CW00922647

JUN 198
WITHDRA
MAY

Senior workshop calculations

Senior workshop calculations

Dr. W. A. J. Chapman

MSc(Eng), FIMechE, HonFIProdE

EDWARD ARNOLD

First published 1941
by Edward Arnold (Publishers) Limited
41 Maddox Street
London W1R OAN

Reprinted 1944, 1947, 1949, 1952
Second edition 1954
Reprinted 1957, 1959, 1961, 1962, 1965
Third edition 1972

ISBN 0 7131 3260 4

Photoset and printed in Malta by St Paul's Press, Ltd

Preface

This book is a revision of the workshop practice material in *Senior Workshop Calculations*. This revision was made necessary by the advent of the SI System and of developments in some aspects of teaching and industrial practice.

Senior Workshop Calculations has enjoyed a vogue of thirty years and is used in many parts of the world. From the various expressions I have received I am sure that it has rendered a useful contribution to the work of countless students as well as to that of mature workers engaged in engineering.

During the revision it was decided to separate out the text dealing with practice calculations as a first priority. The text includes most of the material required by students and practitioners in workshop and production engineering practice and should provide a useful textbook for National Certificates and Diplomas, and for City & Guilds courses in Mechanical and Production Engineering subjects.

In the work of revision I have received considerable advice and help from Mr M. G. Page, BSc(Eng), FIMechE, FIProdE, and I should like here to acknowledge my warm appreciation of his generous and kind assistance.

I hope that in its present form the book will continue to serve the interests of students and other workers in those aspects of engineering it has always been my desire to foster.

Hatfield, 1972 W. A. J. C.

Preface

Contents

1 Introduction

The SI system of units and conventions

The initials SI are an abbreviation for Système International d'Unités (International System of Units), the modern form of the metric system, finally agreed upon at an international conference in 1960. It is now being adopted widely throughout the world and is likely to become the primary world system for units and measurement. As we shall discuss below, the system rationalises the main metric units of measurement and standardises their names and symbolic representation. It also rationalises certain mechanical principles and conventions.

The British system of weights and measures is many centuries old, and the derivation of its units with their multiples and sub-divisions is often obscure. The system has been refurbished from time to time but the yard and the pound with their multiples (e.g. mile) and sub-divisions (e.g. ounce) have persisted; so have such ridiculous measures as $5\frac{1}{2}$ yards = 1 rod, pole and perch, 4 roods = 1 acre or 14lb = 1 stone remained with us to try the mental agility of generations of students, not to mention the more mature, and less mentally agile population.

The metric system was founded during the French Revolution and has been adopted for us by most countries with the notable exceptions of the British Commonwealth and the U.S.A., but even in these countries it is used for precise scientific measurements.

The basic units of the SI metric system are the metre and the kilogramme and it is exclusively *decimal*, so that all multiples and sub-divisions of the standard are found by applying factors of 10 (1 kilometre = 1000 metres; 1 kilogramme = 1000 grammes; 1 hectare (area) = 100 × 100 square metres, and so on). In the English system, of course, there is no such orderly pattern and indeed, the foreigner might well question our sanity when he hears us refer to 112 pounds as a *hundredweight*.

However, we have, at last, been caught up with the progress of the times and as a nation we have decided to change over to the metric system. The entire text of this book conforms with the SI system and the object of this introductory chapter is to provide help and reference for the reader as he finds his way into what may seem, at first, to be a complexity. The best advice that can be given for achieving rapid progress in coping with the change is to become familiar with the new measures and to learn, as soon as possible to *think* in terms of them, and not to persist in making mental conversions back to the old units. This process can be speeded up by acquiring, as soon as possible, a mental appreciation of a range of lengths, weights, capacities, etc. Some of these could be (say) the mental judgement of 25 millimetres, 1 metre, the weight of 1 kilogramme, the amount of fluid comprising 1 litre (1000 cm^3) and the pressure corresponding to 1 bar (approx 1 atmosphere)*. In this way it will soon be possible to think of these measures in their own right and not grope around converting them to their English equivalents (1 kg = 2·2 lb; 1 litre = about $1\frac{3}{4}$ pints and so on). A similar process is concerned in the learning of a foreign language where facility will never be achieved until a student thinks in terms of the language concerned and abandons all attempts to intrepret mentally from, and into, English. It is well known that another language is quickest learned by living amongst those who speak nothing else. If the reader can approach this new mathematical and scientific language in this frame of mind he will find that the former system will rapidly recede, so increasing the ease with which he can cope with the problems involved.

Basic SI units

The SI system is based on six primary units as follows:

Table 1. Basic SI units

Quantity	Unit	Symbol
Length	Metre	m
Mass	Kilogramme	kg
Time	Second	s
Electric current	Ampere	A
Temperature	Kelvin	K
Luminous Intensity	Candela	cd

In addition to these there are a number of supplementary and derived units. We give below a selection of those which are most likely to be required by students using this book. A full list of the SI Units and conventions is given in BSI publication PD 5686.

*The reader has probably heard of the bar in reference to millibars of atmospheric pressure in Met Office forecasts.

Supplementary and derived units

Table 2. Selected supplementary and derived SI units

Quantity	Unit	Symbol
Area	Square metre	m^2
Volume	Cubic metre	m^3
Density	Kilogramme per cubic metre	kg/m^3
Velocity	Metre per second	m/s
Acceleration	Metre per second squared	m/s^2
Force	Newton	$N(kg\,m/s^2)$
Moment of force	Newton metre	N m
Pressure, stress	Newton per square metre	N/m^2
Work, energy Heat quantity	Joule	J (N m)
Power	Watt	W (J/s)
Plane angle	Radian	rad
Temperature (Everyday use)	Degree Celsius*	°C
Specific heat capacity	Joule per kilogramme degree Celsius	J/kg°C
Electric tension Potential difference Electromotive force	Volt	V

*It is probable that the word "centigrade" will remain, but SI recommends the use of Celsius to prevent confusion with another unit.

Multiples and sub-divisions of the unit

In the same way, that in the British system where the yard is divided into feet and inches and multiplied into the furlong and mile, the pound multiplied into the cwt and ton and divided into the ounce, so it is necessary to make similar provisions in the SI system. One of the advantages of the system for this purpose is the simplicity of its multiples and sub-multiples because of its decimal (10) character. We will give, again, a selection of the chief factors likely to be required by the reader leaving him to study the BSI literature if he wishes to pursue the remainder.

It will be noticed that multiples and divisions involving 10^4, 10^5 and certain higher powers are not included in the system. This has been done in order to rationalise the procedure by using, after 10^2 and 10^{-2}, only powers which are multiples of 3, and the full list of such factors extends from 10^{12} at the higher end to 10^{-18} at the lower.

Table 3. SI multiples and sub-multiples

Factor by which unit is multiplied	Prefix	Symbol	Example
One million = 10^6	mego	M	megawatt (MW)
One thousand = 10^3	kilo	k	kilometre (km)
One hundred = 10^2	hecto	h	hectare (ha)
Ten = 10	deca	da	decagramme (dag)
One tenth = 10^{-1}	deci	d	decimetre (dm)
One hundredth = 10^{-2}	centi	c	centimetre (cm)
One thousandth = 10^{-3}	milli	m	millilitre (ml)
One millionth = 10^{-6}	micro	μ	microvolt (μV)

Having now considered the quantitative manipulation of the basic units we may now go on to consider the facilities available for alternative smaller divisions, or larger multiples of the main units, and of certain additional variations allowable in the system. By this means it is possible to employ a unit of suitable proportions for any particular set of circumstances. (Table 4).

Representation of unit symbols and quantities

It often happens that when we move into a new house, or office, or take on something which changes our way of life we take the opportunity of overhauling our methods. So it is with the changeover to this new system where the adoption of SI is accompanied by various conventions regarding the presentation of information.

These are summarised as follows:

(a) *Writing the unit symbols*

- (i) The full stop, usually placed after an abbreviated word, is never used after an abbreviated symbol except at the end of a sentence. Thus, 50 kg, 10 m, 8 kg, 30 s, 5 N/mm^2, all without a full stop, but: "the vehicle had a mass of 1100 kg." end of sentence, full stop.
- (ii) The plural 's' is *not* used. (50 cm *not* 50 cms)
- (iii) The proposition "per" is replaced by the oblique / (rev/min *not* rev per min)
- (iv) Symbols for areas and volumes are qualified by the index. (cm^2 *not* sq cm and cm^3 *not* cu cm)

(Note that when converting quantities denoted by indices: 1 m^3 = (100 cm)^3 = 100^3 cm^3 = 10^6 cm^3) (continued on p. 6).

Table 4. Recommended multiples and sub-divisions of the basic SI units

Quantity	Multiple or sub-multiple	Other units acceptable in the system and likely to persist
Plane angle	m rad	degree° minute′ second″
Length	km	
	cm*	
	min	
	μm	micron ($\frac{1}{1000}$mm)
Area	km²	hectare (ha)(10⁴m²)
	cm²	are (a)(10²m²)
	mm²	
Volume	dm³	litre (*l*)(100 cm³)
	cm³	millilitre (ml)
	mm³	
Time	ms	year, month, week.
	ks	day (d) hour (h)
	ms	minute (m)
	μs	
Velocity	—	km/h
Mass	Mg	tonne (OR metric ton) (t)
	g	metric carat (2×10^{-4} kg)
	mg	
Density	kg/dm³	or kg/l
	g/cm³	g/l
Force	MN : kN : mN : μN	kgf (weight of 1 kg mass) (not included in SI system but likely to be used) 1 kgf = 9·806N
Moment of force	MN m : kN m : μN m	
Pressure	N/mm² : N/cm² : kN/mm² mN/m² : μN/m²	bar = 10N/cm² hectobar (hbar) = 10³N/cm² (Will probably be used for pneumatic pressures. High pressures and stresses will be expressed in units shown opposite)
Stress	kN/mm² : kN/cm² : N/mm² N/cm² : kN/m²	
Work and energy	MJ : kJ : mJ	Kilowatt Hour (kWh = 3·6 MJ)
Power	MW : kW : mW : μW	
Specific heat capacity	kJ/kg°C	

*The cm is not recommended for general use and it is hoped that it will eventually disappear. It is, however, a very convenient unit for certain purposes as will be seen from the uses of it later in our text. It will be observed, however, that the cm² and cm³ are still permissible.

(*b*) *Numerical values*

(i) When a quantity is less than unity (1) always place zero (0) before the decimal point. (0·625:0·0031, etc.)

(ii) As far as possible always express a quantity in terms of a power of 10, so using the index of 10 instead of a row of 0's. ($36{\cdot}2 \times 10^3$ instead of 36 200; $1{\cdot}5 \times 10^{-3}$ instead of 0·0015) and preferably use powers of 10 which are multiples of 3.

(iii) Separate a row of digits into groups of three by a space, instead of using a comma. (71 562 instead of 71,562, or 0·006 13 instead of 0·006,13). But a group of four digits may be left without separation (e.g. 6713 or 0·0036 without separation).

Dimensioning (drawings)

It is customary, when dimensioning drawings, to dimension all sizes in millimetres, and *not* to write the unit (mu) after the dimension. An instruction may be given to the effect that all sizes are in millimetres but this is not always done. All the diagrams in this book are dimensioned according to this rule so that the reader will now recognise that ←65→ means 65 mm.

Mass, weight and force

The reader will observe that kg is the SI unit for *MASS* and that a unit for weight is not mentioned in the scheme. There is, however, the Newton (N) as the unit of *FORCE*. The mass of a body is the amount of matter (or material) of which it is composed and the kilogramme unit is equal to the mass of the international prototype kilogramme which is in the custody of the Bureau International des Poids et Mesures at Sèvres near Paris. The only means of measuring and comparing masses is by weighing them so that the weight of an object is proportional to its mass and indeed, the weight of a body is the downward force its mass exerts under the influence of the earth's gravitational pull. We have seen this concept very effectively illustrated since astronauts have been penetrating beyond the influence of the gravitational pull of the earth and most readers will have seen the fascinating television pictures of the interior of the capsule, with objects floating about, still having their mass, but without weight. The definition of a newton (N) of force is that force which acting on one kilogramme of mass will propel it along with an acceleration of one metre per second per second (i.e. it gains 1 m per second every second). Put into symbols this becomes:

$$1\,\text{N} = 1\,\text{kg m/s}^2$$

The kilogramme weight (kgf)
The gravitational pull where we are (England) is such that it imparts an acceleration of about 9·807 metres per second per second (9·807 m/s^2) on a freely falling body and this pull, acting on a mass of 1 kg causes it to exert a downwards force (its weight) of 9·807 Newton of force (since 1 Newton = 1 kgm/s^2). Thus the weight of a mass of 1 kg expressed in newtons of force is:

1 kg weight (kgf) = 9·807 newtons (usually approximated to 9·81 N)

The weight of a body having a mass of 150 kg = 150 × 9·81 = 1471·5 N)

The mass of a body is a quantity which never changes (unless a piece is cut off or added to it), but the force of gravity varies slightly on different parts of the earth. This means that the weight of 1 kg of mass in England will not be quite the same as its weight at the equator. The variation is very small (about 0·5%) over the surface of the earth so that for all but the very accurate scientific work there is a justification for using the kgf unit of weight in everyday life. The reader will find kg loosely referred to as the "weight" of an article, when what is really meant is the gravitational pull on a kg of mass. However, for some problems, such as those involving weights and costs of materials, it will be convenient to work in kgf rather than newtons, since suppliers of materials will always quote kg or tonne, and not newtons as the weight in their price lists and specifications. The following examples will illustrate the use of force units:

Example 1. A round steel bar, 100 mm diameter, 1 metre long is placed standing on its end. If the contact between the end of the bar and its support is uniformly spread over the whole end face of the bar calculate the intensity of pressure over the area of contact. Take the density of steel as 7·83 g/cm^3.

$$\text{Mass of bar} = (\text{Volume})(\text{density})$$
$$= \frac{\pi}{4} \times 10^2 \times 100 \times 7{\cdot}83 \text{ grams (Working in cm)}$$
$$= \frac{0{\cdot}7854 \times 10^4 \times 7{\cdot}83}{10^3} \text{ kg} = 61{\cdot}5 \text{ kg}$$

Downward force (weight) exerted by bar

$$= (\text{mass})(\text{gravity}) = 61{\cdot}5 \times 9{\cdot}807 = 603 \text{ N}$$
$$\text{Area of bar end} = 0{\cdot}7854 \times 10^2 \text{ cm}^2$$
$$= 78{\cdot}54 \text{ cm}^2$$

$$\text{Intensity of pressure} = \frac{\text{force}}{\text{area}} = \frac{603}{78{\cdot}54}$$
$$= 7{\cdot}68\ \text{N/cm}^2$$

Example 2. A vehicle having a mass (m) of 2000 kilo has a fractional resistance to motion of $m/20$. If the drive is equivalent to an average force of 320 N find the speed attained after 1 min from rest.

$$\text{Resistance to motion} = \frac{2000}{20}\text{N} = 100\ \text{N}$$
$$\text{Effective driving force} = 320\text{N} - 100\text{N} = 220\text{N}$$

and since

$$\text{force } (F) = \text{mass } (m) \times \text{accel } (a)$$
$$220\text{N} = 2000\,a$$
$$a = \frac{220}{2000} = 0{\cdot}11\ \text{m/s}^2$$

Speed after 1 min

$$V = (\text{accel})(\text{time})$$
$$= 0{\cdot}11 \times 60$$
$$= \underline{6{\cdot}6\ \text{m/s}}$$

Example 3. A pin is being driven home by a hammer of mass 1 kg. When the hammer is moving at 1·5 m/s it strikes the pin and drives it 10 mm further in. Assuming the hammer is brought to rest at constant deceleration estimate the average force of the blow.

If the hammer travels 10 mm (0·01 m) whilst decelerating at a constant rate from 1·5 m/s to rest:

Average speed over the stopping period

$$= \frac{1{\cdot}5}{2} = 0{\cdot}75\ \text{m/s}$$

and the space moved $= 0{\cdot}01$ m

Hence:

$$\text{duration of the blow } (t) = \frac{0{\cdot}01}{0{\cdot}75} = 0{\cdot}0133\ \text{sec}$$

We then have for the movement of the hammer after it strikes the pin:

initial speed (u) $= 1{\cdot}5$ m/s: final speed (v) $= 0$

and time (t) $= 0{\cdot}0133$

and from $v = u + at$ (see p. 10)

$$0 = 1{\cdot}5 + 0{\cdot}0133a$$

from which $a = \frac{-1{\cdot}5}{0{\cdot}0133} = -112{\cdot}7\,\text{m/s}^2$ (retardation)

The average force of the blow is found from:

$$F = (\text{mass})(\text{accel}) = 1 \times 112{\cdot}7$$
$$= \underline{112{\cdot}7\,\text{N}}$$

The equations of motion

The reader, no doubt, will have already realised that the SI system is more orderly and coherent than the British system and this might be pursued by considering its application to the equations of motion.

If s = space travelled, v = velocity (or speed) and t = time

$$\text{then } s = vt \qquad \text{or} \qquad v = \frac{s}{t} \tag{1}$$

The basic unit for s is the metre (m) and for t, the second. This gives us the secondary basic unit for velocity as $v = \frac{s}{t}$ = m/s (metres per second). Naturally, it is not always desirable, or possible, to work in metres and seconds but alternative units of larger or smaller dimension are available to suit the conditions or aspects of any particular situation. (e.g. for a road speed we should probably use kilometres and hours).

Thus: 1 kilometre = 1000 metres
1 hour = 3600 seconds

$$\frac{1\text{ km}}{1\text{ h}} = \frac{1000\text{ m}}{3600\text{ s}} = \frac{5\text{ m}}{18\text{ s}} = \frac{5}{18}\text{ m/s}$$

i.e. to convert km/h to m/s multiply by $\frac{5}{18}$.

Acceleration

Acceleration is the rate of change of velocity

$$\text{i.e. acceleration} = \frac{\text{change in velocity}}{\text{time taken for the change}}$$

If a body starts from rest and acquires a velocity of v after time t, and using the symbol a for acceleration

$$a = \frac{v}{t}$$

Since the basic derived unit for v is m/s, and the basic unit for t is s, so the basic unit for acceleration is $\frac{\text{m}}{\text{s}} \div \text{s} = \frac{\text{m}}{\text{s}^2}$ (metres per second squared).

Transposing the above $a = \frac{v}{t}$ to give v we get $v = at$.

If, instead of starting from rest, the body already had an initial velocity of u. Then, final velocity after time t:

$$v = u + at \qquad (2)$$

Instead of accelerating a body may be slowing down or decelerating. Then the acceleration will be a minus quantity and

$$v = u - at$$

This slowing down is termed a retardation.

The above relationships may be illustrated graphically and this is shown at Fig. 1.

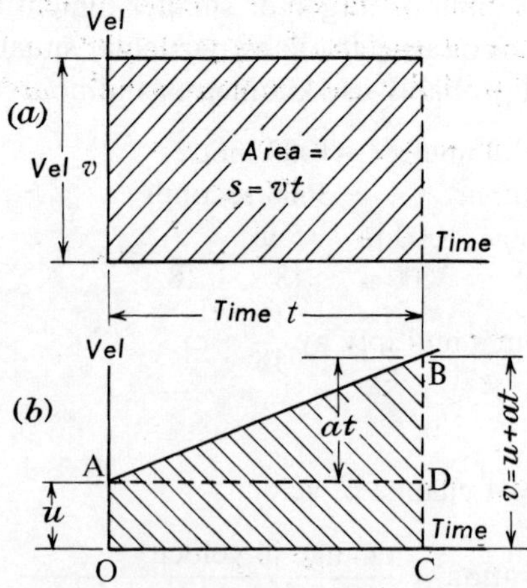

Fig. 1

Example 4. A drop stamp falls freely for 5 metres under the action of gravity. Find: (a) the time of fall and (b) its velocity at the instant it strikes the tup. Take $g = 9{\cdot}81$ m/s².

The graph representing the fall is shown at Fig. 2 and if v is the final velocity after time t:

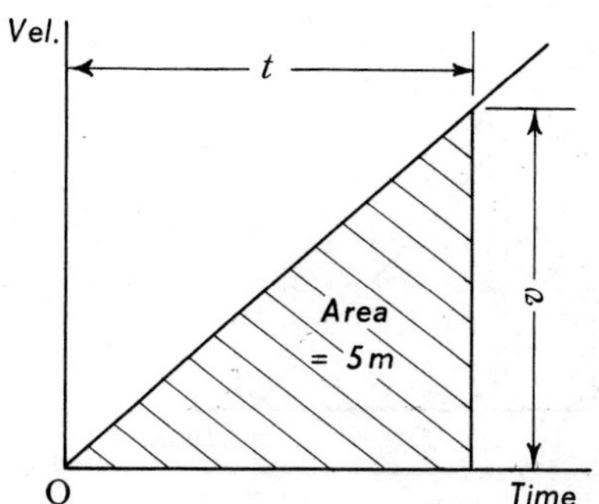

Fig. 2

We get:

$$\tfrac{1}{2}\,vt = 5 \text{ and } v = \frac{10}{t} \qquad (1)$$

But for accelerated motion from rest

$$v = at \text{ where } a = g = 9{\cdot}81 \text{ m/s}^2$$

Hence, equating this to (1):

$$\frac{10}{t} = a = 9{\cdot}81\, t$$

and

$$t^2 = \frac{10}{9{\cdot}81} \quad \therefore \quad \underline{t = 1{\cdot}01\,\text{s}}$$

Substituting in (1) for t we have:

$$v = \frac{10}{1{\cdot}01} = \underline{9{\cdot}9\,\text{m/s}}$$

Example 5. A machine ram is operating on a stroke of 360 mm. It starts from rest, accelerates at a uniform rate until the centre of the stroke and then retards at a uniform rate to a standstill at the end of the stroke. If the stroke occupies 1·5 seconds find the acceleration and the maximum speed attained.

This problem is best solved with the help of a graph and the motion is represented in Fig. 3.

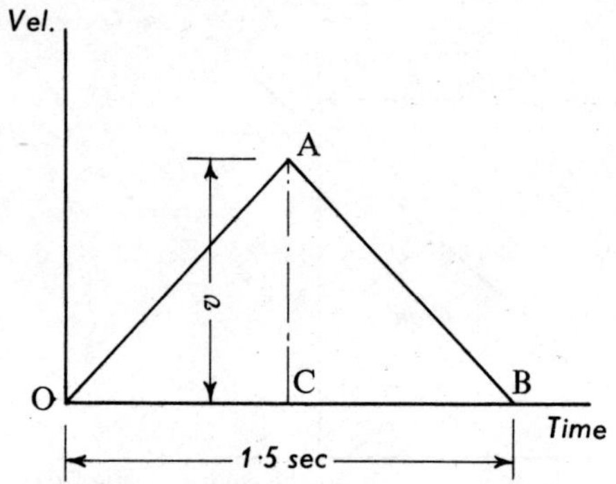

Fig. 3

The ram accelerates from 0 to A, its velocity increasing uniformly, and the reverse process takes place from A to B.

The area OAB represents the space travelled which, in this case, is 360 mm (0.36 m).

Hence $0{\cdot}36\ \text{m} = \frac{1}{2}(\text{OB})(\text{AC})$, and since $\text{OB} = 1{\cdot}5\text{s}$

$$0{\cdot}36\,\text{m} = \tfrac{1}{2}(1{\cdot}5\,\text{s})(\text{AC})$$

$$\text{AC} = v = \frac{2 \times 0{\cdot}36\,\text{m}}{1{\cdot}5\,\text{s}} = \underline{0{\cdot}48\ \text{m/s}}$$

For half the stroke $v = at$

Hence $a = \dfrac{v}{t} = \dfrac{0{\cdot}48}{0{\cdot}75}\text{m/s} = \underline{0{\cdot}64\text{m/s}^2}$

2 Measurement and gauging

Limits and tolerances

When parts which must fit together are being made under conditions which do not permit of each fitting pair to be mated up individually, it becomes necessary to arrange the working dimensions so that if each component is made to them, the required type of fit will be assured. To achieve this, a system of limits and fits is adopted. The definitions used in connection with limit systems will be gathered from the following and Fig. 4.

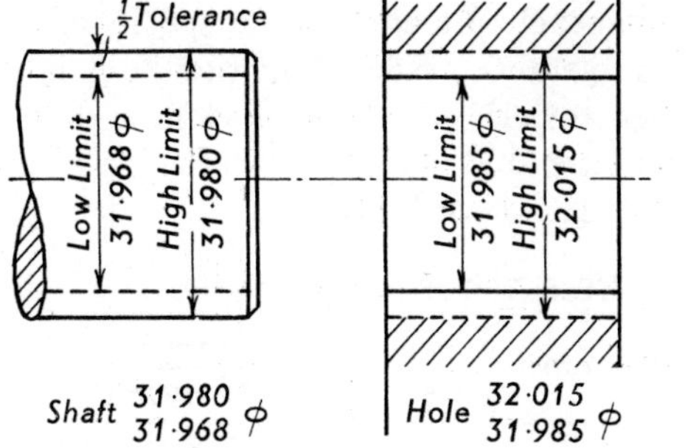

Fig. 4

The low limit is the dimension of the smallest permissible size, and the high limit the largest permissible size. The component is acceptable if its size lies anywhere between the two.

The *tolerance* is the difference between the two limiting dimensions. [The tolerance on the above shaft is 31·980 − 31·968 = 0.012 mm.]

The *allowance* is the variation between the sizes of the hole and shaft necessary to give the type of fit required. For a running fit the shaft must be smaller than the hole (clearance fit), whilst for a driving or force fit, the shaft must be larger than the hole (interference fit). Between the extremes of clearance and interference there is a range of fits such as push fit, slide fit, etc., in which there is only a small variation between the hole and shaft sizes (transition fit).

Limit systems

The numerical value of the limits for any related hole and shaft will depend on:

(*a*) The nominal size (i.e. whether 25 mm, 50 mm, 100 mm, etc.)
(*b*) The class of fit (e.g. running fit, push fit, force fit, etc.)
(*c*) The grade of workmanship desired.

The ISO system, set out in BS Specification No. 4500 (1969), allows for 27 types of fit and 18 grades of tolerance over a size range of zero to 3150 mm. At first sight this seems an enormous provision, but the fits and grades of workmanship covered allow for everything from fine gauge work to the roughest form of production, and even for some classes of raw materials. Average workshop requirements may be met from a limited part of the specification and for this purpose suitable recommendations are given. In the system the 27 possible holes are designated by capital letters A B C D etc., and the shafts by small letters covering the same range. The 18 accuracy grades are denoted by the numbers 01, 0, 1, 2, . . . 16. The nomenclature adopted for specifying any particular hole or shaft with its tolerance grade is to write the hole or shaft letter with its grade number: thus H7 for a hole, or e8 for a shaft of the fit and accuracy given by the letter and numeral concerned. A fit involving these two elements is written H7–e8 or H7/e8.

SELECTED FITS (HOLE BASIS)

Type of Fit	Shaft Tolerance	Hole Tolerances			
		H 7	H 8	H 9	H 11
Clearance (Slack, Running etc.)	c 11				
	d 10				
	e 9				
	f 7				
	g 6				
	h 6				
Transition (Push, Slide etc.)	k 6				
	n 6				
Interference (Force, Drive etc.)	p 6				
	s 6				

(Details of the limits for the above shafts over a diameter range 6 mm to 250 mm are given in Appendix 1, page 225.)

For average workshop use the H hole associated with the accuracy grades 7 to 11 (H7 to H11) are recommended as being satisfactory and details of the limits of these for a diameter range of 6 mm to 250 mm are shown in the table on p. 226.

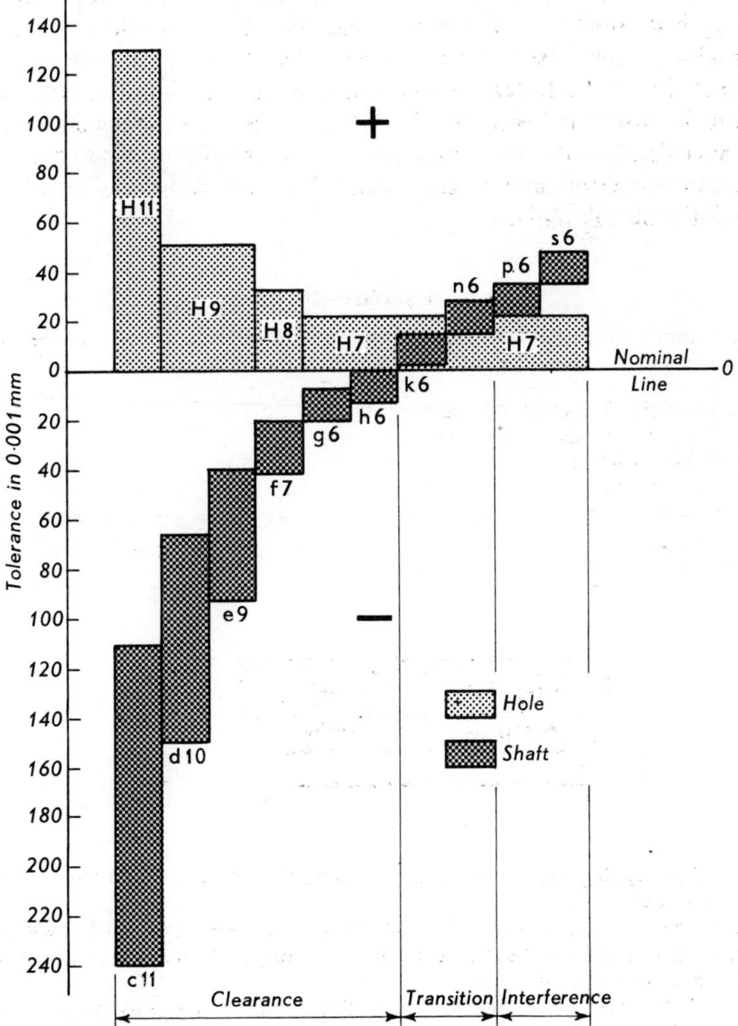

Fig. 5 ISO System of Limits and Fits. Hole and shaft relationships for selected fits (hole basis). (Tolerance scale applies to the diameter range: 18 mm – 30 mm.)

From the shafts included in the specification the table gives a selection of those recommended as likely to be the most useful in coping with the needs of the average workshop. The holes with which they should be associated as well as the approximate type of fit are also given.

Naturally from a selection of 27 fits associated with 18 grades of accuracy it is possible to choose many combinations, but the small selection above should be sufficient to help the reader in his study of the subject. Fig. 5 illustrates the hole and shaft relationship for a selection of the fits associated with the H7 to H11 holes as recommended in the BS Specification. From the diagram the reader will be able to trace the maximum and minimum metal conditions for the range of diameters to which the details apply.

Exercises 2a

Write down for problems Nos. 1 to 4 the hole and shaft limits, and calculate the maximum and minimum clearance or interference. (See tables in appendices)

1. 75 mm BSI H10 hole and e8 shaft.

2. 35 mm BSI H9 hole and k6 shaft.

3. 20 mm BSI H7 hole and f7 shaft.

4. 57 mm BSI H8 hole and s7 shaft.

5. Two 32 mm BSI H8 holes are bored in a plate at 105 mm ± 0·02 mm centres. Their centre distance is to be checked by a gauge of the type shown at Fig. 6. If the "go" ends

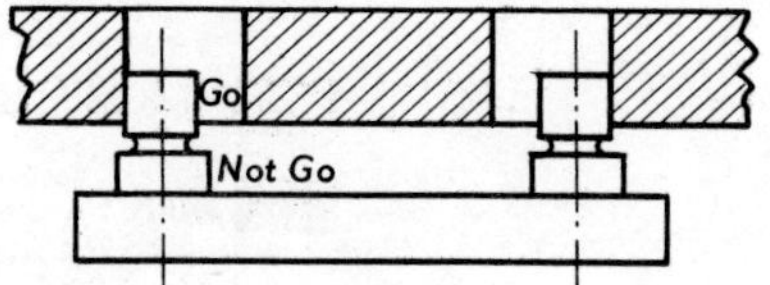

Fig. 6

of the checking plugs are 12 mm diameter calculate their "Not go" diameters and their centre distance.

6. To allow for gauge wear the "Go" end of a limit plug gauge, made for a 40 mm BSI H9 hole, is made larger than the minimum hole size by 10% of the tolerance. Calculate the diameter of this end of the gauge.

7. A limit caliper gauge made for a 50 mm BSI f7 shaft is to be ground out to suit a k7 shaft. Determine the alteration necessary.

8. Two blocks each 25 mm wide are made to BSI h7 limits and a 50 mm slot is made to H8 limits. Compare the fit of these blocks put together with that of a single 50 mm block made to h7 limits. (Assume the width of the blocks put together to be equal to the sum of their individual thicknesses.)

9. A number of limit plug gauges are available, made for the former Newall $\frac{3}{4}$ in. Class B hole $\left(\frac{+0{\cdot}000\,75}{-0{\cdot}0005}\text{in}\right)$. Could these be ground down to suit a 19 mm BSI H8 hole and, if so, what alteration would be necessary?

10. A BS 40 mm b9 shaft is placed in an H8 hole. Determine the greatest and least clearance possible between the shaft and the sides of the hole.

Slip gauges

For the purpose of checking the accuracy of micrometers, verniers and other gauges, it is necessary to have available some means of building up any required length. In most workshops this is achieved by the use of slip gauges. These consist of blocks of different thicknesses, which are made to such a fine degree of accuracy and flatness on their measuring faces, that they may be "wrung" together and the overall length of any number of blocks so joined is the sum of their individual lengths. These gauges are often called Johannsen gauges after their originator. (Fig. 7)

The Coventry Gauge and Tool Co. Ltd.

Fig. 7 A set of slip gauges (107 pieces).
(*Lid of box not shown*)

The number of blocks in a set will depend upon the range of sizes that is required to be made up, and a medium-sized set of such gauges contains 47 pieces of the following sizes.

Metric dimensions: widths of blocks in mm.

Pieces	Range	Steps
1	1·005	—
9	1·01–1·09	0·01
9	1·1–1·9	0·1
24	1–24	1·0
4	25, 50, 75, 100	25·0
47 Total		

From such a selection it is possible to choose blocks to build up almost any dimension that can be named within the capacity of the set. It will be seen that there will be alternative methods of making up a size, but the one should be chosen which employs the smallest number of pieces.

Example 3. Choose blocks to assemble the following sizes: (*a*) 31·31 mm (*b*) 61·685 mm.

To assemble (*a*) we may use the following blocks:

1·01
1·3
10·00
25·00

37·31

Dimension (*b*) may be obtained as follows:

1·005
1·08
1·6
8·00
50·00

61·685

The above example should indicate to the reader how to proceed for any other size, the method being to start at the figure on the extreme right of the dimension required, choosing gauges to accommodate each figure in turn.

English sizes

For routine English work, slip gauges made to inch dimensions may be obtained but it is possible, by calculating the metric equivalent, to use gauges from a metric set.

Example 4. Make up a set of slip gauges to check a gauge measuring 2·1758 in.

The metric equivalent of 2·2758 in is found by multiplying 2·1758 by 25·4 and is equal to 55·26532 mm.

The nearest size to this, that may be assembled from the set of gauges given above, is 55·265 which is 0·00032 mm or 0·000012 in. too small.

Gauges to make up to 55·265 are as follows:

$$\begin{array}{r} 1{\cdot}005 \\ 1{\cdot}06 \\ 1{\cdot}2 \\ 2 \\ 50 \\ \hline 55{\cdot}265 \\ \hline \end{array}$$

Exercises 2b

From the list given on p. 18 make up sets of slip gauges to give the following sizes:

1. 11·11 mm **2.** 23·64 mm **3.** 35·635 mm
4. 68·78 mm **5.** 75·70 mm **6.** 115·36 mm
7. 0·375 in **8.** 1·750 in **9.** 3·1885 in

10. A dimension given as $\frac{34{\cdot}925}{34{\cdot}95}$ mm is to be checked. Make up two separate sets of blocks, one to measure each limit.

11. Make up sets of slip gauges to check the jaws of a limit gap gauge for a 30 mm BSI f7 shaft.

12. Two holes, 0·875 inch diameter and 1·0625 inch diameter, are bored in the face of a casting at 1·5625 inch centres. Convert to mm, and make up a set of slip gauges to test between the insides of test plugs placed in the bores.

The spirit level

The spirit level consists essentially of a glass vial fixed into a frame. The inside top surface of the vial is not straight but is formed to a radius, convex upwards, as shown in Fig. 8. In some instruments the inside of the vial is ground barrel-shaped as shown, whilst in others the glass tube which

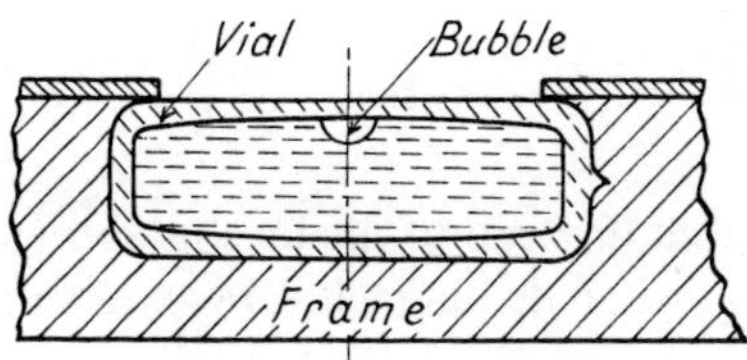

Fig. 8

forms the vial is bent to a radius. The vial contains spirit with sufficient air space to leave a bubble, and is cemented into the frame and accurately located so that when the base of the frame is level the bubble rests at the centre of the scale.

The relations governing the movement of the bubble and the angle of tilt of the level will be followed from Fig. 9 and the following:

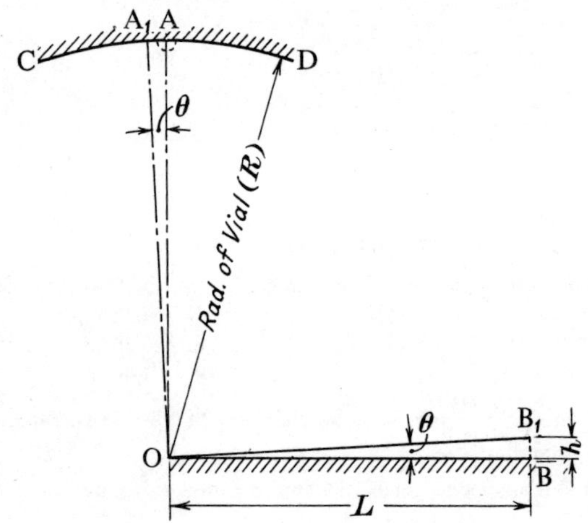

Fig. 9

Arc CAD represents the upper inner surface of the vial and O the centre of its radius. OB represents the base of the level. OB is horizontal and perpendicular to OA. If OB in now tilted to bring B to B_1, point A on the vial will swing to A_1 but the bubble will remain vertically above O and will travel along the vial to A.

If θ is the angle of tilt, then θ (radian) $= \dfrac{A_1A}{R}$

If BB_1 is the length of the arc through which one end of the level (length L) swings, then θ (radian) $= \dfrac{BB_1}{L}$

$$\therefore \frac{BB_1}{L} = \frac{AA_1}{R} \text{ and } BB_1 = \frac{L.\,AA_1}{R}$$

Actually, the height h that one end of the level is above the other is the dimension we require, but when dealing with angles as small as those concerned here, the difference between BB_1 and h is so small as to be negligible.

Thus we can say that $h = \frac{L}{R}$(distance bubble moves)

If the angle of tilt is required in degrees, then since

$$\theta \text{ (radian)} = \frac{\text{Movement of bubble}}{R}$$

$$\theta \text{ (degree)} = \frac{57{\cdot}3 \text{ (Movement of bubble)}}{R}$$

Unfortunately, not many makers of levels mark them with particulars as to the radius (R) of the vial, but this may be determined experimentally by tilting one end of the level by a known amount and after noting the movement of the bubble, calculating the radius from the above expressions.

Example 5. A spirit level is 300 mm long, and it is found that when one end is raised 0·02 mm above the other, the bubble moves 1·50 mm along the vial. Calculate the radius of the vial.

We have that $$\frac{h}{L} = \frac{\text{Movement of bubble}}{R}$$

$$\frac{0{\cdot}02}{300} = \frac{1{\cdot}5}{R}$$

From which $$R = \frac{300 \times 1{\cdot}5}{0{\cdot}02} = 22\,500 \text{ mm or } 22{\cdot}5 \text{ m}$$

Example 6. The base of level is 450 mm long and the radius of the vial is 30 m. Find (*a*) the height of one end above the other, and (*b*) the angle of tilt, corresponding to a bubble movement of 3 mm.

$$\frac{h}{L} = \frac{\text{Movement of bubble}}{R}$$

and $$h = \frac{L \text{ (movement of bubble)}}{R}$$

$$= \frac{450 \times 3}{30 \times 1000} = \underline{0{\cdot}045 \text{mm}}$$

Angle of tilt in degree $= \dfrac{57{\cdot}3 \times 3}{30 \times 1000} = 0{\cdot}005\,73° = \underline{20{\cdot}6 \text{ second}}$

The sine bar

For accurate work in connection with angles the sine bar possesses advantages over the usual forms of protractor. Sine bars differ in form, but the considerations affecting their setting are the same in every case. Two common types of sine bar are shown in Fig. 10.

The bar shown at (*a*) has two plugs which are let in and project about 12 mm from the front face. At (*b*) is shown a bar which is stepped at the ends and a roller is secured into each step, being pulled in by a screw so as to contact with each of the faces of the step. Both at (*a*) and (*b*) the following points are important if the sine bar is to be of any use:

(i) The rollers or plugs should both be of the same diameter.

(ii) Their centre distance must be absolutely correct. (The diagram is dimensioned as 200 mm centres, but sine bars are available in 100, 250 and 300 mm centres as well.

(iii) The centre line AB of the plugs must be absolutely parallel with the edge of the bar used for measuring (generally the bottom). It is desirable for the two edges of the bar to be parallel, with AB parallel with both.

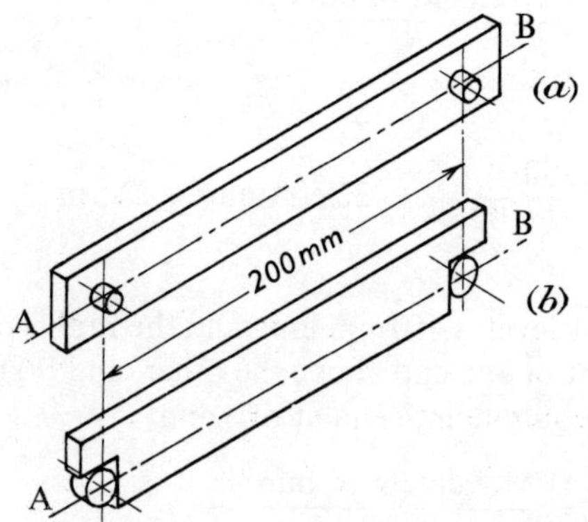

Fig. 10.

When in use, the bar shown at (*a*) lends itself to clamping against an angle plate, whilst that at (*b*) can be rested on two piles of Johannson gauges to give it the correct inclination.

Calculation for sine bar setting

In Fig. 11, C is the centre distance of the plugs, h is the height of one plug above the other and α is the angle to which the bar must be set.

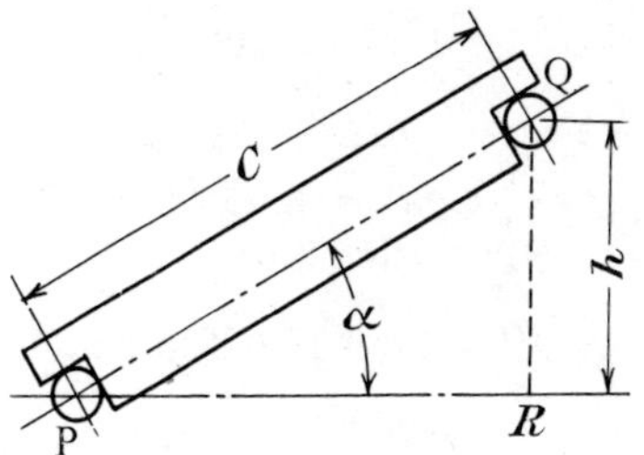

Fig. 11

Then

$$\frac{QR}{PQ} = \frac{h}{C} = \sin \alpha$$

and $$h = C \sin \alpha$$

i.e. difference in height of plugs = (centre distance) (sine of angle).

Example 7. Calculate the setting of a 200 mm sine bar to measure an angle of 36° 38′.

We have that $\sin 36° 38' = 0{\cdot}5967$

$$h = 200 \times 0{\cdot}5967 = 119.34$$

Hence one plug must be set 119·34 mm above the other.

Example 8. Calculate the setting of a 250 mm sine bar to check the angle of a taper of 1 in 16 on the diameter.

The taper is shown in Fig. 12(*a*) and, if it is assumed to be 16 units long, then in triangle ABC,

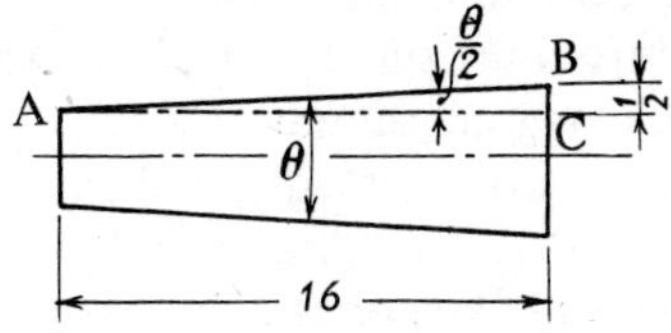

Fig. 12(*a*)

AC = 16, BC = ½, and $\widehat{BAC} = \dfrac{\theta}{2}$

$$\tan \frac{\theta}{2} = \frac{\frac{1}{2}}{16} = \frac{1}{32} = 0{\cdot}031\,25$$

From which $\frac{\theta}{2} = 1° \ 47' \ 30''$

and $\theta = 3° \ 35'$

Now $\sin \theta = \sin 3° \ 35' = 0{\cdot}0625$

and since the setting is for a 250 mm sine bar:

$$h = 250 \times 0{\cdot}0625 = 15{\cdot}625 \text{ mm}$$

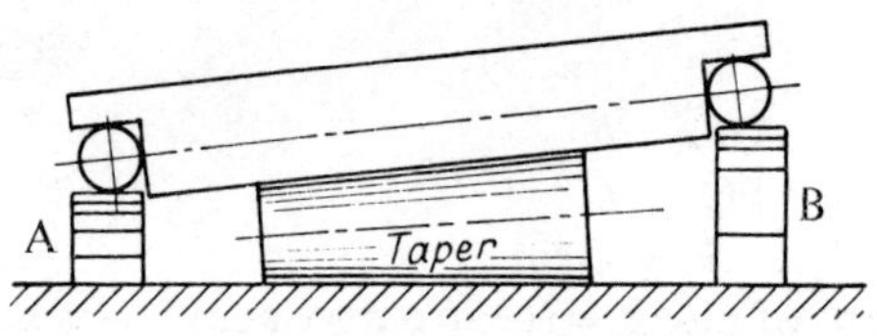

Fig. 12(*b*)

The set-up shown at Fig. 12(*b*), A and B being two sets of block gauges assembled to give the setting calculated above.

Precaution when checking plane surfaces with the sine bar

The reader should observe that when using the sine bar to check the angle between two plane surfaces (e.g. the surfaces of an angle plate) the bar must be set accurately at right angles to the slope of the face being measured. The following example will illustrate how an error may be introduced if this is not done.

Example 9. A surface was being checked by a 100 mm sine bar which, due to an error in setting, was placed 6 mm out of square with the slope of the surface. The angle obtained from the sine bar readings was 59° 30′. Find the true angle of the surface being measured.

The conditions are shown diagrammatically, and exaggerated, in Fig. 13.

The readings should have been taken on the line of greatest slope AB, but were actually taken on AC.

CH is a perpendicular drawn from C on to AB, and from the conditions of the problem, CH = 6 mm.

AB = AC = 100 mm, E, F and G are points where horizontal lines through A meet verticals through B, C and H.

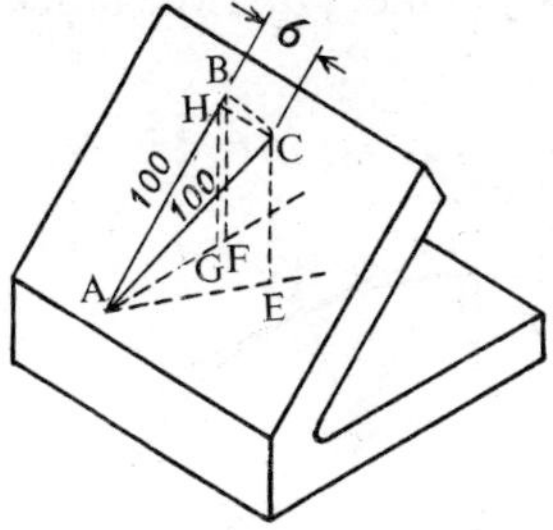

Fig. 13

In triangle ACH: $AH^2 = AC^2 - CH^2$

$$100^2 - 6^2 = 9964$$

$$AH = \sqrt{9964} = 99{\cdot}82$$

Now since CH is parallel to the slope, C and H are the same height and CE = HG

In triangle CAE:

$$AC = 100, \text{ and } C\hat{A}E = 59°30'$$
$$\therefore CE = 100 \sin 59°30'$$
$$= 100 \times 0{\cdot}8616 = 86{\cdot}16\,\text{mm}$$

Then since CE = HG; in triangle $H\hat{A}G$

HA = 99·82 mm, HG = 86·16 mm and $H\hat{A}G$ is the true angle of the plate

Sine HAG $= \dfrac{86{\cdot}16}{99{\cdot}82} = 0{\cdot}8631$ from which, $H\hat{A}G$, the true angle of the plate $= 59°40'$

i.e. an error of 10′

Gauging large radii

From some classes of work it is necessary to measure the radii of circles which are too large to be straddled by calipers or a micrometer. Where the complete circle is available its circumference may be measured by a tape and the diameter obtained by dividing by π. This method, however, is by no means perfect, and is not at all convenient when the radius to be measured is not part of a complete circle.

An alternative method is to determine the radius by reference to the distance of its surface from the corner of a vee block resting on it.

In Fig. 14 ABC represents the faces of a vee block resting on a circle, centre O and radius R.

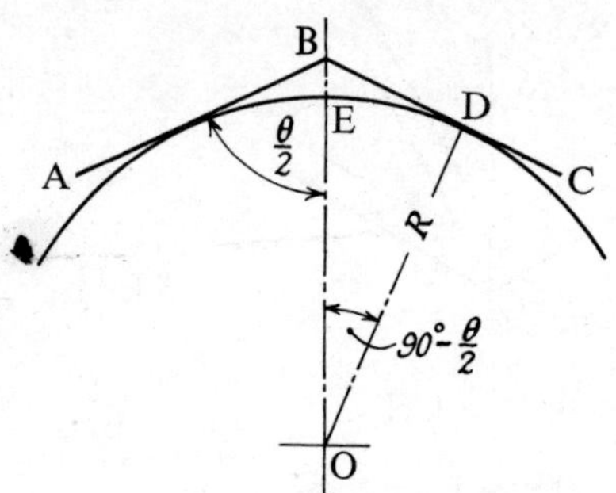

Fig. 14

If θ is the included angle of ABC, its half angle ABO will be $\frac{\theta}{2}$ as shown. The circle and the block contact at D, and in triangle BOD, since D is a right angle, angle BOD $= 90 - \frac{\theta}{2}$

For different-sized circles placed in the vee, the variable length that we can measure is BE, so that the problem becomes one of finding a suitable expression for R in terms of this length and the angle of the vee.

Now BE $=$ BO $-$ EO and EO $=$ OD $= R$

But
$$\frac{\text{BO}}{\text{OD}} = \text{secant}\left(90 - \frac{\theta}{2}\right)$$

$$\therefore \text{BO} = \text{OD sec}\left(90 - \frac{\theta}{2}\right)$$

$$= R \text{ cosec}\frac{\theta}{2}$$

since $\sec\left(90 - \frac{\theta}{2}\right) = \text{cosec}\,\frac{\theta}{2}$

Note:

$$\text{secant} = \frac{1}{\cos}$$

$$\text{cosecant} = \frac{1}{\sin}$$

Hence
$$\text{BE} = R\,\text{cosec}\frac{\theta}{2} - R$$

$$= R\left(\text{cosec}\frac{\theta}{2} - 1\right)$$

From which
$$R = \frac{\text{BE}}{\text{cosec}\,\frac{\theta}{2} - 1}$$

For any given angle of vee, the quantity $\operatorname{cosec}\frac{\theta}{2} - 1$ is constant and can be calculated and stamped on the gauge. All that is then necessary is to measure BE, and divide it by this number to give R.

Example 10. A gauge of the type shown in Fig. 14 having an included angle of 120° is placed on a tube and the length BE measures 21·25 mm. Find the diameter of the tube.

Here $$R = \frac{BE}{\operatorname{cosec}\frac{\theta}{2} - 1} = \frac{21{\cdot}25}{\operatorname{cosec} 60° - 1} = \frac{21{\cdot}25}{1{\cdot}1547 - 1}$$

$$= \frac{21{\cdot}25}{0{\cdot}1547} = 137{\cdot}36\,\text{mm}$$

and $$\text{dia. of tube} = 2 \times 137{\cdot}36 = \underline{274{\cdot}72\,\text{mm}}$$

The main difficulty in the use of a gauge of this type is the accurate measurement of the distance BE. This may be overcome by constructing the gauge and incorporating a depth gauge or micrometer head on the centre line at B. An alternative construction is to make the gauge with a flat portion as shown at Fig. 15, using slip gauges to check the distance between the work and the flat.

It will be an interesting example to plan such a gauge as this:

Example 11. Plan out a vee gauge to measure round work, to cover a range of diameters varying from 250 mm to 750 mm.

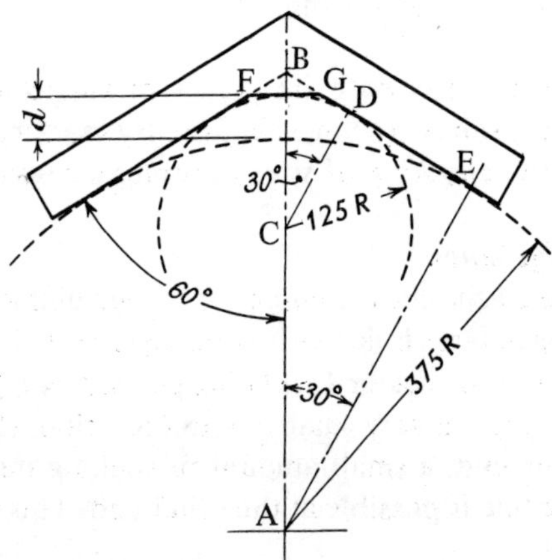

Fig. 15

We will make the gauge with an included angle of 120°, and the flat portion FG filling in the corner of the vee such that it just contacts with a 250 mm circle placed in the vee, as shown in Fig. 15. The length of the gauge must be sufficient to accomodate a 750 mm circle.

The length must exceed twice the distance from E to line AB, i.e. > 2AE sin 30° = > 2 × 375 × ½, say, 400 mm.

If flat FG just touches a 250 mm circle placed in the vee,

then

$$CB = CD \sec 30° = 125 \times 1{\cdot}1547 = 144{\cdot}34\,\text{mm}$$

and from the vee corner B to FG the distance is 144·34 − 125 = 19·34 mm.

It now remains to find the relation between the radius of any circle placed in the vee, and the distance from its circumference to line FG.

From Fig. 14 we have that from B to the circumference of a circle radius R,

$$= R \operatorname{cosec} \frac{\theta}{2} - 1$$

which becomes $0{\cdot}1547R$ when $\frac{\theta}{2} = 60°$.

We have to subtract 19·34 mm from this, so that

$$d = 0{\cdot}1547R - 19{\cdot}34\,\text{mm}$$

and transposing to give R results in

$$R = \frac{d + 19{\cdot}34}{0{\cdot}1547}\,\text{mm}$$

The distance d can be measured with slip gauges, or a micrometer depth gauge incorporated in the construction as before. By marking the above formula on the gauge, the checking of sizes becomes a routine job.

The measurement of large bores

An interesting example of the measurement of a large diameter is available to us in the gauging of large holes with a point gauge. This is shown in Fig. 16(a), where a hole of diameter D is being gauged by a point gauge of length L. In practice, L is a very small amount less than D, and when the gauge is held at one end, a small amount of rocking movement on either side of the centre line is possible at the other end. This is indicated by w.

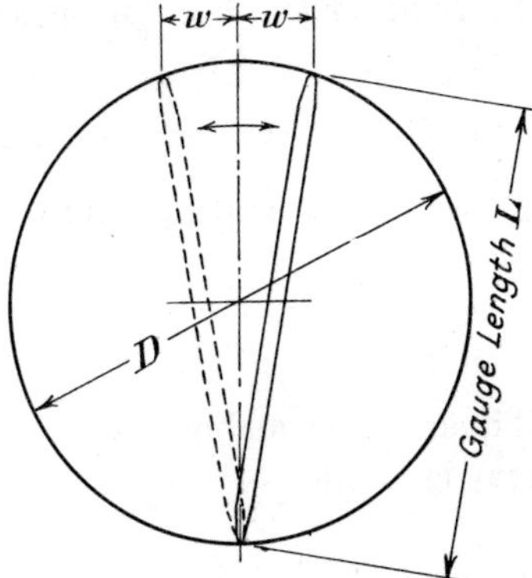

Fig. 16(*a*)

The conditions are shown exaggerated at Fig. 16(*b*). The full circle is the hole being gauged, and the dotted circle (centre A) is that which the end of the point gauge would describe if it made a full sweep. Actually, the end of the gauge only moves over the arc BHF. The amount by which this guage is smaller than D is shown by CH. Let this be δ.

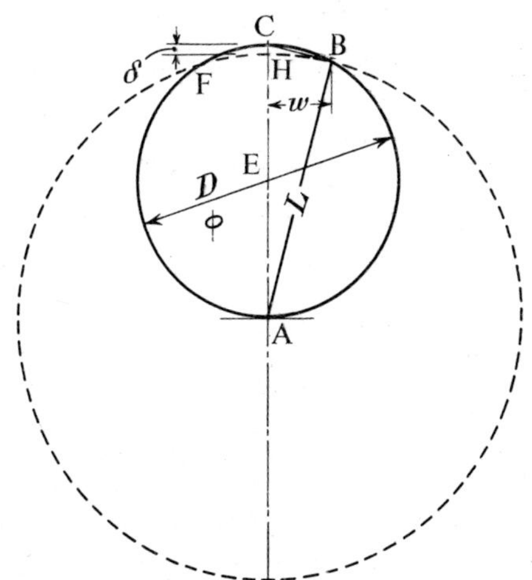

Fig. 16(*b*)

An approximate solution to the problem which will be accurate enough for most practical purposes is as follows:

If BC is joined, angle B is a right angle, since it is the angle in a semicircle, and in triangle ABC: $AC^2 = CB^2 + AB^2$.

$$AC = D;\ AB = L \text{ and CB is very nearly equal to } w.$$

Hence we may say: $D^2 = L^2 + w^2$ approximately.

But

$$D = L + \delta$$
$$(L + \delta)^2 = L^2 + w^2$$
$$L^2 + 2L\delta + \delta^2 = L^2 + w^2$$

Now δ will be a very small quantity, probably less than 0·02 mm so that δ^2 will be so small that we may ignore it.

Hence

$$L^2 + 2L\delta = L^2 + w^2$$
$$2L\delta = w^2$$
$$\delta = \frac{w^2}{2L}$$

This enables us to find the amount the gauge is smaller than the hole when we know how far the end may be rocked on either side of the centre line.

Example 12. If a 375 mm point gauge rocked 6 mm at one end, calculate the diameter of the hole being gauged.

The difference (δ) $= \dfrac{w^2}{2L}$ and if the total movement is 6 mm, $w = 3$ mm

$$\therefore \quad \delta = \frac{3^2}{2 \times 375} = \frac{9}{750} = 0{\cdot}012\,\text{mm}$$

Hence, Hole diameter = <u>375·012 mm</u>

Exercises 2c

1. The radius of the vial of a spirit level is 25 m. When this is placed on the bed of a machine $2\frac{1}{2}$ m long, the bubble is 3 mm from its central position. What is the end to end error in the machine?

2. A machine bed is 1·8 m long and is tested by a level 150 mm long. One division on the level corresponds to an inclination of 0·06 mm per m. The level is transversed in steps of its length, from the LH to the RH end of the bed, with the following results:

Position of Level	1	2	3	4	5	6
Reading (Division) [+ LH end high, – RH end high]	0	0	$+\frac{1}{2}$	$+1$	$+1\frac{1}{2}$	$+\frac{1}{2}$

(continued on p. 31)

Position of Level	7	8	9	10	11	12
Reading (Division) [+ LH end high / – RH end high]	0	$-\frac{1}{2}$	-1	$-1\frac{1}{2}$	-1	0

Make a scale diagram showing the dip in the bed to an enlarged scale, and calculate the total error.

3. If a level is to be sensitive enough to indicate 1 minute of angle by 3 mm of movement of the bubble, what must be the radius of the vial?

4. Calculate the ietting of a 250 mm iine bar to sheck a taper of 1 in 6 on the diameter.

5. A 100 mm sine bar is used to check the inclination of a surface which is given on the drawing as 26°36′ ± 4′. The height of one plug above the other is found to be 45·03 mm. What is the error in the angle of the surface?

6. A sine square has 4 plugs spaced at the corners of a 125 mm square. To mark out the template shown at Fig. 17, the template is secured to the sine square and line AB is first marked parallel to two of the plugsı The square is then tilted and set to the correct angles for marking BC, CD and AD. Calculate the settings for marking these lines and also the lengths x and y.

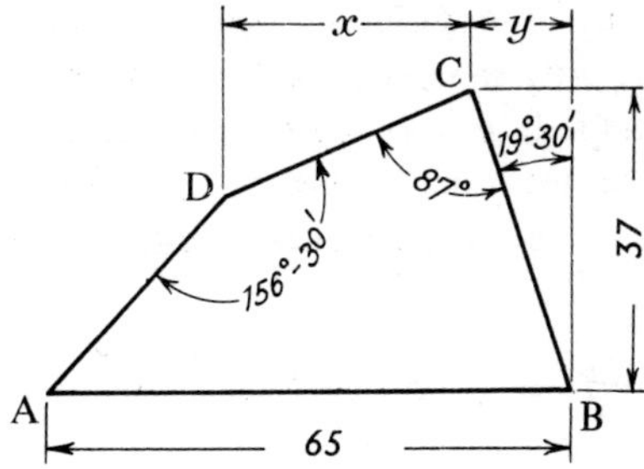

Fig. 17

7. In testing an angular surface with a 200 mm sine bar, the reading obtained is 122·30 mm for the height of one plug above the other. If the bar is 6 mm out of alignment with the line of maximum slope, calculate the true angle of the surface and state the error in the reading.

8. A point gauge 500 mm long, when tried in a bore, rocks a total amount of 12 mm at one end. When it is tried in a position at 90° to the first position, the movement is 24 mm. Calculate the mean diameter of the bore and the out of roundness.

9. A vee of 120° with a 12 mm flat at its bottom is placed on a cylinder and the distance from the flat to the curved surface of the cylinder is 2·40 mm. Calculate the diameter of the cylinder.

10. In Fig. 18 A and B are two spherical seating pins 14 mm diameter.

Calculate the height H so that the distance between the circle and the setting pin C shall be 0·50 mm.

(A and B are true half spheres.)

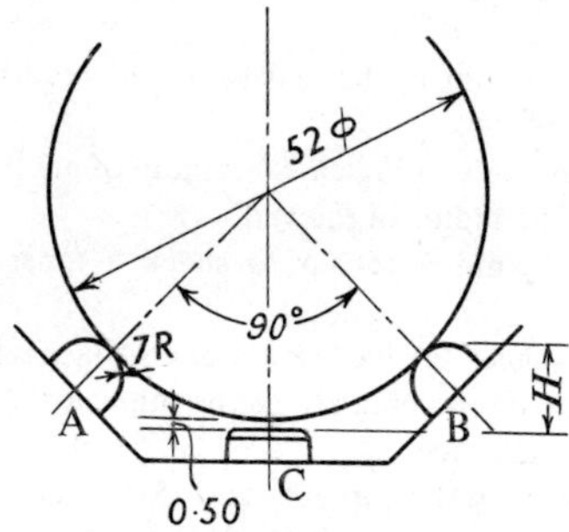

Fig. 18

11. How much rock must be allowed on a point gauge 460 mm long if the bore is to be finished to 460·06 mm diameter?

The location of points on angular surfaces

When a component having an angular surface is shown in orthographic projection on a drawing, only the projected view is given, and unless a true auxiliary view is added to give particulars of points located on the surface, some means must be found to calculate their position. Two or three problems of this type will be illustrated in the following examples:

Example 13. The plan and elevation of a block with two holes is shown in Fig. 19 (*a*).

Find (*a*) the centre distance of the holes,

(*b*) the angle between XX and AB, both dimensions *as measured on the sloping surface*.

In dealing with problems of this type it is well to cultivate the sense of visualizing lengths in 3 perpendicular directions, and also of being able to make a rough pictorial sketch of the data. The sketch is generally very useful in helping to show up how the problem should be treated.

In Fig. 19 (*b*), A and B are the hole centres, C is a point on the sloping surface where the centre lines intersect, and D is the point where a vertical through A meets a horizontal through C.

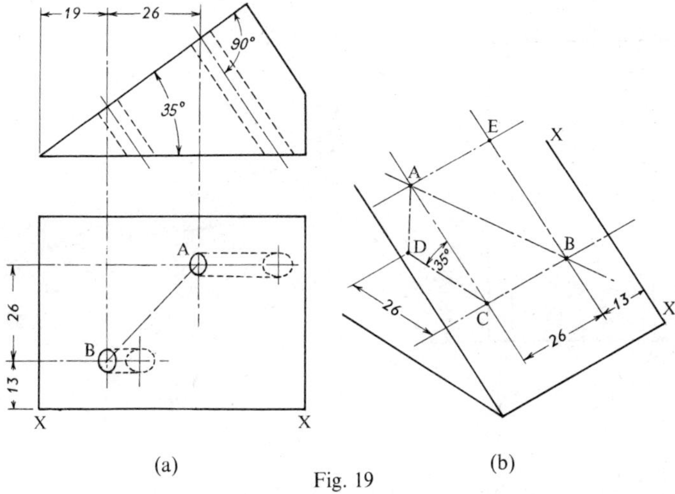

(a) Fig. 19 (b)

Then in triangle ACD:

$$CD = 26\,\text{mm},\ \hat{D} = 90^\circ \text{ and } \hat{C} = 35^\circ$$

$$AC = \frac{CD}{\cos 35^\circ} = \frac{26}{0{\cdot}8192} = 31{\cdot}74\,\text{mm}$$

The centre distance AB is the hypotenuse of the right-angled triangle ABC.

$$AB^2 = 26^2 + 31{\cdot}74^2 = 1684$$

$$AB = \sqrt{1684} = \underline{41{\cdot}04\,\text{mm}}$$

The angle made by AB with the side of the block is the angle ABE and

$$\frac{AE}{AB} = \sin ABE = \frac{26}{41{\cdot}04}$$

$$= 0{\cdot}6335$$

From which $\widehat{ABE} = \underline{39^\circ 18'}$

Example 14. Fig. 20 (*a*) shows the plan and elevation of a block in which a hole has to be drilled, entering at the point A, and leaving at B. Calculate the angular settings of the block for drilling.

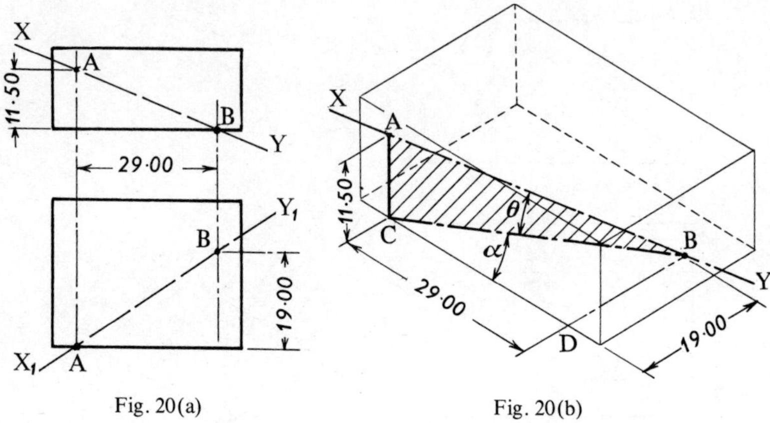

Fig. 20(a) Fig. 20(b)

The centre line of the hole is lettered XY in the elevation, and X_1Y_1 in the plan, point B being underneath the block as drawn. A pictorial view of the job is shown at Fig. 20 (*b*), and in that diagram AC is a vertical and BC a horizontal line. For drilling the hole, the base of the block must be set at an angle of θ, and the face containing A must be set at α, both angles being with the vertical.

In triangle CDB:

$$CD = 29\,\text{mm},\ DB = 19\,\text{mm and } \hat{D} = 90°$$

$$\therefore\quad CB^2 = 29^2 + 19^2 = 1202$$

$$CB = \sqrt{1202} = 34{\cdot}67\,\text{mm}$$

$$\tan\theta = \frac{AC}{CB} = \frac{11{\cdot}5}{34{\cdot}67} = 0{\cdot}3317$$

$$\theta = 18°21'$$

$$\tan\alpha = \frac{DB}{CD} = \frac{19}{29} = 0.6552$$

$$\alpha = 33°14'$$

Example 15. Calculate the angular settings for drilling a hole on the line AB shown in Fig. 21.

If A is joined to C, triangle ABC is formed and AC is parallel and equal to the line DE, shown on the end of the bar.

$$DE = OE \sec 45° = OE \times 1{\cdot}414 = 26 \times 1{\cdot}414 = 36{\cdot}76\,\text{mm}$$

and in triangle ABC:

$$\frac{BC}{AC} = \tan \hat{A} = \frac{52}{36{\cdot}76} = 1{\cdot}4146$$

from which $\hat{A} = 54° 45'$.

Hence, if lines DE and EC are marked on the bar, and the end of the bar set at 54° 45′ to the horizontal with DE parallel to the line of greatest slope, a hole started at B will break through at A.

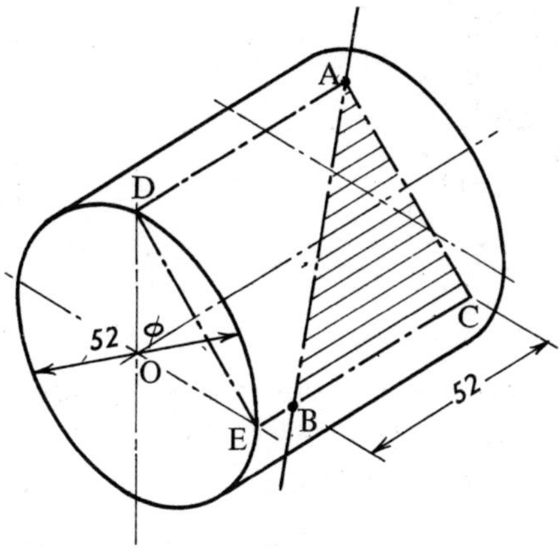

Fig. 21

Example 16. In the drawing of the component shown at Fig. 22 (*x*) the two sloping holes starting at A and B must meet at a point 10 mm from the base of the block. Find the starting heights *a* and *b* of the angular holes.

A diagrammatic view of the base of the block is shown at Fig. 22 (*y*) in which the lines AB, BC and AC are assumed to be horizontal ones (i.e. the projections of lines joining the points A, B and C).

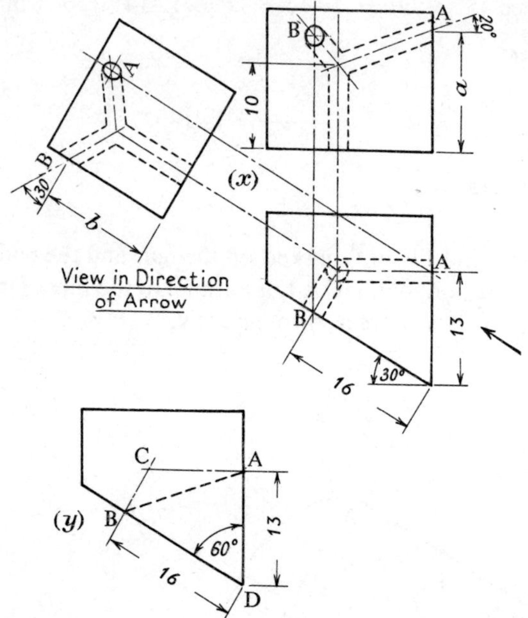

Fig. 22

In triangle ABD:

$$
\begin{aligned}
AB^2 &= 13^2 + 16^2 - 2 \times 13 \times 16 \cos 60^\circ \text{ (cosine rule)} \\
&= 169 + 256 - 208 = 217 \\
AB &= \sqrt{217} = 14{\cdot}73\,\text{mm}
\end{aligned}
$$

$$
\text{also } \frac{AB}{\sin 60^\circ} = \frac{13}{\sin B}
$$

$$
\sin \hat{B} = \frac{13 \sin 60^\circ}{14{\cdot}73} = 0{\cdot}7644
$$

$$
\hat{B} = 49^\circ 51'
$$

$$
\text{Hence} \quad \hat{A} = 180^\circ - (60^\circ + 49^\circ 51') = 70^\circ 9'
$$

$$
\text{Since } \widehat{DBC} = 90^\circ;\ \widehat{ABC} = 90^\circ - 49^\circ 51' = 40^\circ 9'
$$

$$
\text{also } \widehat{BAC} = 90^\circ - 70^\circ 9' = 19^\circ 51'
$$

In triangle ABC; AB = 14·73. $\hat{B} = 40^\circ 9'$ $\hat{A} = 19^\circ 51'$

$$\text{also } \hat{C} = 180° - (19°51' + 40°9') = 120°$$

and
$$\frac{BC}{\sin 19°51'} = \frac{14{\cdot}73}{\sin 120°} \text{ from which } BC = 5{\cdot}77\,\text{mm}$$

also in the same triangle:

$$\frac{AC}{\sin 40°9'} = \frac{14{\cdot}73}{\sin 120°} \text{ whence } AC = 10{\cdot}97\,\text{mm}$$

The centre lines of the holes of which AC and BC are projections, slope upwards at 20° and 30° respectively.

Hence, height of A above C = AC tan 20° = 10·97 × 0·364 = 3·99 mm and height of B above C = BC tan 30 = 5·77 × 0·5774 = 3·33 mm.

This completes the solution of the problem and gives us the following data:

$$\text{dimension } a = 3{\cdot}99 + 10 = \underline{13{\cdot}99\,\text{mm}}$$
$$\text{dimension } b = 3{\cdot}33 + 10 = \underline{13{\cdot}33\,\text{mm}}$$

Exercises 2d

1. A straight-edge is placed on a surface sloping at 36° 45′ and is set at an angle of 15° to the line of greatest slope. Calculate the inclination of the straight-edge to the horizontal.

2. In Fig. 23 a hole is to be drilled, starting in the centre of the sloping face, and breaking out at the corner B. Calculate the angle between the vertical plane containing centre line AB of the hole, and the face BCD of the block.

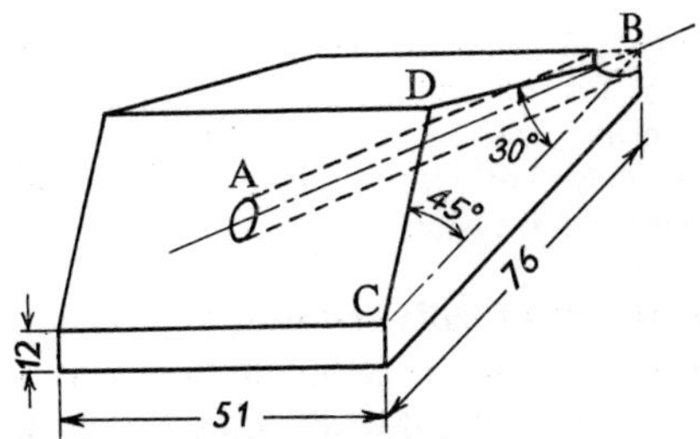

Fig. 23

3. For Fig. 23, calculate the angle between the centre line of the hole and the base of the block, for a hole starting at A and breaking out in the centre of the base.

4. In Fig. 24 A and B are two points on the sloping surface shown, and line AB is parallel to the sloping edge. Find (i) angle line AB makes with the horizontal, (ii) dimensions a and b, and (iii) distance AB.

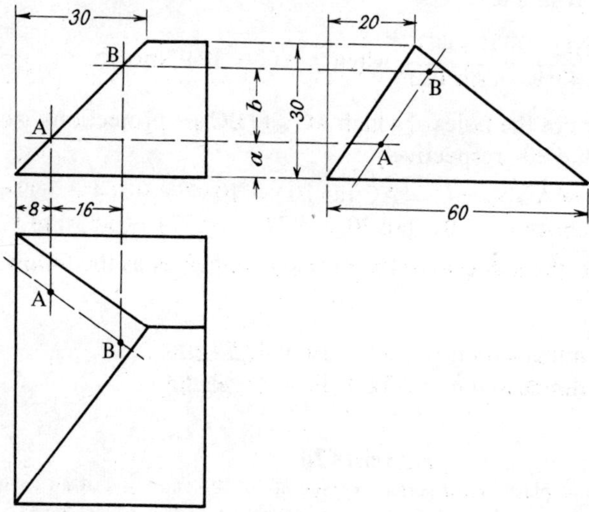

Fig. 24

5. In Fig. 25, 6 holes are equally spaced, start on an 80 mm pitch circle and break through on a 130 mm circle. Calculate the angle between the centre lines of one hole and the next.

6. In Fig. 26 find the distance a and the angle α for a hole whose centre line AB shall be tangential to the 60 mm circle.

7. Calculate the height from the base to the centres of holes A and B in Fig. 27.

8. In Fig. 28 a hole AB starts at A and leaves the bottom of the block at B. Find the length of this hole and the angle it makes with the base of the block. Another hole is to start at H, and be drilled in a plane parallel to the plane CDEF. The second hole must run into the first (i.e. their centre lines must intersect). Calculate the angle that the centre line of the second hole must make with the base.

Measurement of tapers by means of balls and rollers

Male taper with rollers (Fig. 29 (a)). If two similar rollers are placed in contact with the taper on opposite sides as shown, then for rollers of diameter d and centers c:

$$h = c \tan \frac{\alpha}{2} \tag{1}$$

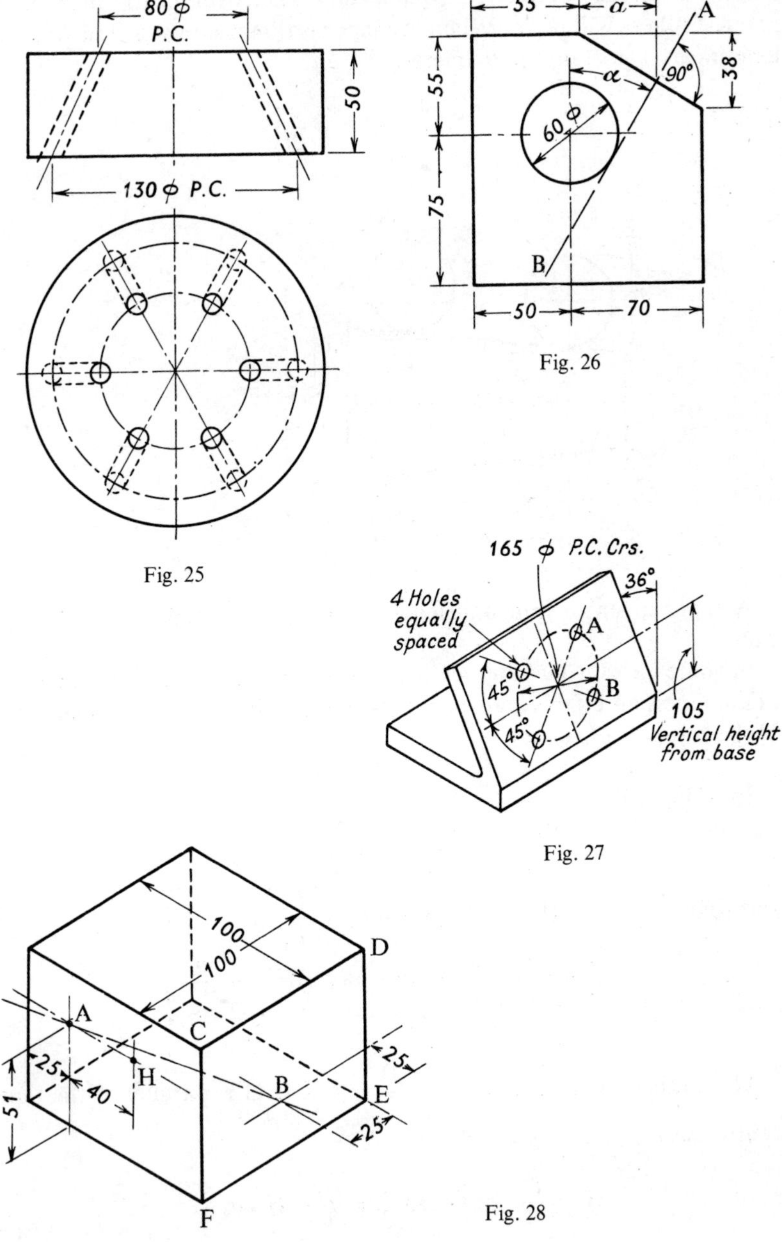

Fig. 25

Fig. 26

Fig. 27

Fig. 28

and the difference between the dimensions taken over the top and bottom pairs of rollers will be $2h$. When the taper is dimensioned as 1 in a certain length (say 1 in l) on the diameter,

then $$\frac{h}{c} = \frac{1}{2l} \text{ and } h = \frac{c}{2l} \qquad (2)$$

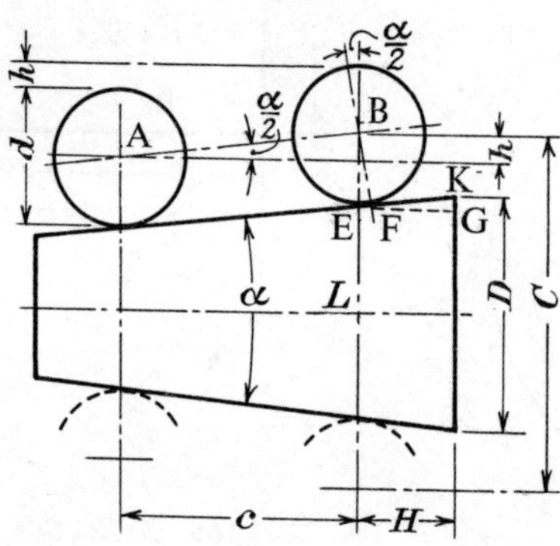

Fig. 29 (*a*).

A taper given in mm/unit length may be converted to 1·in l by division.

In some cases it may be necessary to have a check on the diameter D of the taper, and if this diameter is situated at a distance H from the centre of the top pair of rollers:

In triangle BEF:

$$\frac{\text{BF}}{\text{BE}} = \cos\frac{\alpha}{2},$$

and since $$\text{BF} = \tfrac{1}{2} \text{ dia of roller} = \frac{d}{2}$$

$$\frac{d}{2\text{BE}} = \cos\frac{\alpha}{2}, \text{ from which BE} = \frac{d}{2\cos\frac{\alpha}{2}}$$

The radius EL of the taper $= \dfrac{D}{2} -$ GK (EG is parallel to the taper centre line).

$$\text{EL} = \frac{D}{2} - \text{EG}\tan\frac{\alpha}{2} = \frac{D}{2} - H\tan\frac{\alpha}{2}$$

$$C\text{(centre distance of rollers)} = 2(\text{BE} + \text{EL})$$
$$= 2\left(\frac{d}{2\cos\frac{\alpha}{2}} + \frac{D}{2} - H\tan\frac{\alpha}{2}\right) \quad (3)$$

In practice, C, d and H would be known, so we require to transpose for D.

This gives that

$$\frac{C}{2} + H\tan\frac{\alpha}{2} - \frac{d}{2\cos\frac{\alpha}{2}} = \frac{D}{2}$$

and
$$D = C + 2H\tan\frac{\alpha}{2} - \frac{d}{\cos\frac{\alpha}{2}} \quad (4)$$

If the taper is dimensioned as 1 in l:

Then
$$\tan\frac{\alpha}{2} = \frac{1}{2l}$$

and
$$\cos\frac{\alpha}{2} = \frac{l}{\sqrt{\frac{1}{4} + l^2}} \text{ (Fig. 29}(b)\text{)}.$$

D then becomes

$$D = C + \frac{H}{l} - \frac{d\sqrt{\frac{1}{4} + l^2}}{l} \quad (5)$$

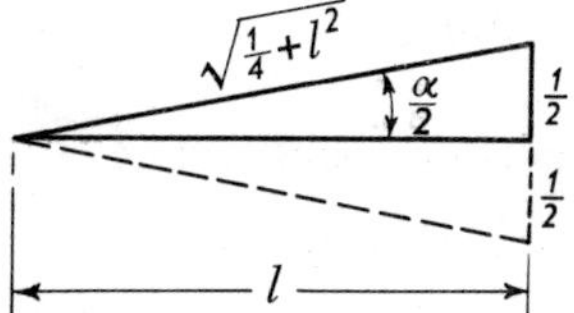

Fig. 29 (*b*).

In practice, for the measurement of tapers in this way, it is helpful to have a fixture of some kind which will support the taper and provide supporting and gauging arrangements for the rollers.

Example 17. A taper of 1 in 10 on the diameter is 80 mm long. Two pairs of rollers 12 mm dia. are used to check it, and the spacing of the rollers is as shown in Fig. 30. If the reading over the top rollers is 105 mm, calculate (*a*) the reading for the bottom rollers, (*b*) the diameter of the taper on a circle 14 mm from the top.

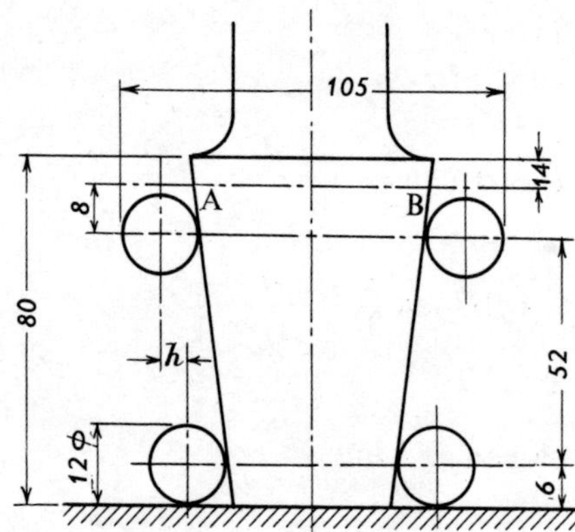

Fig. 30.

If the top rollers are situated at 58 mm from the face on which the taper and bottom rollers are resting, the roller centres will be 52 mm as shown.

Centre distance of top rollers = 105 − 12 = 93 mm and applying the formula to find h we have

$$h = \frac{c}{2l}[\text{where } c = 52 \text{ and } l = 10]$$

$$= \frac{52}{20} = 2{\cdot}60\,\text{mm}$$

Hence the reading over the bottom roller will be

$$93 - 5{\cdot}2 + 12 = 99{\cdot}8\,\text{mm}$$

For calculating the diameter D of AB we have from (5) above that

$$D = c + \frac{H}{l} - \frac{d\sqrt{\frac{1}{4} + l^2}}{l}$$

and $C = 93$, $H = 8$, $d = 12$, $l = 10$

So that

$$D = 93 + \frac{8}{10} - \frac{12\sqrt{\frac{1}{4} + 100}}{10}$$

$$= 93{\cdot}8 - 12{\cdot}012 = \underline{81{\cdot}788\,\text{mm}}$$

Checking a taper hole by means of balls

For this it is necessary to use two balls of different diameters which will rest in the hole, touching its sides. The ball sizes should be chosen to give a reasonable centre distance (c), and this may be measured by employing a depth gauge from the top face of the hole to the top of the lower ball, and a height or depth gauge to the top of the upper one.

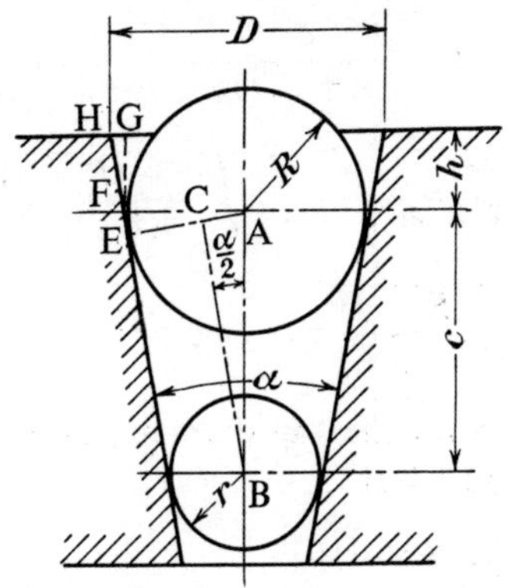

Fig. 31

Generally, the dimensions R, r, c and h in Fig. 31 would be known, and we require to derive formulae for finding α and D.

E is the point where the ball contacts with the side of the hole and BC is parallel to the side of the taper.

Then in triangle ABC:

$$\text{AB} = c,\ \text{C} = 90^\circ,\ \text{and}\ \hat{\text{B}} = \frac{\alpha}{2}$$

$$\text{AC} = R - r\ (\text{since CE} = r),$$

so that

$$\frac{\text{AC}}{\text{AB}} = \sin\frac{\alpha}{2}$$

$$\frac{R - r}{c} = \sin\frac{\alpha}{2} \qquad (6)$$

which enables us to find the angle α of the taper.

If the taper is dimensioned as 1 in l on the diameter, then from Fig. 29 (b),

$$\sin\frac{\alpha}{2} = \frac{\frac{1}{2}}{\sqrt{\frac{1}{4} + l^2}}$$

and from above,

$$\frac{R - r}{c} = \frac{\frac{1}{2}}{\sqrt{\frac{1}{4} + l^2}}$$

$$\sqrt{\tfrac{1}{4} + l^2} = \frac{c}{2(R - r)}.$$

Square both sides:

$$\tfrac{1}{4} + l^2 = \frac{c^2}{4(R - r)^2},$$

from which

$$l^2 = \frac{c^2}{4(R - r)^2} - \tfrac{1}{4}$$

and

$$l = \sqrt{\frac{c^2}{4(R - r)^2} - \tfrac{1}{4}} = \sqrt{\frac{c^2 - (R - r)^2}{4(R - r)^2}}$$

$$= \frac{\sqrt{c^2 - (R - r)^2}}{2(R - r)}. \qquad (7)$$

To obtain an expression for the top diameter D of the hole we must consider triangles AEF and FGH

and

$$D = 2(\text{AF} + \text{GH})$$

$$= 2\left(\text{AE}\sec\frac{\alpha}{2} + \text{FG}\tan\frac{\alpha}{2}\right)\left[\text{since } \hat{\text{E}} = \text{G} = 90°\right]$$

$$= 2\left(R\sec\frac{\alpha}{2} + h\tan\frac{\alpha}{2}\right) \qquad (8)$$

For a taper of 1 in l on the diameter

$$\sec\frac{\alpha}{2} = \frac{\sqrt{\frac{1}{4} + l^2}}{l} \text{ and } \tan\frac{\alpha}{2} = \frac{1}{2l} \text{ [Fig. 29 (}b\text{)]}$$

and D becomes

$$2\left[\frac{R\sqrt{\frac{1}{4} + l^2}}{l} + \frac{h}{2l}\right] \qquad (9)$$

Example 18. In a check on a taper hole, using the symbols and method given in Fig. 31, the following results were obtained:

$R = 15\,\text{mm}$, $r = 12{\cdot}5\,\text{mm}$, $c = 37{\cdot}4\,\text{mm}$ and $h = 7{\cdot}3\,\text{mm}$.
Calculate the total angle of taper and the top diameter.

Here we have from above, that $\sin\frac{\alpha}{2} = \frac{R - r}{c}$

$$= \frac{15 - 12{\cdot}5}{37{\cdot}4} = 0{\cdot}0668$$

This gives $\frac{\alpha}{2} = 3°\ 50'$ and $\alpha = \underline{7°\ 40'}$.

$$D = 2\left(R \sec\frac{\alpha}{2} + h \tan\frac{\alpha}{2}\right)$$

$$\sec\frac{\alpha}{2} = 1{\cdot}0022$$

$$\tan\frac{\alpha}{2} = 0{\cdot}0670$$

$$D = 2(15 \times 1{\cdot}0022 + 7{\cdot}3 \times 0{\cdot}0670) = \underline{31{\cdot}04\,\text{mm}}$$

Exercises 2e

1. Calculate the diameter D and the included angle of the taper for the case shown in Fig. 32.

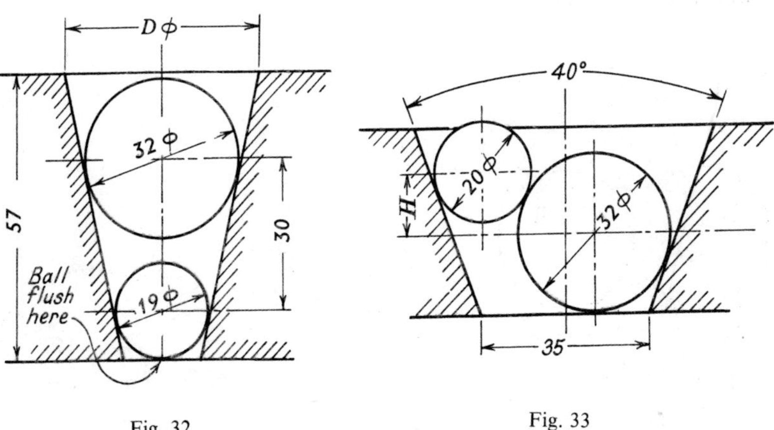

Fig. 32

Fig. 33

2. For the gauge shown in Fig. 33 calculate the centre height H between the two balls. (See Example 22, p. 52.)

3. Calculate, for the set-up shown in Fig. 34, the dimensions A and B. (The rollers are all 20 mm dia.)

4. For the example shown in Fig. 35, make up an expression connecting H with the centre distance D of the rollers. Find H when $D = 77$ mm.

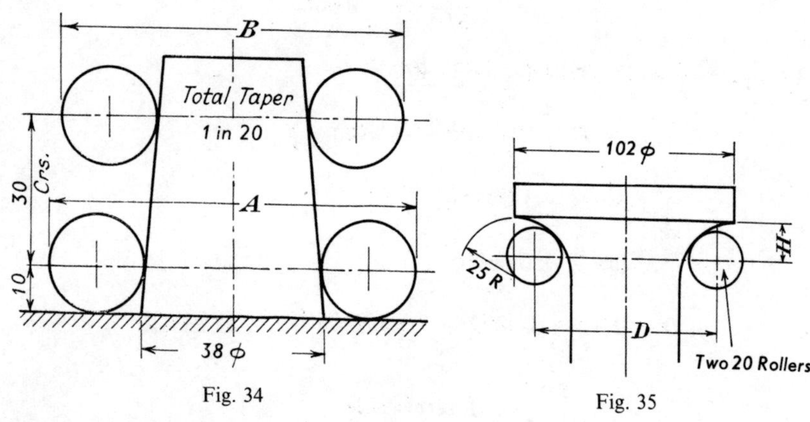

Fig. 34

Fig. 35

5. A hole A of diameter D has two equal plugs, B, which just fit into it. Obtain an expression in terms of D for the diameter d, of two more plugs C, which will just fit into the spaces left (Fig. 36).

Find d when $D = 80$ mm.

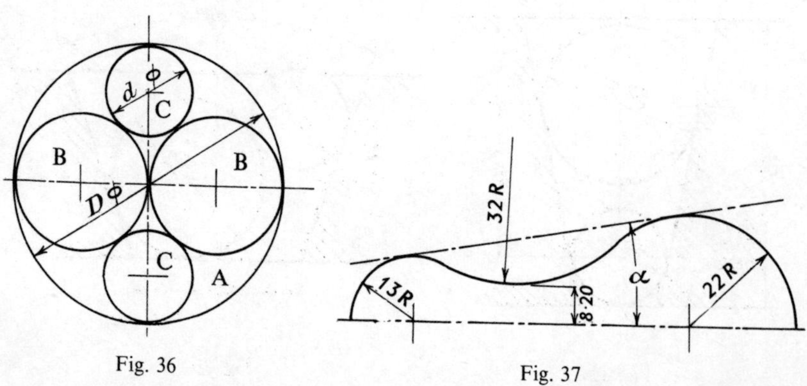

Fig. 36

Fig. 37

6. In Fig. 37 the three radii blend together.
Calculate the angle α.

Wire measurement of screw threads

For the fundamental accurate measurement of a screw thread such as is necessary in turning taps and screw gauges, the method employing 3 wires is a very useful one. The wires are arranged as shown in Fig. 38 (*a*).

We will work out a general case, and in Fig. 38 (*b*) is shown a wire, radius r, resting in a sharp pointed thread of angle α, pitch p and effective (or mean) diameter D_E. The wire size is not important, providing the three are the same diameter, touch at the flat portion of the thread, and are large enough to project above the thread for gauging. The best results

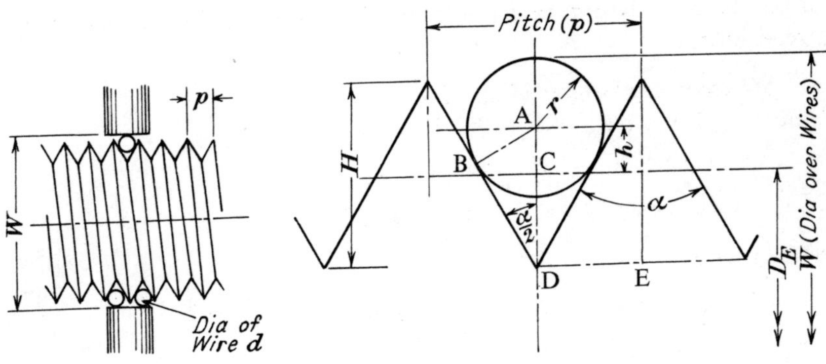

Fig. 138

are obtained, however, if the wires touch the thread at the effective diameter, and for this reason the wires should be near to the following diameters:

For ISO Metric and Unified $d = 0{\cdot}577\,p$

For Whitworth $d = 0{\cdot}564\,p$

In Fig. 38 (*b*), $\quad AD = AB \operatorname{cosec}\frac{\alpha}{2} = r \operatorname{cosec}\frac{\alpha}{2}$

$$H = DE \cot\frac{\alpha}{2} = \frac{p}{2}\cot\frac{\alpha}{2}$$

$$CD = \tfrac{1}{2}H = \frac{p}{4}\cot\frac{\alpha}{2}$$

$$h = AD - CD = r \operatorname{cosec}\frac{\alpha}{2} - \frac{p}{4}\cot\frac{\alpha}{2}$$

and distance over wires (W)

$$= D_E + 2h + 2r$$

$$= D_E + 2\left(r \operatorname{cosec}\frac{\alpha}{2} - \frac{p}{4}\cot\frac{\alpha}{2}\right) + 2r$$

$$= D_E + 2r\left(1 + \operatorname{cosec}\frac{\alpha}{2}\right) - \frac{p}{2}\cot\frac{\alpha}{2}$$

$$= D_E + d\left(1 + \operatorname{cosec}\frac{\alpha}{2}\right) - \frac{p}{2}\cot\frac{\alpha}{2} \text{ (where } d = \text{dia. of wires)}$$

Having established this general formula, which may be applied to any thread, we will determine its special adaptation for the most common thread forms.

(a) *ISO metric and unified* (Fig. 39)

Here $D_E = D - 2(0{\cdot}325p) = D - 0{\cdot}65p$

$$\alpha = 60^\circ$$

$$\operatorname{cosec}\frac{\alpha}{2} = 2 : \cot\frac{\alpha}{2} = 1{\cdot}732$$

W(over wires)

$$= D_E + d\left(1 + \operatorname{cosec}\frac{\alpha}{2}\right) - \frac{p}{2}\cot\frac{\alpha}{2}$$

$$= D - 0{\cdot}65p + d(3) - \frac{p}{2}(1{\cdot}732)$$

$$= D + 3d - 1{\cdot}516p$$

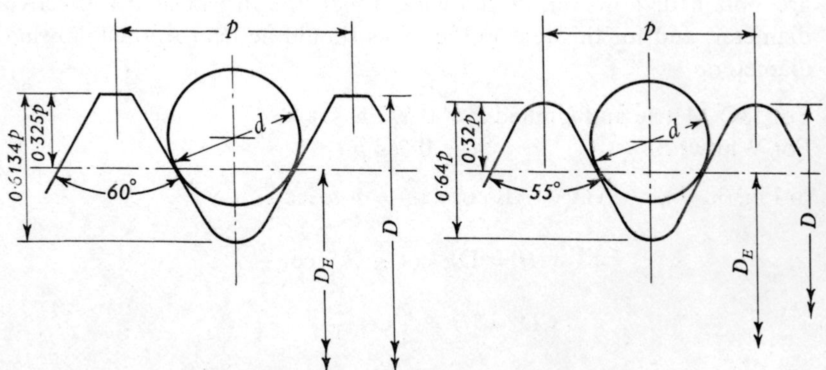

Fig. 39 ISO metric and unified

Fig. 40 Whitworth

(*b*) *Whitworth* (Fig. 40).

Here the depth of thread is $0{\cdot}64p$, so that $D_E = D - 0{\cdot}64p$

Also since

$$\alpha = 55^\circ$$

$$\operatorname{cosec}\frac{\alpha}{2} = 2{\cdot}1657$$

$$\cot\frac{\alpha}{2} = 1{\cdot}921$$

$$W \text{ (over wires)} = D_E + d\left(1 + \operatorname{cosec}\frac{\alpha}{2}\right) - \frac{p}{2}\cot\frac{\alpha}{2}$$

$$= D - 0{\cdot}64p + d(3{\cdot}1657) - \frac{p}{2}\cdot 1{\cdot}921$$

$$= D + 3{\cdot}1657d - 1{\cdot}60p$$

Example 19. Determine the measurement over wires for the following cases:

(a) $M30 \times 3{\cdot}5$ ISO metric using wires 2 mm dia.
(b) 1 in dia. × 10 t.p.i. Whitworth using wires 0·062 in dia.

(a) M30 × 3.5 ISO metric using 2 mm wires.

$$W = D + 3d - 1{\cdot}516p$$

$$D = 30,\ d = 2 \text{ and } p = 3{\cdot}5$$

$$\therefore W = 30 + 3 \times 2 - 1{\cdot}516 \times 3{\cdot}5$$

$$= \underline{30{\cdot}694 \text{ mm}}$$

(b) 1 in dia. × 10 t.p.i. Whitworth using 0·062 wires

$$W = D + 3{\cdot}1657d - 1{\cdot}60p$$

$$D = 1,\ d = 0{\cdot}062 \text{ and } p = 0{\cdot}1$$

$$W = 1 + 3{\cdot}1657 \times 0{\cdot}062 - 1{\cdot}60 \times 0{\cdot}1$$

$$= \underline{1{\cdot}036 \text{ in.}}$$

Checking the thread angle of a screw

By taking measurements over two sets of wires of diferent diameters a check on the thread angle may be made. The underlying theory of this is similar to that given on page 43 for the measurement of taper holes by means of two balls.

Miscellaneous problems in measurement

Examples in gauging and measurement are so many and varied that it is impossible to establish set rules for application to every problem. If the fundamental rules of geometry and trigonometry are known thoroughly it is nearly always possible to apply some of them to the solution of the problem. The following miscellaneous examples will serve to indicate possible methods of dealing with problems of a similar type.

Example 20. Two 25 mm circles centres D and B, touch a 100 mm circle, and their centres subtend an angle of 50° at its centre. Find the diameter of a circle which will touch the other three. The problem is shown at Fig. 41 and we require to obtain the diameter of circle C.

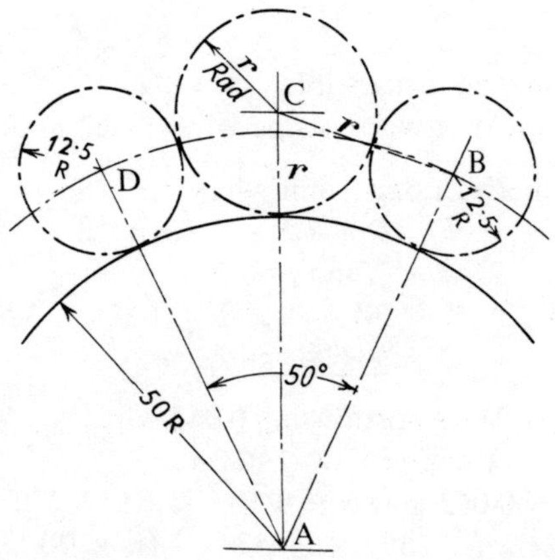

Fig. 41

If C and B are joined and triangle ABC is considered, we have:

$$AC = 50 + r;\ CB = 12{\cdot}5 + r,\ AB = 62{\cdot}5 \text{ and } \hat{A} = 25° \ (r = \text{rad of C})$$

Applying the cosine rule for triangle ABC

$$CB^2 = AC^2 + AB^2 - 2AC.AB\cos\hat{A}$$

Substituting the values from above gives us

$$(12{\cdot}5 + r)^2 = (50 + r)^2 + (62{\cdot}5)^2 - 2(50 + r)(62{\cdot}5)(0{\cdot}9063)$$

Multiplying out the brackets gives:

$$156{\cdot}3 + 25r + r^2 = 2500 + 100r + r^2 + 3906 - 5664 - 113{\cdot}29r$$

eliminate r^2 from both sides and collect terms

$$25r - 100r + 113{\cdot}29r = 2500 + 3906 - 5664 - 156{\cdot}3$$
$$38{\cdot}29r = 585{\cdot}7$$
$$r = \frac{585{\cdot}7}{38{\cdot}29} = 15{\cdot}29 \text{ mm}$$

giving a circle of $2 \times 15{\cdot}29 = \underline{30{\cdot}58 \text{ mm dia}}$

Example 21. From a piece of round material 40 mm radius, a piece 50 mm radius is cut as shown in Fig. 42. Find the distance x.

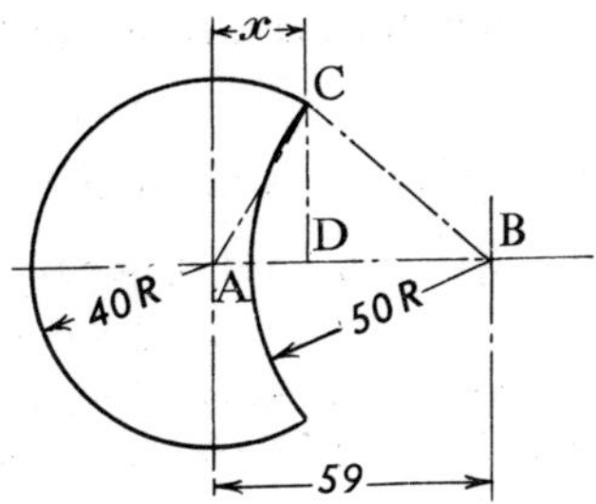

Fig. 42

If AC and BC are joined as shown in the figure, then in triangle ABC:

AB = 59, AC = 40 and BC = 50

$$\text{also } AC^2 = AB^2 + BC^2 - 2AB.BC \cos B \text{ (cosine rule)}$$

$$\cos B = \frac{AB^2 + BC^2 - AC^2}{2\,AB.BC} = \frac{5{\cdot}9^2 + 5^2 - 4^2}{2{\cdot}5{\cdot}9{\cdot}5} \text{(working in cm)}$$

$$= \frac{43{\cdot}81}{59} = 0{\cdot}7425$$

$$\hat{B} = 42°3'$$

If CD is $\perp r$ to AB, then

$$DB = CB \cos B = 50 \cos 42°3'$$
$$= 50 \times 0{\cdot}7425 = 37{\cdot}125 \text{ mm}$$
$$x = AB - DB = 59 - 37{\cdot}125 = \underline{21{\cdot}875 \text{ mm}}$$

Example 22. A profile gauge is as shown by ABCD in Fig. 43. Two plugs are placed in the gauge and dimension h is required as a check.

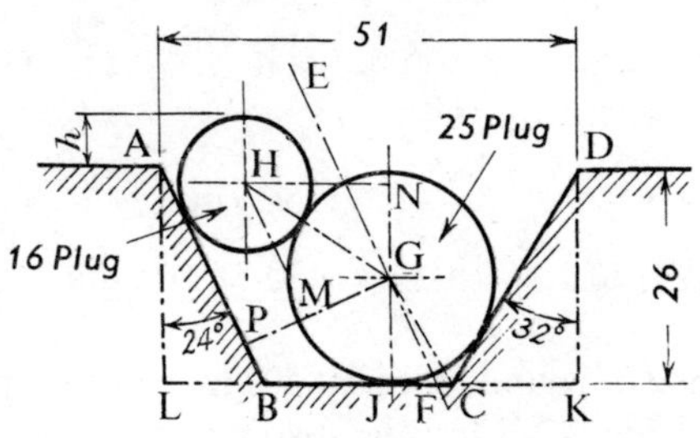

Fig. 43

In the diagram, EF and HM are drawn parallel to AB and PG in perpendicular to it. HN is a horizonatl line, and if we can find GN we shall be able to determine h.

$$CK = 26 \times \tan 32° = 16{\cdot}25\,\text{mm}$$

In triangle JCG: $\widehat{JCG} = \frac{122}{2} = 61°$, JG $= 12{\cdot}5$ and JC $=$ JG cot 61° $=$ $12{\cdot}5 \cot 61° = 6{\cdot}93\,\text{mm}$

In triangle ACB: $CB = AC \tan 24° = 26 \tan 24° = 11{\cdot}57\,\text{mm}$

In triangle JGF: $JF = JG \tan 24° = 12{\cdot}5 \tan 24° = 5{\cdot}56\,\text{mm}$

$$FC = JC - JF = 6{\cdot}93 - 5{\cdot}56 = 1{\cdot}37\,\text{mm}$$

$$BF = LK - (LB + FC + CK) = 51 - (11{\cdot}57 + 1{\cdot}37 + 16{\cdot}25) = 21{\cdot}81\,\text{mm}$$

$$GP = BF \cos 24° = 21{\cdot}81 \cos 24° = 20{\cdot}01\,\text{mm}$$

PM $=$ rad of small plug so that $GM = 20{\cdot}01 - 8 = 12{\cdot}01\,\text{mm}$

GH $=$ sum of plug radii $= 12{\cdot}5 + 8 = 20{\cdot}5\,\text{mm}$

$$\cos \widehat{HGM} = \frac{GM}{GH} = \frac{12{\cdot}01}{20{\cdot}5} = 0{\cdot}5858 \text{ and } \widehat{HGM} = 54°8'$$

Now $\widehat{HGN} = \widehat{PGN} - \widehat{HGM}$

and since $\widehat{PGN} = 90° + 24° = 114°$

$$\widehat{HGN} = 114 - 54°\,8' = 59°\,52'$$

$$GN = HG \cos \widehat{HGN} = 20{\cdot}5 \cos 59°\,52' = 20{\cdot}5 \times 0{\cdot}5020 = 10{\cdot}29\,\text{mm}$$

Distance $h = [\text{JG} + \text{GN} + \text{rad of small plug}] - 26$

$= 12{\cdot}5 + 10{\cdot}29 + 8 - 26$

$= \underline{4{\cdot}79\,\text{mm}}$

Example 23. For the turned part shown in Fig. 44, calculate the radius (R) so that the diameter at the throat may be 20 mm as shown.

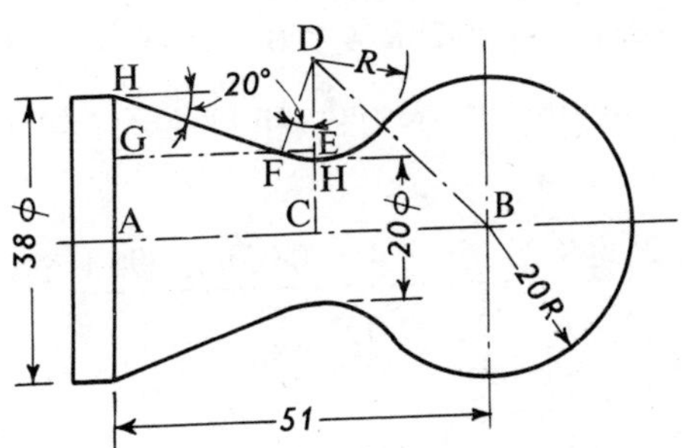

Fig. 44

The radius R blends into the 20° angular portion, and into the 20 mm radius, spherical end.

We have to construct and solve an equation to give us R.

DC is drawn perpendicular to AB, and DF is drawn to the point where R blends into the 20° angular portion so that FDE = 20°. GFE is parallel to AB.

Then we have that GF + FE + CB = AB = 51 mm.

$$\begin{aligned} GF &= GH \cot 20° = (AH - AG) \cot 20° = (AH - CE) \cot 20° \\ &= [AH - (CD - DE)] \cot 20° \\ &= [19 - \{(R + 10) - R \cos 20°\}] \cot 20° \\ &= [19 - R - 10 + 0{\cdot}9397R] \cot 20° \\ &= [9 - 0{\cdot}0603R] \cot 20° \\ &= 24{\cdot}73 - 0{\cdot}166R \end{aligned}$$

$$FE = R \sin 20° = 0{\cdot}342R$$

$$CB = \sqrt{DB^2 - DC^2} = \sqrt{(R + 20)^2 - (R + 10)^2}$$

Hence equating (GF + FE + CB) to AB = 51

$$24{\cdot}73 - 0{\cdot}166R + 0{\cdot}342R + \sqrt{(R + 20)^2 - (R + 10)^2} = 51$$

and this reduces to

$$\sqrt{(R + 20)^2 - (R + 10)^2} = 26{\cdot}27 - 0{\cdot}176R$$

Square both sides:

$$(R + 20)^2 - (R + 10)^2 = (26{\cdot}27 - 0{\cdot}176R)^2$$

i.e. by squaring out the brackets

$$R^2 + 40R + 400 - R^2 - 20R - 100 = 690{\cdot}1 - 9{\cdot}25R + 0{\cdot}031R^2$$

Collecting and re-arranging on the RH side:

$$0{\cdot}031R^2 - 29{\cdot}25R + 390{\cdot}1 = 0$$

This is a quadratic equation in R, and can be solved by the formula method.

$$R = \frac{29{\cdot}25 \pm \sqrt{29{\cdot}25^2 - 4 \times 0{\cdot}031 \times 390{\cdot}1}}{2 \times 0{\cdot}031}$$

From which $R = 930$ or $13{\cdot}55$

The smaller root, $R = 13{\cdot}55$ is obviously the one we require

Hence $\underline{R = 13{\cdot}55\,\text{mm}}$

Exercises 2f

1. Calculate the diameter over wires for the following screw threads:

(*a*) M20 × 2·5 ISO metric over 0·577*p* mm wires
(*b*) M36 × 2 ISO metric over 0·577*p* mm wires
(*c*) $\frac{3}{4}$in × 10t.p.i. Whitworth over 0·564*p* wires

2. A screw thread has the form and angle shown in Fig. 45. Calculate the reading W over 8 mm plugs placed in opposite threads.

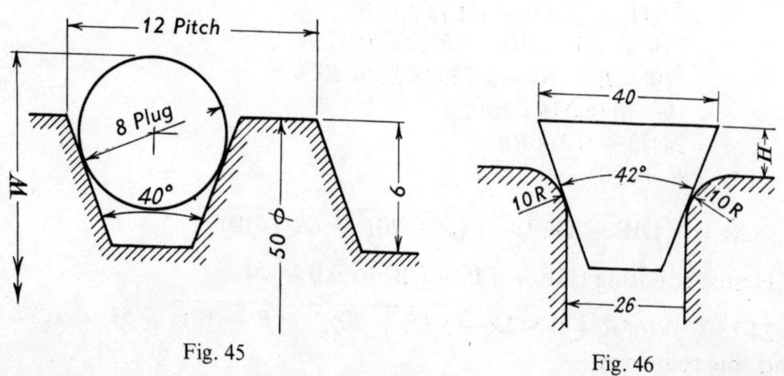

Fig. 45

Fig. 46

3. A wedge rests between two radiused jaws as shown in Fig. 46. When the top of the wedge is level, calculate the distance H.

4. Solve the previous problem, when the radius on the right-hand side jaw is 3 mm.

5. In Example 3, if the wedge has an included angle of 40°, and is tilted through an angle of 10°, calculate the distance H to its higher corner.

6. Calculate the distance from the centre of the circle (O) to the centre of the 20 mm plug placed in the slot shown in Fig. 47.

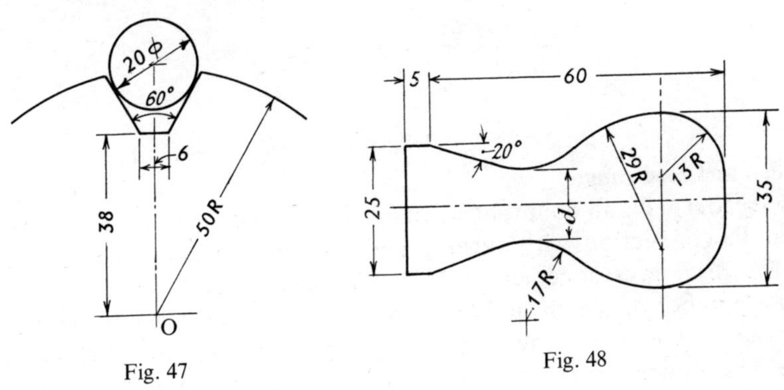

Fig. 47

Fig. 48

7. Fig. 48 shows the profile of a die form. From the information given, calculate the width d at the narrowest portion.

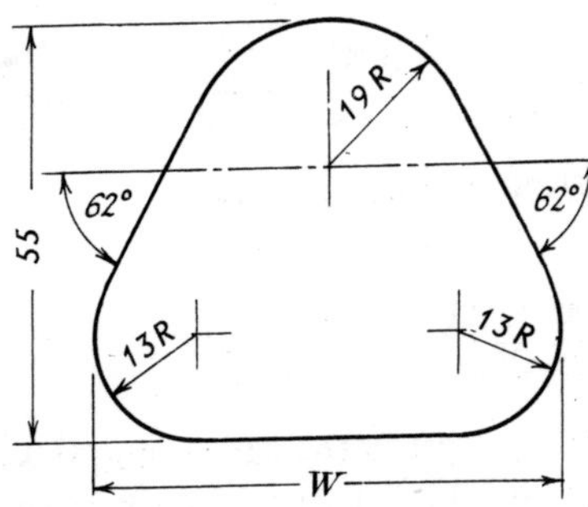

Fig. 49

8. From the information given in Fig. 49 calculate the width W of the profile shown.

3 Calculations for cutting, turning and boring

Speed and feed range

The reader will, no doubt, be acquainted with the meaning of speed and feed in connection with turning and boring operations.

The driving arrangements of machine tools usually make provision for a number of speeds and feeds, so that a suitable one may be chosen for the work in hand. The reader will probably be curious as to how these are determined. In the case of spindle speeds, the highest and lowest speeds in the range are generally related to the extremes of size for which the machine is designed. For example: a lathe might be designed to take a range of work varying from 10 mm to 250 mm diameter. Allowing for a cutting speed of 22 m/min, this would give for the top speed:

$$N = \frac{1000 \times 22}{\pi \times 10} = \frac{1000 \times 22 \times 7}{22 \times 10} = 700 \text{ rev/min}$$

as being suitable for the 10 mm diameter work.

For the lowest speed:

$$N = \frac{1000 \times 22}{\pi \times 250} = \frac{1000 \times 22 \times 7}{22 \times 250} = 28 \text{ rev/min}$$

These will be the highest and lowest in the range, and if we assume there are eight speeds altogether, six intermediate speeds must be chosen and fitted in, the intermediate speeds being so calculated that the whole series is in some regular order.

One method of arranging the speeds would be to make them in straight line form, in which each speed would be the same amount greater than the one below it. In this case, as there are 8 speeds and 7 intervals, each interval would be:

$$\frac{\text{Top speed} - \text{bottom speed}}{7} = \frac{700 - 28}{7} = \frac{672}{7} = 96$$

and the speeds would be:

1st 28 rev/mm, 2nd 28 + 96 = 124 rev/min
3rd 124 + 96 = 220 rev/min

and so on.

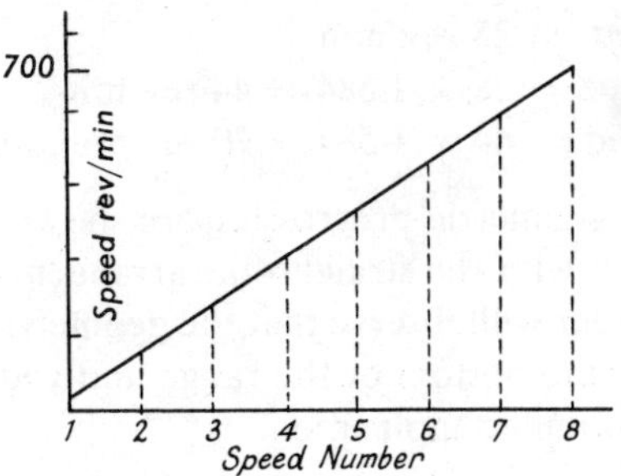

Fig. 50

If these were plotted on a graph, the result would be as shown in Fig. 50, and the series is known as an *Arithmetic Progression*.

In practice, speeds arranged in this way are not suitable, as the steps between the speeds at the lower end (28 rev/min, 124 rev/min, 220 rev/min) are too great, whilst at the upper end of the range (700, 604, 508 rev/min, etc.) a larger interval value could be tolerated without inconvenience.

To overcome these objections and provide a convenient range of speeds, they are generally arranged in *Geometric Progression*. When arranged in this way, instead of each speed being a constant amount greater than the one below it, the speed is a *constant multiple* of the one below it. The calculation for determining speeds arranged in geometric progression is as follows:

Considering the case we have taken, where the extremes are 28 and 700 rev/min with 8 speeds.

The 2nd speed will be a constant amount multiplied by the 1st, and the 3rd will be the same constant multiplied by the 2nd, and so on.

Let this constant be denoted by K.

Then 1st speed $= 28$
2nd speed $= 28 \times K = 28K$
3rd speed $= 28K \times K = 28K^2$
4th speed $= 28K^2 \times K = 28K^3$

and so on to the 8th speed, which we can see will be $28K^7$.

Now the 8th speed is 700 rev/min, so that

$$28K^7 = 700$$

$$K^7 = \frac{700}{28} = 25$$

$$K = \sqrt[7]{25} = 1{\cdot}584$$

No.	Log.
25	7)1·397 9(0·1997)

Hence we have 1st speed $= 28$ rev/min
2nd speed $= 28 \times 1{\cdot}584 = 44$ rev/min
3rd speed $= 44 \times 1{\cdot}584 = 70$ rev/min, and so on.

The speeds arranged in geometric pregression are shown plotted in Fig. 51, and their comparison with the straight-line arrangement is shown in the table below. The reader will observe that the geometric arrangement gives closer intervals at the bottom of the range and wider ones at the top which is more useful under application.

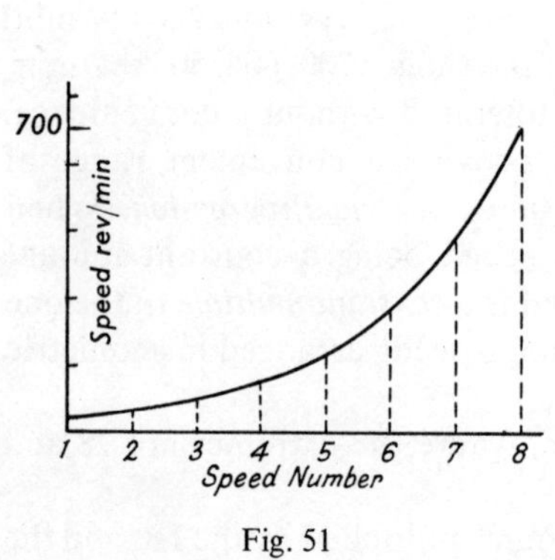

Fig. 51

Speed	Arithmetic Progression rev/min	Geometric Progression rev/min
1	28	28
2	124	44
3	220	70
4	316	111
5	412	176
6	508	279
7	604	442
8	700	700

We might put a geometric progression in general symbolic form as follows:

Let
$A_1 =$ 1st term
$A_2 =$ 2nd term
$A_n = n$th term
$K =$ constant multiplier
$n =$ number of terms

$$
\begin{aligned}
\text{1st term} &= A_1 \\
\text{2nd term} &= A_2 = A_1K \\
\text{3rd term} &= A_3 = A_2K = A_1K^2 \\
n\text{th term} &= A_n = A_1K_n^{\,n-1}
\end{aligned}
$$

(i.e. if $n = 8$, then the index of K is $8 - 1 = 7$).

Hence if $\quad A_n = A_1K^{n-1}$

$$K^{n-1} = \frac{A_n}{A_1} \text{ and } K = \sqrt[n-1]{\frac{A_n}{A_1}}.$$

In an example, A_1, A_n and n would be given and the expression above would enable K to be found and the whole series calculated.

Example 1. Calculate a suitable range of six speeds for a drilling machine, if the size range of the machine is to be from 2·5 mm to 10 mm drills and a cutting speed of 22 m/min is to be given. Show a speed table with suitable drill size for each speed.

We have that $N = \dfrac{1000S}{\pi d}$ where N = Spindle speed (rev/min).
S = Cutting speed (m/min).
d = Drill diameter.

For the top speed (2·5 mm drill)

$$N_6 = \frac{1000 \times 22}{\pi \times 2{\cdot}5} = \frac{1000 \times 22 \times 7}{22 \times 2{\cdot}5} = 2800 \text{ rev/min}$$

Lowest speed (10 mm drill)

$$N_1 = \frac{1000 \times 22}{\pi \times 10} = \frac{1000 \times 22 \times 7}{22 \times 10} = 700 \text{ rev/min}$$

$$K \text{ (the multiplier)} = \sqrt[5]{\frac{N_6}{N_1}} = \sqrt[5]{\frac{2800}{700}} = \sqrt[5]{4}$$

No.	Log.
4	5)0·6021(0·1204

Antilog 0·1204 = 1·319 = K.

We may now calculate the range of speeds as follows:

1st speed = 700 rev/min
2nd speed = 700 × 1·319 = 924 rev/min
3rd speed = 924 × 1·319 = 1220 rev/min

4th speed = 1220 × 1·319 = 1610 rev/min
5th speed = 1610 × 1·319 = 2120 rev/min
6th speed = 2120 × 1·319 = 2800 rev/min

The relationship between the speeds and the drill sizes they will accommodate may now be calculated:

	Nearest 0·25 mm
1st speed, 700 rev/min suitable for 10 mm drill	10 mm
2nd speed, 924 rev/min suitable for $10 \times \frac{700}{924}$	7·5 mm
3rd speed, 1220 rev/min suitable for $10 \times \frac{700}{1220}$	5·75 mm
4th speed, 1610 rev/min suitable for $10 \times \frac{700}{1610}$	4·25 mm
5th speed, 2120 rev/min suitable for $10 \times \frac{700}{2120}$	3·25 mm
6th speed, 2800 rev/min suitable for 2·5 mm drill	2·5 mm

The speed and drill diameter table is shown below.

Spindle Speed (rev/min)	700	924	1220	1610	2120	2800
Suitable drill diameter (mm)	10·0	7·5	5·75	4·25	3·25	2·5

Feeds

The factors governing the choice of feed-range limits is rather beyond our scope, but when the limits of the range have been fixed, together with the number of intermediates in the range, the steps usually follow the rules for geometric progression in the same way as the speeds.

Exercises 3a

1. A lathe is operating on a range of work varying from 25 mm to 250 mm diameter. Allowing for a cutting speed of 22 m/min, calculate the highest and lowest speeds necessary. If there are 8 speeds in the complete range, find the range of speeds if they are in geometric progression. Make out a table showing the most suitable diameter to be turned on each speed.

2. A drill has 4 speeds and drills a range of holes from 2 mm to 6 mm diameter. Calculate the four speeds if they are in geometric progression, and make a drill diameter speed table. Cutting speed = 16·5 m/min.

3. For Example No. **1.** Plot a graph showing spindle speeds vertical, and speed number horizontal.

4. On a 400 mm stroke single-pulley, all-geared shaping machine the number of turns of the driving pulley required to make one complete double stroke of the ram were found to be as follows:

1st speed, 27 turns
2nd speed, 16 turns
3rd speed, 8 turns
4th speed, 4 turns

Assuming the ratio $\frac{\text{Cutting time}}{\text{Return time}}$ to be $\frac{1{\cdot}25}{1}$ and to remain constant, estimate a suitable pulley speed to give an average cutting speed of 11 m/min in the lowest gear and on the longest stroke.

With this pulley speed, find the most suitable stroke for each of the other speeds.

5. The highest spindle speed for a small lathe is 1500 rev/min. In order to obtain a suitable cutting speed for drilling some 3 mm holes in brass, a drill head is mounted on the carriage, and driven in the opposite direction to the spindle. At what speed must the drilling spindle be driven to give a cutting speed of 66 m/min?

Cutting tool life

As a cutting tool does its work it becomes blunted, and a time ultimately arrives when it must be taken out and re-sharpened. The life of the tool between the times of re-grinding is influenced by the severity of its treatment whilst it is cutting. Depending upon circumstances, there is a best economic tool life for every tool; if the cutting duty is made such as to allow the tool to last longer than the best economic time, then it is cutting below an efficient rate and is doing less work then it might. On the other hand, if its performance is raised to a level such as to cause it to become blunted in less than the economic time, then undue expense and lost time are being incurred in the additional sharpening and re-setting necessary.

The problem of tool life and of cutting generally is rather complicated and indeterminate, since there are so many variable factors involved. From experimental data, however, cutting speed and tool life have been found to conform roughly to the following rule:

$$VT^n = C,$$

where V = Cutting speed in metres per minute
T = Corresponding life in minutes
C = A constant depending on cutting conditions

$n = \frac{1}{7}$ to $\frac{1}{8}$	for roughing cuts in steel	Using H.S.S. tools.
$= \frac{1}{12}$	for roughing cuts in cast iron	
$= \frac{1}{10}$	for light cuts in steel	
$= \frac{1}{5}$	for roughing cuts in steel	Using tungsten carbide tools.

The above values of n are only approximate and are influenced by tool shape, use of cutting compound, etc. The above relationship enables us to estimate probable tool life as shown in the following examples:

Example 2. When operating with roughing cuts on mild steel at 20 m/min a certain tool gave a life of 3 hours between re-grinds. Estimate the life of this tool on similar cuts at a speed of 30 m/min.

In the $VT^n = C$ expression for this case we will take $n = \frac{1}{8}$.

The first step is to calculate the value of the constant C.

We have that when $V = 20$, $T = 180$ min and $n = \frac{1}{8}$.

Hence $$C = 20 \times 180^{\frac{1}{8}}.$$

Taking logs

$$\text{Log } C = \log 20 + \frac{\log 180}{8}$$
$$= 1{\cdot}5829$$

No.	log
180	8)2·2553
$180^{\frac{1}{8}}$	0·2819
20	1·3010
	1·5829

Antilog 1·5829 = 38·27 = C.

Hence we may write:

$$VT^{\frac{1}{8}} = 38{\cdot}27$$

We now require T when

$$V = 30$$
$$30T^{\frac{1}{8}} = 38{\cdot}27$$
$$T^{\frac{1}{8}} = \frac{38{\cdot}27}{30} = 1{\cdot}2757$$
$$T = (1{\cdot}2757)^8$$
$$T = \text{antilog } 0{\cdot}8456$$
$$= \underline{7{\cdot}008, \text{ say } 7 \text{ min.}}$$

No.	Log
1·2757	0·1057
	8
	0·8456

Example 3. A tool cutting at 20 m/min gave a life of 1 hour between regrinds when operating on roughing cuts with mild steel. What will be its probable life when engaged on light finishing cuts? [Take $n = \frac{1}{8}$ for roughing, and $\frac{1}{10}$ for finishing cuts.]

Here we have for roughing:

$$20 \times 60^{\frac{1}{8}} = C$$

$$C = \text{antilog } 1{\cdot}5233 = 33{\cdot}38$$

No.	log
60	8)1·7782(
$60^{\frac{1}{8}}$	0·2223
20	1·3010
	1·5233

Applying to the finishing conditions

$$20 \times T^{\frac{1}{10}} = 33{\cdot}38$$

$$T^{\frac{1}{10}} = \frac{33{\cdot}38}{20} = 1{\cdot}669$$

$$T = (1{\cdot}669)^{10}$$

No.	log
1·669	0·2225
$(1{\cdot}669)^{10}$	2·225

$$T = \text{antilog } 2{\cdot}225 \quad = 167{\cdot}9, \text{ say } 168 \text{ min.}$$

Tool cutting angles

The principal angles on a cutting tool are its rakes and clearances, and these are shown in Fig. 52.

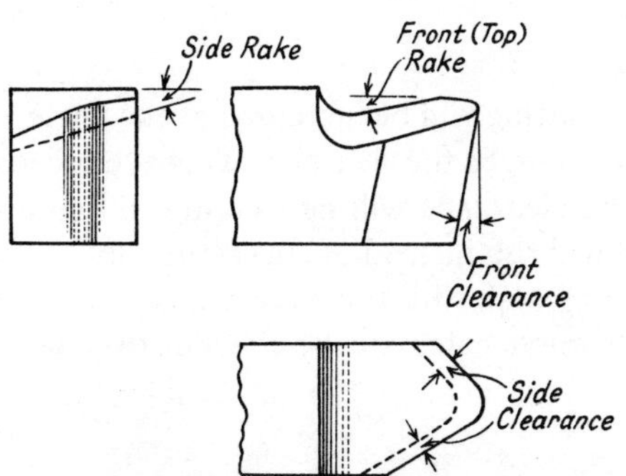

Fig. 52

The choice of suitable cutting angles depends upon the material being cut, and the reader should look up particulars in books dealing with

Workshop Technology. We might consider here the effect on the cutting angles of various tool settings.

When a tool is cutting a circular bar of material it is operating relative to a radial line drawn from the centre of the work to the cutting point. Thus in Fig. 53(a) the tool is cutting relative to the line OA. If the tool point is is level with the centre of the work the line OA is horizontal and the cutting angles operating are the true values put on the tool.

If, however, the tool point is placed above or below the centre, the cutting angles will be modified since the line OA is not now horizontal.

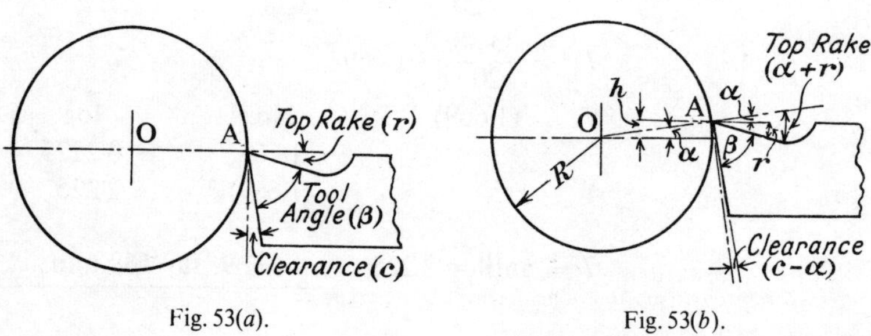

Fig. 53(a). Fig. 53(b).

In Fig. 53 (b) the tool point is shown a distance h above the work centre. The line OA is now tilted up an angle α, and if R is the radius of the work we have that $\sin \alpha = \dfrac{h}{R}$

The top rake angle of cutting will be increased by the angle α, and since the total angle β has not changed the clearance will be reduced by α. If the tool is put very high, the clearance will be so reduced that it will vanish altogether and the tool will rub instead of cut. If the tool is placed below the centre the effects are opposite, the rake being decreased and the clearance increased. We might calculate the effect on the cutting angles of a numerical example.

Example 4. A bar of material 60 mm diameter is being turned with a tool having 20° top rake and 6° front clearance. Calculate (a) the cutting angles when the tool is 2·5 mm above centre, and (b) the amount the tool must be above centre for the clearance to become zero.

The conditions are as shown at Fig. 53 (*b*).

(*a*) $\sin \alpha = \frac{2{\cdot}5}{30} = \frac{1}{12} = 0{\cdot}0833.$

From which $\alpha = 4° 47'$.

The rake is increased and the clearance decreased by this amount. Thus the rake becomes $20° + 4° 47' = 24° 47'$ and the clearance becomes $6° - 4° 47' = \underline{1° 13'}$.

(*b*) If the clearance is to vanish, then angle α must be 6°.

$$\sin \alpha = \frac{h}{30} \text{ and since } \sin 6° = 0{\cdot}1045$$

$$0{\cdot}1045 = \frac{h}{30}$$

$$h = 30 \times 0{\cdot}1045$$
$$= \underline{3{\cdot}14\,\text{mm}}$$

Exercise 3b

1. A certain tool when cutting cast iron had a life between regrinds of 2 hours when cutting at 20 m/min. If the relationship between life and speed is given by $VT^{\frac{1}{10}} = C$, calculate C, and estimate the tool life at a speed of 15 m/min.

2. For the tool in Question **1**, plot a graph of tool life-cutting speed over a range of speeds from 30 m/min to 15 m/min.

3. For a certain tool it was found that the relationship between speed and tool life was given by $VT^{\frac{1}{7}} = 50$. Estimate the cutting speed to give a time of 2 hours between regrinding.

4. If the relationship for high-speed steel tools is $VT^{\frac{1}{8}} = C_1$, and for tungsten carbide tools $VT^{\frac{1}{5}} = C_2$, and assuming that at a speed of 25 m/min the tool life was 3 hours in each case, compare their cutting lives at 35 m/min.

5. For a certain tool it was found that the relationship between cutting speed (V) and tool life (T) was as follows:

$$V = \frac{500}{27 + T} + 20$$

Express T in terms of V and find T when $V = 25$ m/min.

6. A cutting tool has a top rake of 20° and a clearance of 7°. Calculate the modified values of these angles when the tool is cutting 3 mm below centre on a bar 44 mm diameter.

7. When turning a bar 50 mm diameter, how much above centre may a tool with a clearance of 6° be set before the clearance vanishes? When the tool is in this position, what is the effective value of the top rake, if the rake on the tool is 15°?

8. A boring tool 10 mm deep is required to bore out holes to 40 mm diameter. If the body of the tool is horizontal, how much clearance will be necessary if the bottom corner of the tool is to clear?

9. If the clearance face of the tool in Question **8** is made with two angles as shown in Fig. 54, calculate the angles α and β for the tool to clear the hole.

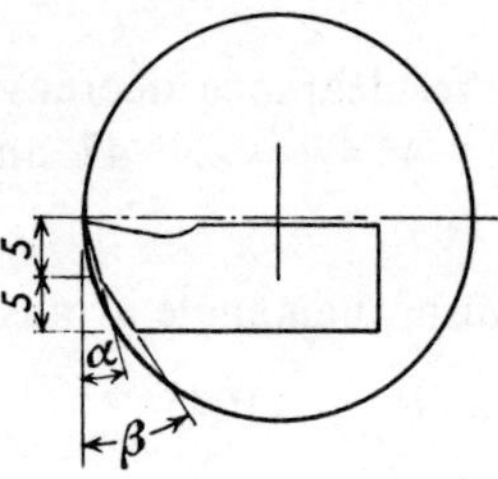

Fig. 54

10. A 50 mm diameter boring bar is concentric with a 72 mm hole which is being bored. The tool is 12 mm square and passes through the centre of the bar. Calculate the tool angles necessary so that the cutting rake shall be 10°, and the clearance 6°.

Taper turning

When a tapered or formed surface is being turned the accuracy of the surface is influenced by the position of the tool point relative to the centre of the work. The conditions in the case of taper work are shown in Fig. 55 (a). If the tool is set on the centre, and its movement controlled so as to turn the correct taper, it starts at A, and when it has travelled the line AB, the correct taper has been produced.

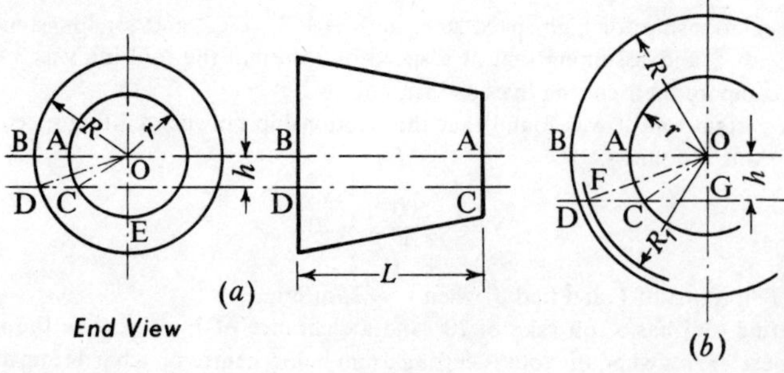

Fig. 55

If, now, instead of being on the centre, the tool is a distance h below centre and starts at C, it will travel along the line CD, and if D is on the same circle as B, the length CD is greater than AB. The tool being set to move the distance AB will therefore not reach the point D, and consequently if A and C are on the same circle, the top diameter of the taper will be less than it should be. The reader will probably appreciate the point better if he considers the extreme case of the tool being at E and travelling parallel to AB. In such a case, if the tool could cut in this position, it would not turn a true taper, but would produce a tapered shape faintly hollow in form.

In order to follow the problem mathematically we will show an enlarged diagram (Fig. 55 (*b*)).

The tool starts at C and moves out the distance CF, equal to AB. If it turns the end of the bar to radius r, instead of reaching the radius OB $= R$ it will only attain OF $= R_1$.

Let the work be L long as shown in Fig. 55 (*a*).

$$\text{True taper} = \frac{2(R - r)}{L}$$

$$\text{Actual taper obtained} = \frac{2(R_1 - r)}{L}$$

An attempt to reduce R_1 to an expression in terms of the other quantities involves rather awkward terms, and cases will be best evaluated from the information available. Such an example is illustrated as follows:

Example 5. In turning a taper of 1 in 6 on the diameter, the tool is set to move the correct angle relative to the work, but is 4 mm below centre. If the work is 32 mm diameter at the small end, calculate the actual taper obtained.

Referring to Fig. 55 (*b*), if we assume the work to be 60 mm long, then the large diameter will be 32 + 10 = 42 and we shall have

$$r = 16\,\text{mm}$$
$$R = 21\,\text{mm}$$
$$h = 4\,\text{mm}$$

The tool, starting at C where OC = 16 mm, will move out to F where CF = 21 mm.

We require the distance OF.

$$\text{OF}^2 = \text{FG}^2 + \text{OG}^2 = (\text{FC} + \text{CG})^2 + \text{OG}^2$$

But $\text{FC} = 5 \text{ and } \text{OG} = 4$

$$\therefore \text{OF} = (5 + \text{CG})^2 + 4^2$$

But $CG^2 = CO^2 - OG^2$

$= r^2 - h^2 = 16^2 - 4^2$

$= 240$

$CG = \sqrt{240} = 15{\cdot}49$

Hence $OF^2 = (5 + 15{\cdot}49)^2 + 4^2$

$= 20{\cdot}49^2 + 4^2 = 435{\cdot}8$

$OF = \sqrt{435{\cdot}8} = 20{\cdot}88$

The top diameter of the taper will therefore be $2 \times 20{\cdot}88 = 41{\cdot}76$ instead of 42 mm.

Since the bottom diameter is 32 mm and length 60 mm

$$\text{Actual taper} = \frac{41{\cdot}76 - 32}{60} = \frac{9{\cdot}76}{60}$$

This gives a taper of 1 in 6·15.

Form tools

For turning forms from the cross-slides of turret and automatic lathes and sometimes from centre lathes as well, a tool is used which gives the correct form on the work. If the tool is set on centre as shown in Fig. 56, it must have the correct form in plane OAB. Since, however, the tool must have clearance as shown, lengths such as BC, taken perpendicular to the front clearance face will be less than lengths such as AB taken on the horizontal, and the form of the tool on a plane parallel to BC will be different from its form on AB. When the tool is being made, the shaping and other machining operations are carried out parallel to the clearance face, so that for the purpose of making the tool it may be necessary to determine its form when taken on a plane such as BC, perpendicular to the front clearance face.

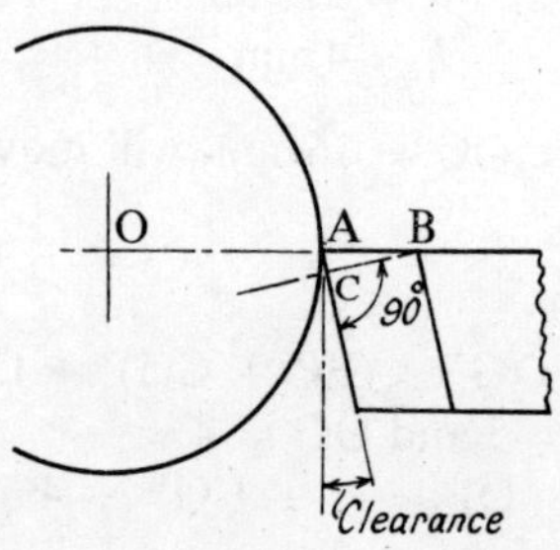

Fig. 56

We shall best illustrate the method of determining the modified form of the tool in planes perpendicular to the front clearance face by working one or two examples:

Example 6. A tool is to have the form shown in Fig. 57 (*a*) on its top horizontal face. If the clearance is 10°, determine and sketch the form on a plane perpendicular to the front clearance face.

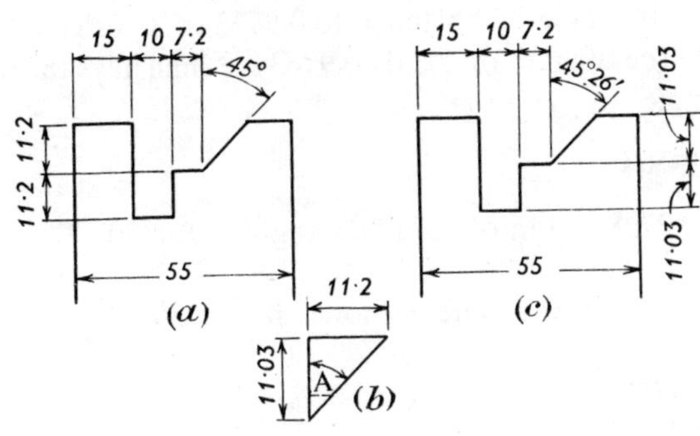

Fig. 57

In Fig. 57 (*a*) horizontal dimensions will not be affected, but vertical dimensions will not be shortened in the ratio of $\frac{BC}{AB}$ in Fig. 56, and since $\widehat{ABC}$ is equal to the clearance angle, $\frac{BC}{AB}$ = cos of clearance angle

$$= \cos 10° = 0{\cdot}9848$$

Hence the 11·2 in dimensions become $11{\cdot}2 \times 0{\cdot}9848 = 11{\cdot}03$ mm and the 45° angle will become a triangle as shown in Fig. 57 (*b*).

$$\tan A = \frac{11{\cdot}2}{11{\cdot}03} = 1{\cdot}0154. \text{ From which } \hat{A} = 45° \ 26'$$

Hence the revised sketch of the tool profile taken along the clearance face will be as shown in Fig. 57 (*c*).

When the form of the tool incorporates circular shapes the problem becomes rather more involved, since the effect of shortening the depth but not the width converts the circular form into a portion of an ellipse.

Example 7. Calculate and sketch the form of the tool shown in Fig. 58 (*a*) when taken perpendicular to the front clearance of $12\frac{1}{2}°$.

As before, the vertical dimensions are shortened in the ratio of the clearance angle cosine, i.e. $\cos 12\frac{1}{2}° = 0{\cdot}9763$.

We thus have $12{\cdot}8 \times 0{\cdot}9763 = 12{\cdot}50$ mm

$8 \times 0{\cdot}9763 = 7{\cdot}81$ mm

and for the 15 mm radius,

$$15 \times 0{\cdot}9763 = 14{\cdot}64 \text{ mm}$$

The base of the 20° angle is shortened to 0·9763 of its original length, so that if we divide the tangent of 20° by 0·9763 we shall have the tangent of the modified angle

$$\tan 20° = 0{\cdot}364$$

$$\frac{0{\cdot}364}{0{\cdot}9763} = 0{\cdot}3728 = \text{tan of modified angle} = \tan 20°\ 27'$$

The sketch of the modified profile is shown at Fig. 58 (*b*) .

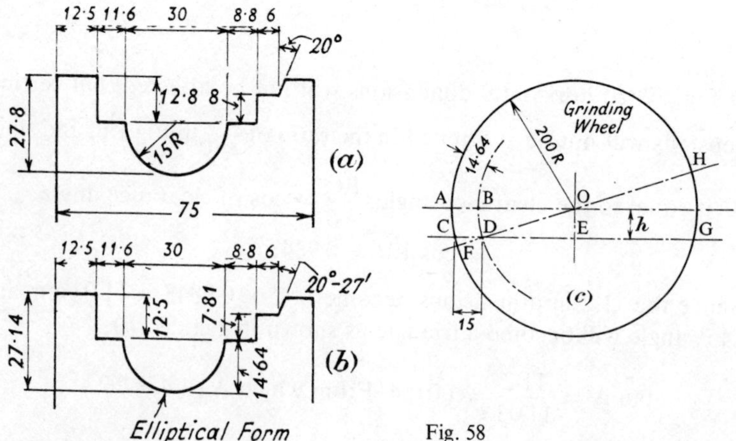

Fig. 58

The finishing of the elliptical form given to the circular portion is apt to be troublesome, but such a shape can be produced on a grinding wheel by trimming it with a radius forming attachment set off centre. This is shown in Fig. 58 (*c*), and if the radius truing attachment is set with the diamond rotating in plane CDE it will trim the wheel to a semicircle, 15 mm rad., in that plane. Since AB is less than CD, the true form of the wheel on a radial plane such as ABO will be elliptical, because the width of the wheel at B = width at D. The semi-minor axis of the elliptical form will be AB = FD, and the major axis will be 2 × 15 mm = 30 mm. As the profile on a radial plane is the one imparted by the wheel to the work we can, by forming the wheel in this way, obtain the required elliptical shape for the tool in question and we require to determine h in order that when CD = 15 mm, FD will be 14·64 mm.

Let us assume a grinding whell of 200 mm radius, and consider the problem from the aspect of two intersecting chords of a circle.

Then $$FD.DH = CD.DG$$

But $FD = 14{\cdot}64$, $DH = 400 - 14{\cdot}64 = 385{\cdot}36$ and $CD = 15$

Hence $$(14{\cdot}64)(385{\cdot}36) = 15.DG$$

$$DG = \frac{14{\cdot}64 \times 385{\cdot}36}{15} = 376{\cdot}1\,\text{mm}$$

and $$CG = 376{\cdot}1 + 15 = 391{\cdot}1$$

$$CE = \tfrac{1}{2}CG = \frac{391{\cdot}1}{2} = 195{\cdot}55$$

But $$h^2 = R^2 - CE^2 = 200^2 - 195{\cdot}55^2 = 1760$$

from which $h = 42$ mm

Hence by trimming the wheel to a 15 mm radius in a plane 42 mm off-centre, the required elliptical form will be produced.

Form tools with "top rake"

If back slope is put on the cutting face of a form tool the cutting effect of the tool is rather curious, because for the purpose of obtaining an accurate relative reproduction of the tool form on the work, the tool, at the finish of the cut, must have its top face lying on a radial line. This is shown at Fig. 59 (*a*), where the tool is shown at the completion of its cut, and its top face lies on the radial line OA. The reader will notice that at this position the effective top rake is zero, since the tool is cutting relative to tangent BC, which is perpendicular to OA.

When this tool starts its cut, however, the conditions are as shown at (*b*), and it will be seen that if the back slope α on the tool is made large enough, the tool will start cutting with an effective top rake of $\beta = \alpha - \delta$. As the tool feeds in, this rake will gradually get less until, as we have seen above, there is zero rake at the final position. The reader will notice that a tool of this type must be set below the centre by the amount h, where

$$\frac{h}{r} = \sin \alpha \text{ and } r = \text{smallest radius being turned.}$$

The calculation for the modified form to which the front face of such a tool should be made is similar to that we have already dealt with, except that the angle α must be taken into account.

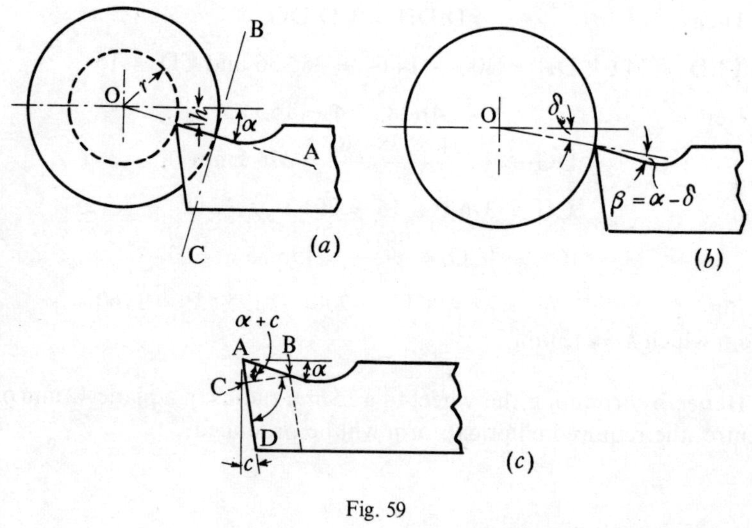

Fig. 59

In Fig. 59 (c), α is the back-slope angle and c the clearance.

The tool finishes its cut relative to face AB, but the depths of the form are put on parallel to AD (i.e. along CB).

Hence a length AB on the top of the tool will correspond to CB, perpendicular to the clearance face.

$$\text{In triangle ABC: } \hat{C} = 90° \text{ and } \widehat{ABC} = \alpha + c$$
$$CB = AB \cos(\alpha + c).$$

Hence depths in the form must be shortened in the ratio of $\cos(\alpha + c)$.

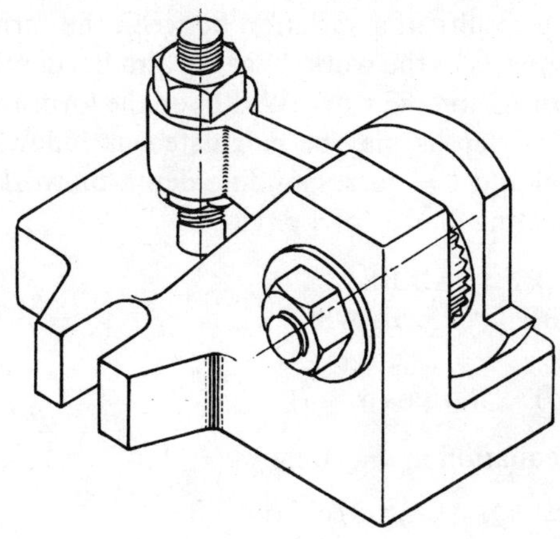

Fig. 60 Circular Form Tool.

Circular form tools

On some types of automatic lathes forming is done from the cross-slide by means of a circular form tool, a sketch of which is shown at Fig. 60.

These tools have the advantage that the form may be turned on their rim and they may be used all round the rim by continual re-sharpenings.

Cutting clearance is obtained by making the cutting edge AB some distance h below the centre, and the tool is applied to the work as shown at Fig. 61. The clearance angle α is then the angle CAO and

$$\sin \alpha = \frac{h}{\text{AO}} = \frac{h}{\text{Tool radius } (r)}$$

$$\text{and } h = r \sin \alpha$$

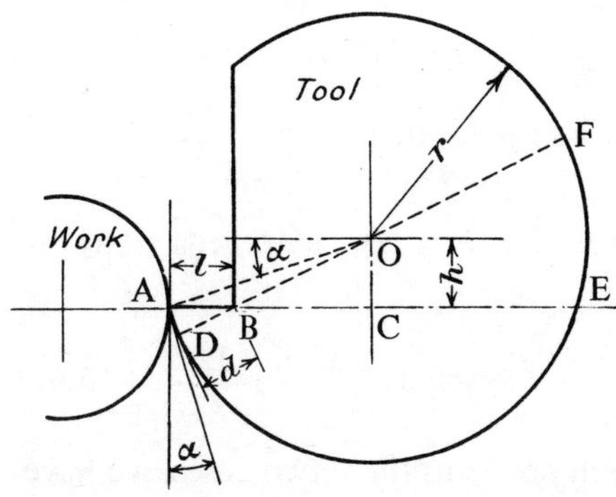

Fig. 61

Gashing the tool in this way results in a variation between the form turned on it and the form it imparts to the work, because a radial depth DB on the tool will turn a depth AB on the work. Widths on the form are unaffected, and corrections for depths may be calculated as follows, where d = a depth on the tool and l = corresponding depth on work.

From the property of intersecting chords of a circle

$$DB.BF = AB.BE.$$

But $\quad DB = d; \; BF = 2r - d; \; AB = l$

and $\quad BE = AE - l = 2r \cos \alpha - l$

Hence $\quad d(2r - d) = l(2r \cos \alpha - l)$

which reduces to a quadratic equation in d as follows:

$$d^2 - 2rd + l(2r \cos \alpha - l) = 0$$

in which all the quantities except d are known.

The following example will illustrate the application of this.

Example 8. A circular form tool, 100 mm diameter, is to be made to produce the form shown in Fig. 62 (*a*). If the gashing is to give a cutting clearance of 10°, determine the form to be turned on its periphery.

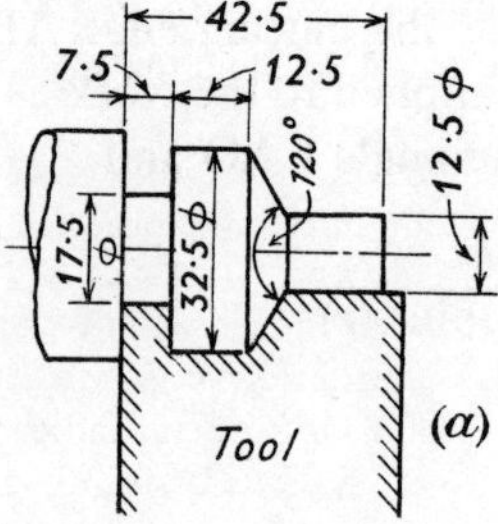

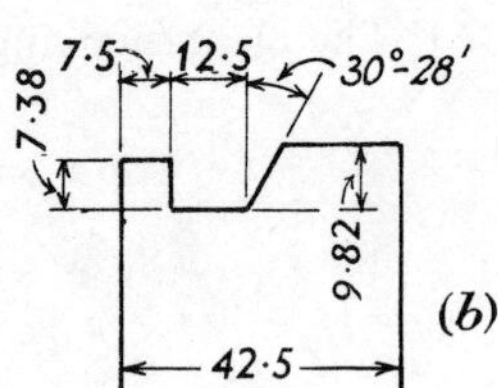

Fig. 62

Here r = 50 mm and α = 10°, so that

$$h = 50 \sin 10° = 50 \times 0{\cdot}1736 = 8{\cdot}68 \text{ mm}.$$

To turn the correct diameters on the work, the steps on the face AB of the tool must be:

$$\frac{32{\cdot}5 - 17{\cdot}5}{2} = 7{\cdot}5 \text{ mm, and } \frac{32{\cdot}5 - 12{\cdot}5}{2} = 10 \text{ mm}$$

Applying the equation above to these two cases, we have

(*i*) $l = 7{\cdot}5$, $r = 50$, $\cos\alpha = \cos 10° = 0{\cdot}9848$

$$d^2 - 100d - 7{\cdot}5(100.0{\cdot}9848 - 7{\cdot}5) = 0$$

from which $d = 7{\cdot}38$ mm

(*ii*) $l = 10$, $r = 50$, and $\cos\alpha = 0{\cdot}9848$

$$d^2 - 100d - 10(100.0{\cdot}9848 - 10) = 0$$

from which $d = 9{\cdot}82$ mm

The angle on the tool to give an included angle of 120° on the work must now be corrected. Its width is

$$\frac{32{\cdot}5 - 12{\cdot}5}{2}\tan 30° = 10\tan 30° = 5{\cdot}774\,\text{mm}$$

and its corrected depth from (*ii*) above is 9·82.

Hence $\dfrac{5{\cdot}774}{9{\cdot}82}$ = tan of its angle = 0·5882 from which the angle is found to be 30° 28′.

The turned profile of the tool is shown at Fig. 62 (*b*).

Exercises 3c

1. A lathe centre is being ground up by a 70 mm diameter grinding wheel fixed to a tool-post grinder on the compound slide. If the centre of the wheel is set 10 mm below the axis of the lathe centre, and the compound slide fed at 30°, find the angle to which the centre will be ground.

2. A lathe is set correctly for turning a taper of 1 in 6 when the tool is on the centre. What taper will be produced on a piece of work 120 mm long and 60 mm top diameter when the tool is 5 mm below centre?

3. A form tool is straight, and set at an angle of 15° with the axis of the work (i.e. to form an included angle of 30° on the work). If the tool is set to the above angle, but 5 mm below centre, calculate the actual angle produced on a job 50 mm top diameter and 40 mm long.

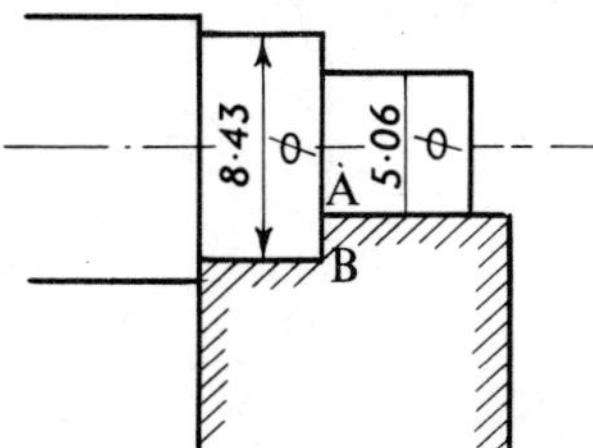

Fig. 63

4. A form tool having 8° clearance and 15° back slope is required to turn the diameters shown at Fig. 63. Calculate (*a*) the depth AB on the clearance face of the tool, (*b*) the amount the tool should be below centre, (*c*) the top cutting rake at the commencement of cutting. (Top diameter of work = 10 mm).

5. Calculate the tailstock set-over for turning a taper of 8° included, on a job 115 mm long. What variation in taper will be produced by a variation of ± 2·5 mm in the length of the work?

6. Calculate the depths and the angle on a form tool for producing the form shown in Fig. 64. Tool has no top rake and 10° clearance.

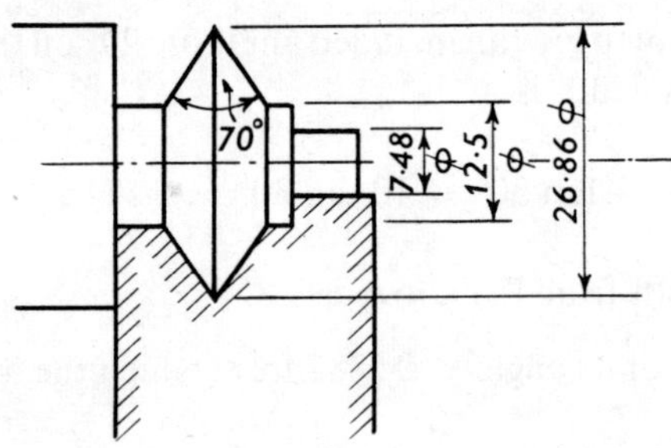

Fig. 64

7. At Fig. 65 is shown a thread form which is to be finished by the form tool indicated. Calculate the angle, depth and bottom land as measured from the clearance face of a tool having no top rake and 15° clearance.

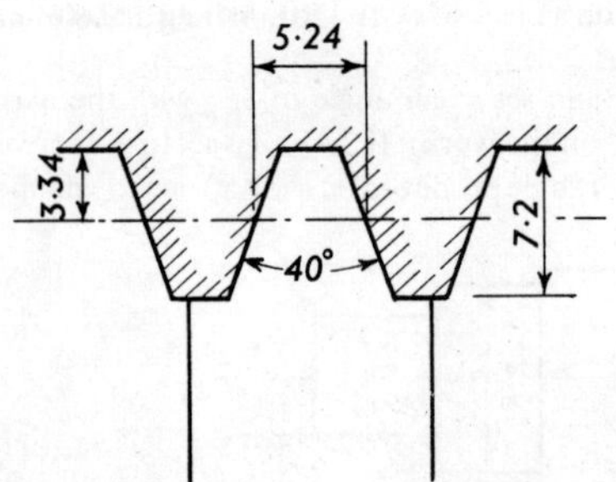

Fig. 65

8. A circular form tool 55 mm diameter is gashed to give 10° clearance, and is to turn the form indicated at Fig. 63. Calculate the amount off-centre for the gashing and the depth AB on the tool.

9. Calculate the depths and angle to be turned on a circular form tool 60 mm diameter to give the profile shown at Fig. 66, if the tool is gashed to give 12° clearance.

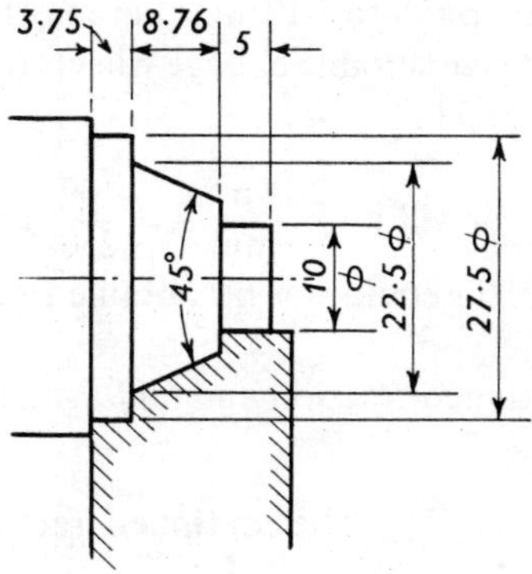

Fig. 66

10. In cutting the thread on a core for a die-casting mould, the pitch of the thread is to be made 2% longer than standard to allow for contraction. To do this, the tailstock of the lathe is set over, the lathe taper attachment is set parallel to the work, and then the thread is cut in the usual way. Calculate:

(*a*) The actual pitch required if the nominal thread is 2 mm pitch.
(*b*) The tailstock set-over if the core is 150 mm long between centres.
(*c*) The angle to which the taper attachment must be set.

Calculating approximate change wheels for odd threads

Sometimes a case may arise where an odd thread must be cut, the exact pitch of which cannot be obtained with the standard machine change-wheels. Also, if a lathe is not supplied with the special 127T wheel, and a metric pitch is required, some alternative way of getting a suitable pitch becomes necessary.

The method of continued fractions will often provide a very near ratio to that required, and enable a pitch to be cut which is near enough for the purpose.

In Appendix VII it will be seen, that the convergents of a continued fraction are a series of fractions, each succeeding one approaching closer to the true value of the original ratio. If, therefore, we have a complicated ratio, the exact value of which cannot be obtained on the machine, it is quite possible that by converting to a continued fraction and finding the convergents, one of these convergents will be a ratio that can be used, and its value will probably be close enough for the purpose. The method will be best illustrated by examples.

Example 9. Find the nearest pitch to 2·18 mm that may be cut on a lathe with a 5 mm leadscrew, and give suitable change wheels from a set ranging from 20T to 120T in steps of 5T.

The ratio of gears: $\frac{\text{Drivers}}{\text{Driven}}$ will be $\frac{2\cdot18\,\text{mm}}{5\,\text{mm}} = \frac{109}{250}$, and since 109 is a prime number, the exact ratio could not be obtained without a gear of this size.

Converting this to a continued fraction and finding the convergents we have:

```
109)250(2
    218
     32)109(3
         96
         13)32(2
            26
             6)13(2
               12
                1)6(6
```

The continued fraction is:

$$\cfrac{1}{2+\cfrac{1}{3+\cfrac{1}{2+\cfrac{1}{2+\frac{1}{6}}}}}$$

and the convergents are: 1st $= \frac{1}{2}$, 2nd $= \frac{3}{7}$, 3rd $= \frac{7}{16}$, 4th $= \frac{17}{39}$, 5th $= \frac{109}{250}$.

If we take the 4th convergent ($\frac{17}{39}$) we may obtain a gear ratio as follows:

$$\frac{17}{39} = \frac{2 \times 8\cdot5}{6 \times 6\cdot5} = \frac{20 \times 85}{60 \times 65}\,\frac{\text{Drivers}}{\text{Driven}}$$

To find the actual pitch obtained we must multiply the ratio $\frac{17}{39}$ by the pitch of the leadscrew, i.e. $\frac{17}{39} \times 5 = \frac{85}{39}$, which when converted to a decimal gives 2·1795 mm. This is less than 0·03% in error on the required pitch of 2·18 mm.

Example 10. Find the nearest pitch obtainable to $2\frac{1}{4}$ mm, on a lathe with a 6 t.p.i. leadscrew and a set of wheels as in the last example.

The pitch of the leadscrew is $\frac{1}{6}$ in and the ratio required $= \frac{2\frac{1}{4}\,\text{mm}}{\frac{1}{6}\,\text{in}}$

Converting the inches to millimeters (1 in = 25·4 mm)

$$= \frac{2\frac{1}{4}}{\frac{25\cdot4}{6}} = 2\tfrac{1}{4} \times \frac{6}{25\cdot4} = \frac{9 \times 6}{4 \times 25\cdot4} = \frac{27}{50\cdot8} = \frac{270}{508}$$

The continued fraction is

```
270)508(1
    270
    238)270(1
        238
         32)238(7
            224
             14)32(2
                28
                 4)14(3
                   12
                    2)4(2
```

$$\cfrac{1}{1+\cfrac{1}{1+\cfrac{1}{7+\cfrac{1}{2+\cfrac{1}{3+\frac{1}{2}}}}}}$$

and the convergents: 1st $= \frac{1}{1}$; 2nd $= \frac{1}{2}$; 3rd $= \frac{8}{15}$; 4th $= \frac{17}{32}$; 5th $= \frac{59}{111}$; 6th $= \frac{270}{508}$

The 4th convergent is the last one which can be made into a ratio and gives:

$$\frac{17}{32} = \frac{2 \times 8{\cdot}5}{4 \times 8} = \frac{20 \times 85}{40 \times 80}\frac{\text{Drivers}}{\text{Driven}}$$

The actual pitch obtained will be $\frac{17}{32} \times \frac{1}{6} \times 25{\cdot}4 = 2{\cdot}2489$ mm, being 0·0011 mm short.

Power required for cutting

Turning and Boring. When metal is being cut with a single-point tool as in turning and boring, the tool is subjected to pressure in three directions at right angles: (1) vertical chip pressure, (2) horizontal work pressure across the lathe, (3) horizontal feeding pressure along the lathe.

The first of these is of greatest importance from the aspect of the power absorbed. The other two, although absorbing some power, are of small effect when compared with the vertical pressure and are generally neglected.

From numerous experiments that have been made it has been established that the cutting force on a single point tool is connected in an expression of the form

$$F = Cd^a f^b$$

where F = force; d = depth of cut; f = feed, and C = a constant. a and b depend on the metal being cut and other factors.

For most practical purposes the expression

$F = Kdf = K(\text{Cut area})$ gives results good enough.

K is a constant depending on the metal being cut.

If $S =$ cutting speed in metres per minute, the work done per minute will be $F \times S$, and the power $\frac{F \times S}{60}$ Watts.

Hence $$\text{Power} = \frac{KdfS}{60\,000} \text{ Kilowatts}$$

Approximate values for K are as follows:

Metal being cut	Steel 100–150 Brinell	Steel 150–200 Brinell	Steel 200–300 Brinell	Steel 300–400 Brinell	Cast Iron	Brass	Bronze	Alu-min-ium
K (N/mm^2)	1200	1600	2400	3000	900	1250	1750	700

[From the form of the expression, the reader will observe that K is the force on the tool per square millimetre of cut area.]

Wehn the power required to do the cutting has been calculated, the total power to run the cut and overcome friction in the machine may be found by adding on about 30%.

Example 11. Calculate the power being absorbed in running a cut 3 mm deep with a feed of 1·5 mm, on a mild steel bar 50 mm diameter turning at 140 rev/min.

$$\text{Cutting speed} = \frac{\pi \times 50 \times 140}{1000}$$

$$= \frac{22 \times 50 \times 140}{7 \times 1000} = 22 \text{ m/min}$$

If we take the constant K as 1200

$$\text{Power} = \frac{1200 \times 3 \times 1{\cdot}5 \times 22}{60\,000} = 1{\cdot}98 \text{ kW}$$

Adding 30% for frictional losses in the machine we have

$1{\cdot}98 + 1{\cdot}98 \times \frac{3}{10} = 1{\cdot}98 + 0{\cdot}594 =$ <u>2·574 say, 2·5 kW to run the machine.</u>

Power for drilling
When a drill is cutting it has to overcome the resistance offered by the metal and a twisting effort is necessary to turn it. This effort is called the Turning Moment or Torque on the drill. The units for torque are those of a force multiplied by a length and the most usual is the Nm unit. The turning effect of a force, or a pair of forces, acting at a certain radius, is found by multiplying the force by the radius, or for two forces the turning effect is the sum of the product of each force by its radius. Thus in Fig. 67, if the drill required a torque of 10 Nm to turn it, the torque would be equivalent to equal and opposite forces of 250 N each operating at 20 mm radius. [$T = 250 \times 0{\cdot}02 + 250 \times 0{\cdot}02 = 10\,\text{Nm}$]

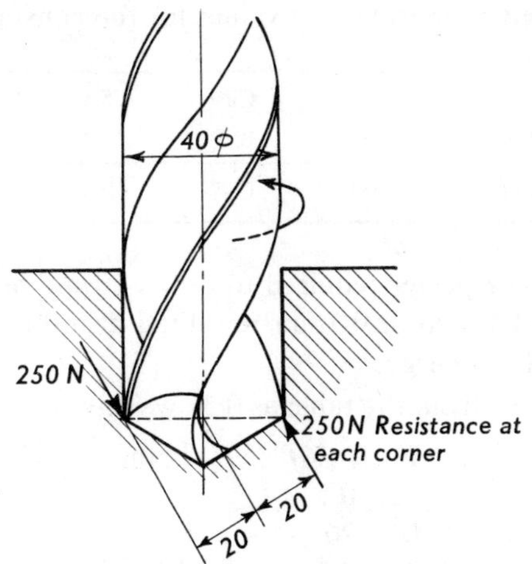

Fig. 67

In addition to the torque, a drill requires an axial force to feed it through the work, but in power calculations this is generally neglected.

When the torque is known, the work done is found by multiplying it by the number of turns made and by 2π.

Thus if T = torque in Nm and N = speed in rev/min,

$$\text{the work done per minute} = 2\pi NT \text{ Nm}$$

$$\text{and the power} = \frac{2\pi NT}{60\,000} \text{ kW}$$

The torque required to operate a drill depends upon various factors, but for the purpose of being able to obtain an approximate calculation for it we will omit all but the drill diameter, the feed and the material being drilled. The relation between the torque, the diameter and the feed has been found experimentally to be that torque varies as $f^{0\cdot75}D^{1\cdot8}$.

Using this, we may say that

$$\text{Torque } (T) = C.f^{0\cdot75}D^{1\cdot8} \text{ newton metres}$$

where C = a constant depending on the material
f = drill feed (mm/rev)
D = diameter of drill (mm).

When the torque has been found, the power can be calculated as shown above.

The following table gives approximate values for the constant (C).

Material being drilled	Alu-minium	Soft brass	Cast iron	Steel (mild)	Carbon tool steel
C	0·11	0·084	0·07	0·36	0·4

Example 12. Calculate the power required to drill a 20 mm hole in mild steel at 250 rev/min and a feed or 0·5 mm/rev. Find also the volume of metal removed per unit of energy.

Taking the constant, C, from the table as 0·36 we have

$$T = 0\cdot36 f^{0.75}\, D^{1.8} \text{ Nm}$$
$$f = 0\cdot5$$
$$D = 20$$
$$T = 0\cdot36\,(0\cdot5)^{0\cdot75}\,(20)^{1\cdot8}$$

and taking logarithms.

$$\log T = \log 0\cdot36 + 0\cdot75 \log 0\cdot5 + 1\cdot8 \log 20$$
$$= \bar{1}\cdot5563 + 0\cdot75(\bar{1}\cdot6990) + 1\cdot8(1\cdot3010)$$
$$= \bar{1}\cdot5563 + 0\cdot75(-0\cdot3010) + 1\cdot8(1\cdot3010)$$
$$= -0\cdot4437 - 0\cdot2258 + 2\cdot3418 = 1\cdot6723$$
$$T = \text{antilog } 1\cdot6723 = 47 \text{ Nm}$$

Since the speed is 250 rev/min

$$P = \frac{2\pi.250.47}{60\,000} = 1\cdot23 \text{ kW}$$

Volume of metal removed per minute

$$= (\text{Area of hole})(\text{Feed})(\text{Speed})$$

$$= \frac{\pi}{4} \times 20^2 \times 0.5 \times 250 = 39\,275\,\text{mm}^3$$

$$\text{Energy consumption} = \frac{39\,275\,\text{mm}^3}{\text{min} \times 1230\,\text{W}} = 31.9\,\text{mm}^3/\text{watt minute}.$$

$$= \underline{0.53\,\text{mm}^3/\text{joule}}$$

Exercises 3d

1. Calculate the nearest change wheels for cutting a sparking-plug thread ($1\frac{1}{2}$-mm pitch) on a lathe with a 4 t.p.i. leadscrew and a set of wheels ranging from 20T to 120T in steps of 5T. For the ratio you select, find the actual pitch of thread obtained.

2. A worm having a lead of π mm is to be cut on a lathe with a 5 mm leadscrew. Taking π as 3·1416, express the ratio required as a continued fraction, and find the nearest convergent that can be used with a set of wheels specified for the last example. What was the actual error in the lead obtained for the worm?

3. A shaft revolves at 15 rev/min and requires a thread cutting on it which will cause a nut to move along the shaft at 66·5 mm/min, when it turns at the above speed. Find the lead of the thread required and calculate the nearest that can be cut to it on a 5 mm leadscrew with change wheels specified for Question **1**. What is the actual speed of the nut with the thread you obtain?

4. Estimate (*a*) the power input to a lathe when it is taking a 6 mm cut in cast iron with 0·75 mm in feed at 20 m/min. (*b*) The volume of metal removed per unit of energy. Take the overall efficiency of the machine as 70%.

5. A lathe is just able to run a cut of 5 mm depth at a feed of 0·8 mm in steel of 120 Brinell, at 150 rev/min on a 50 mm diameter bar. Estimate what cut could be taken on 25 mm bars of 250 Brinell material, at 240 rev/min and the same feed as before. [Take values of K from the table on p. 80.]

6. Taking the value of K from the table on page 80, estimate what cut could be taken on a lathe turning bronze bars at 0·6 mm feed and 20 m/min, if 5 kW were available, and 30% of the power were lost in friction.

7. For the lathe in Question **4**, estimate the power cost per 8-hour day, with power at 2*p* per kWh and the efficiency of the motor is 80%.

8. Calculate the torque required to drill 20 mm diameter holes in mild steel, at a feed of 0·25 mm/rev. If the drill speed is 300 rev/min, calculate (*a*) the power absorbed in cutting, (*b*) the energy absorbed per cubic millimeter removed per minute.

9. A 25 mm drill is drilling aluminium at 110 m/min. Calculate its speed. If the feed is 0·3 mm/rev, calculate the torque, and the input power if frictional losses are equivalent to 30% of the cutting power.

10. For the drill in Question **8**, calculate the drilling time for 100 holes, each 40 mm deep. If the electrical efficiency is 80%, calculate the cost to drill these 100 holes using the same electrical data as in Question **7**.

11. By using a continued fraction calculate the nearest set of change wheels to cut the thread specified in Example 10(a) Exercises 3c, leadscrew 5 mm pitch.

4 Calculations for gears and gear cutting

Formation of the involute tooth

For various practical and theoretical reasons, the tooth shape most commonly used for gearing is the involute. Before we commence our consideration of various problems connected with involute teeth, it will be as well to examine the involute curve itself.

Involute

If a cord is wrapped tightly round a circular form and then unwound, at the same time being kept tight, the end of the cord will trace out an involute. This is shown at the top of Fig. 68, where CB is the portion of the cord that has been unwound and AC is the involute. Another method

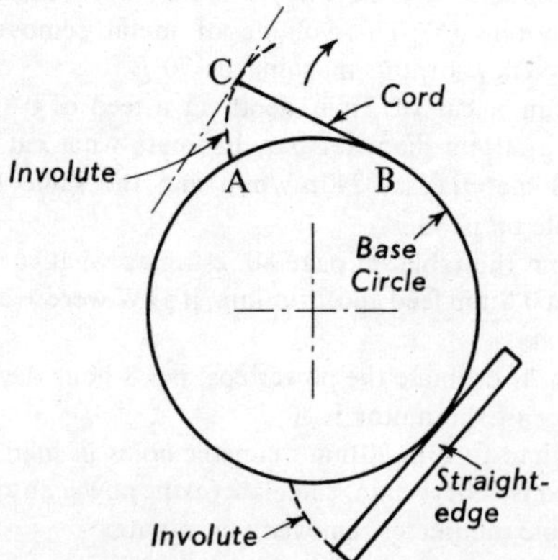

Fig. 68

of tracing an involute is to roll a line (e.g. a straight-edge) on a circle when the end of the line will trace out an involute. The size of circle will, of course, influence the shape of the involute, but there are certain properties which are common to all involutes. Those properties which are interesting from the aspect of the involute as a tooth form, are as follows:

(1) A tangent to the involute is always perpendicular to a tangent from the same point on the involute to the circle from which it is formed. In Fig. 68 the cord CB is tangential to the circle at B, and a tangent to the involute at C is perpendicular to CB.

(2) The length of the cord CB is equal to the length of the arc AB.

Tooth form

O_1 and O_2 are the centres of a pinion and gear of which the pitch circles are shown tangential at P, which is called the *pitch point*.

AB is a line through P perpendicular to line O_1O_2. CD also passes through P and is included at the angle ψ to AB. CD is called the *line of action* and ψ the *pressure angle*. The name "line of action" is given to CD because it is on, and along that line, that the pressure between the teeth takes place. The angle ψ nowadays is virtually always 20°, but at one time $14\frac{1}{2}$° was more common, being related to half the included angle of the Acme thread form. With the changeover of the pressure angle from $14\frac{1}{2}$° to 20° the clearance between the top of the tooth of one gear and the base of its mating tooth form has been increased from 5% of the circular patch (=0·157 of the module), to 0·25 of the module. The cutting depth for gears of 20° pressure angle is thus 2·25 times the module. To

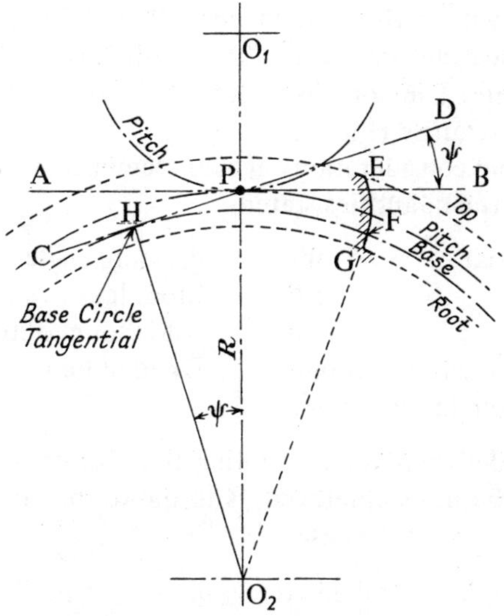

Fig. 69 Formation of Involute Tooth.

obtain the tooth shape a circle is drawn tangential to CD called the *base circle*. The portion of the tooth between this circle and the top (EF) takes the form of an involute to this circle; the portion of the tooth below this circle (FG) is radial (i.e. on a line joining the end of the involute to the gear centre). This is all shown in Fig. 69, where for the sake of clearness the construction has only been carried out on the lower gear. The construction also only shows one side of a tooth; the other side is merely the same shape reversed, and spaced away, a distance equal to the tooth thickness.

The involute rack

The rack is a gear of infinite diameter so that its pitch circle will be a straight line (AB, Fig. 70). A base circle of infinite diameter tangential

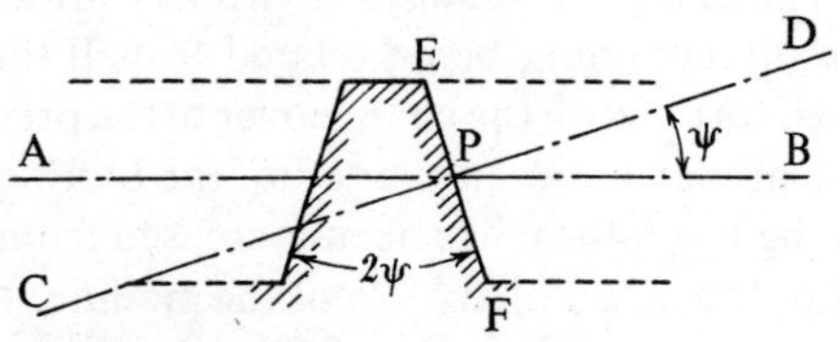

Fig. 70

to the line of action CD will be a straight line coinciding with CD. The involute to this will be the straight line EP, and the radial continuation will be PF. Hence the side of the rack tooth is straight, and inclined at the pressure angle. The complete tooth will have a total angle equal to twice the pressure angle (Fig. 70).

In the following considerations of gear elements the following symbols will be used for the quantities stated:

No. of teeth in gear	T or t	Pressure angle	ψ
Diametral pitch	P	Module	m
Circular pitch	p	Addendum of tooth	Add.
Diameter of pitch circle	D or d	Dendendum	Ded.
Radius of pitch circle	R or r		

The recommended manner of quoting the size of a gear tooth form, irrespective of the units employed, is to quote the addendum and refer to it as a module. In which case,

$$\text{pitch circle diameter} = \text{module} \times \text{number of teeth}$$

$$\text{or } D = mT$$

The module is therefore the reciprocal of the diametral pitch, irrespective of whether measurements are made in millimetres or inches. All the formulae which follow can be used for diametral pitch, by substituting $\frac{1}{P}$ for *m*. Until the use of the metric module becomes the preferred usage in describing gear tooth sizes, the reader may find gears listed in a diametral pitch series. The diametral pitch is simply the number of teeth per unit of pitch circle diameter, and consequently it is necessary to be particularly careful in stating that unit, e.g.

diametral pitch of 8	(inch series)
or diametral pitch of 0·2	(mm series).

In any case, conversion to a module is simply effected from the relationship that the module is equal to the addendum; furthermore

$$\text{circular pitch } P = \pi \times \text{module } m$$

The tooth vernier

The gear-tooth vernier is an instrument for measuring the pitch line thickness of a tooth. It has two scales and must be set for the width (w) of the tooth, and the depth (h) from the top of the tooth, at which w occurs (Fig. 71).

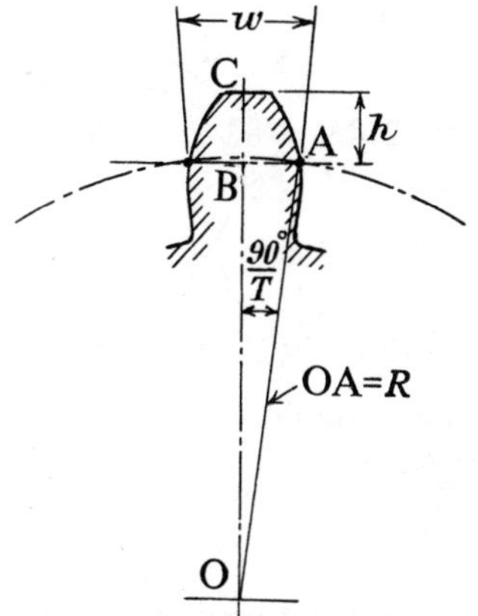

Fig. 71

The angle subtended by a half tooth at the centre of the gear (AOB) in Fig. 71).

$$= \tfrac{1}{4} \text{ of } \frac{360}{T} = \frac{90}{T}$$

$$AB = \frac{w}{2} = AO \sin\frac{90}{T} = R \sin\frac{90}{T}$$

$$D = \text{module} \times \text{number of teeth}$$

$$D = 2R = mT$$

and $$R = \frac{mT}{2}$$

Hence $$\frac{w}{2} = R \sin\frac{90}{T} = \frac{mT}{2} \sin\frac{90}{T}$$

and $$w = mT \sin\frac{90}{T} \qquad (1)$$

To find h we have that $h = CB = OC - OB$.

But $$OC = R + \text{Add.} = \frac{mT}{2} + m$$

and $$OB = R \cos\frac{90}{T} = \frac{mT}{2} \cos\frac{90}{T}.$$

$$\text{Hence } h = \frac{mT}{2} + m - \frac{mT}{2}\cos\frac{90}{T} = m + \frac{mT}{2}\left[1 - \cos\frac{90}{T}\right]. \qquad (2)$$

Example 1. Calculate the gear tooth vernier settings to measure a gear of 33T, 2·5 metric module

$$w = mT \sin\frac{90}{T} = 2{\cdot}5 \times 33 \sin\frac{90}{33}$$

$$= 82{\cdot}5 \sin 2°43' = 82{\cdot}5 \times 0{\cdot}0474$$

$$= \underline{3{\cdot}91 \text{ mm}}$$

$$h = m + \frac{mT}{2}\left(1 - \cos\frac{90}{T}\right)$$

$$= 2{\cdot}5 + \frac{2{\cdot}5 \times 33}{2}(1 - \cos 2°43')$$

$$= 2{\cdot}5 + 41{\cdot}25(0{\cdot}0011)$$

$$= \underline{2{\cdot}545 \text{ mm}}$$

Constant chord method

One drawback to the method just outlined is that the measurements w and h depend on the number of teeth (T) in the gear, and for each different gear a fresh calculation has to be made. The following method avoids this and gives a constant pair of readings for all gears of the same pitch and pressure angle.

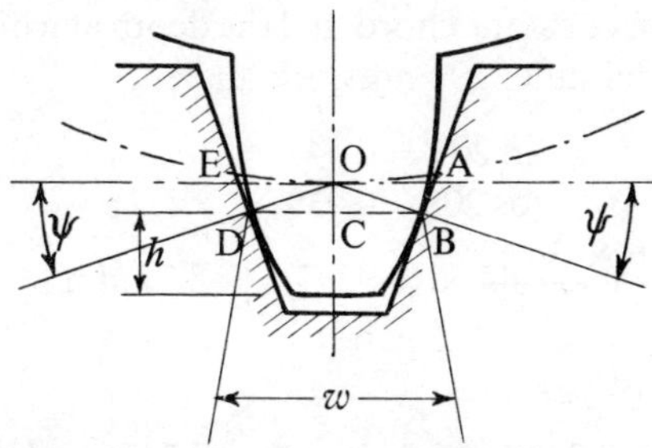

Fig. 72

In Fig. 72 is shown a gear tooth meshing symmetrically with a rack. O is the pitch point, and as we have seen above, the gear tooth will contact with the straight-sided rack tooth at the points B and D, lying on the line of action.

Then DB $= w$ will thus be constant for all teeth of the same pitch and pressure angle.

Since EOA is the pitch line of the rack

$$\text{EA} = \tfrac{1}{2}\,\text{circular pitch} = \tfrac{1}{2}p = \frac{\pi m}{2}$$

and $$\text{OA} = \tfrac{1}{2}\text{EA} = \frac{\pi m}{4}$$

In triangle OAB: $\hat{\text{B}} = 90°$ and $\hat{\text{O}} = \psi$

$$\therefore \text{OB} = \text{OA} \cos v,$$

and in triangle OCB: $\hat{\text{C}} = 90°$ and $\hat{\text{B}} = \psi$

$$\therefore \text{CB} = \text{OB} \cos \psi.$$

Hence $\text{CB} = \text{OA} \cos \psi \cos \psi = \text{OA} \cos^2 \psi = \dfrac{\pi m}{4} \cos^2 \psi$

and $$\text{DB} = 2\text{CB} = w = \frac{\pi m}{2} \cos^2 \psi \tag{3}$$

$$h = \text{Add.} - \text{OC} = m - \text{OC}.$$

But $\text{OC} = \text{OB} \sin \psi$ and $\text{OB} = \text{OA} \cos \psi$.

Hence $\text{OC} = \text{OA} \cos \psi \sin \psi = \dfrac{\pi m}{4} \cos \psi \sin \psi$

and $$h = m - \frac{\pi m}{4} \cos \psi \sin \psi = m\left[1 - \frac{\pi}{4} \cos \psi \sin \psi\right] \tag{4}$$

It will be seen that expressions (3) and (4) remain constant if module (m) and pressure angle (ψ) do not alter.

Example 2. Calculate the constant chord and the depth at which it occurs, for a 30T gear of 6 mm module, 20° pressure angle.

Here we have $\sin 20° = 0{\cdot}342$
$\cos 20° = 0{\cdot}9397$

$$w = \frac{\pi m}{2}\cos^2 20 = \frac{6 \times 3{\cdot}142}{2} \times (0{\cdot}9397)^2 = 8{\cdot}32\,\text{mm}$$

$$h = m(1 - \frac{\pi}{4}\cos\psi \sin\psi)$$
$$= 6(1 - 0{\cdot}7854 \times 0{\cdot}9397 \times 0{\cdot}342) = 6 \times 0{\cdot}7476 = 4{\cdot}49\,\text{mm}$$

Plug method of checking for pitch diameter and divide of teeth

The tooth vernier gives us a check on the size of the individual tooth, but does not give a measure of either the pitch diameter or the accuracy of the division of the teeth.

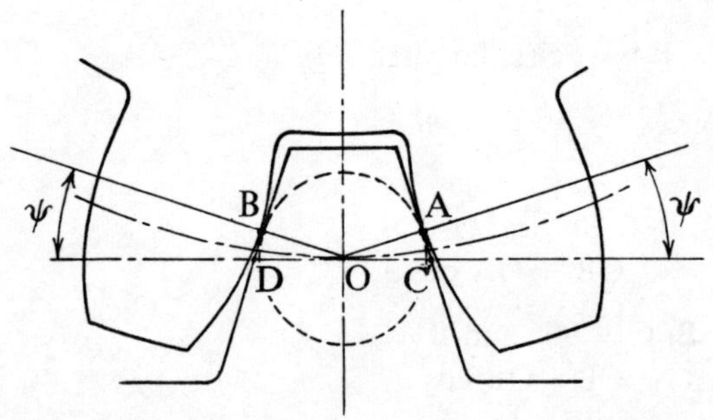

Fig. 73

Fig. 73 shows a rack tooth symmetrically in mesh with a gear tooth space, the curved sides of the gear teeth touching the straight rack tooth at the points A and B on the lines of action. O is the pitch point. If now we consider the rack tooth as an empty space bounded by its outline, a circle with centre at O and radius OB would fit in the rack tooth and touch it at A and B (since OA and OB are perpendicular to the side of the rack tooth). Since the rack touches the gear at these points, the above circle (shown dotted) will rest against the gear teeth at points A and B and will have its centre on the pitch circle.

In triangle OBD: OB = radius of plug required.

$$OD = \tfrac{1}{4} \text{ circular pitch} = \frac{\pi m}{4}$$

$$\hat{B} = 90° \quad \hat{O} = \psi.$$

$$OB = OD \cos \psi = \frac{\pi m}{4} \cos \psi.$$

$$\text{Dia of plug} = 2OB = \frac{\pi m}{2} \cos \psi \qquad (5)$$

This is the diameter of a plug which will rest in the tooth space and have its centre on the pitch circle. Notice that the plug size remains the same for all gears having the same pitch and pressure angle.

With such plugs placed in diametrically opposite tooth spaces, it is a simple matter to verify the gear pitch diameter. The accuracy of the spacing over any number of teeth may be found as shown in chordal calculations.

Example 3. Calculate for a 36T gear of 5 mm module and 20° pressure angle, (*a*) plug size (*b*) distance over two plugs placed in opposite spaces, (*c*) distance over two plugs spaced 10 teeth apart.

(*a*) Dia of plug $= \dfrac{\pi m}{2} \cos \psi = \dfrac{5\pi}{2} \cos 20° = 7{\cdot}854 \times 0{\cdot}9397$

$= 7{\cdot}38$ mm

Pitch dia of gear $= mT = 5 \times 36 = 180$ mm

(*b*) Distance across plugs in opposite spaces

$= 180 + 7{\cdot}38 = 187{\cdot}38$ mm

(*c*) Distance across plugs spaced 10 teeth apart (Fig. 74).

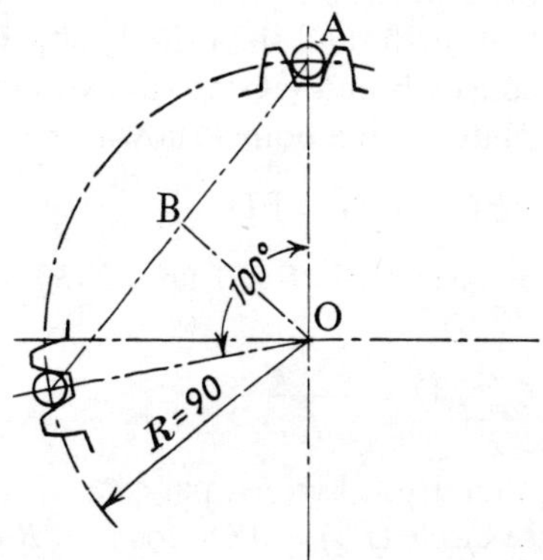

Fig. 74

Angle subtended by 10 teeth $= 10 \times \dfrac{360}{36} = 100°$. In triangle OAB:

$$AB = OA \sin 50° = 90 \times 0{\cdot}766 = 68{\cdot}94$$

Centre distance of plugs $= 2 \times AB = 2 \times 68{\cdot}94 = 137{\cdot}88$ mm
Distance over plugs $= 137{\cdot}88 + 7{\cdot}38 = 145{\cdot}26$ mm

Base pitch

The base pitch is the circular pitch of the teeth measured on the base circle. It is useful for checking the angle between adjacent teeth and for checking a tooth against "drunkenness."

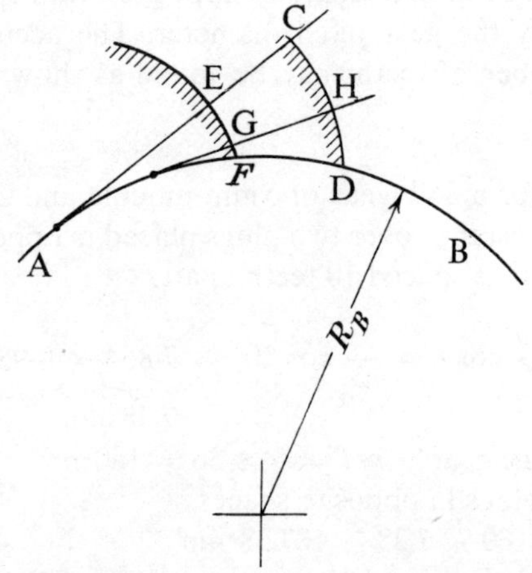

Fig. 75

If AB (Fig. 75) represents a portion of the base circle of a gear, and CD and EF the sides of two teeth, and then the length FD is the base pitch. But if any lines such as CE and HG are drawn tangential to the base circle cutting the involutes at the points shown, then

$$EC = GH = FD$$

If there are T teeth in the gear, then $T \times FD = 2\pi R_B$ and

$$FD = \frac{2\pi R_B}{T}$$

If ψ is the pressure angle, then from Fig. 69, page 85,

$$HO_2 = \text{rad. of base circle } (R_B) = PO_2 \cos \psi = R \cos \psi.$$

Hence $$\text{FD} = \text{base pitch} = \frac{2\pi R \cos \psi}{T}$$

But $$\frac{2\pi R}{T} = \frac{\pi D}{T} = \pi m \quad \left(\text{since } \frac{D}{T} = m\right)$$

Hence $$\text{base pitch} = \pi m \cos \psi \qquad (6)$$

This is the distance between the curved portions of any two adjacent teeth and can be measured either with a height gauge or on an enlarged projected image of the teeth.

Exercises 4a

1. Determine the diameter of a plug which will rest in the tooth space of a 4 mm module 20° rack, and touch the teeth at the pitch line. Calculate (*a*) the distance over two such plugs spaced 5 teeth apart. (*b*) The depth from the top of the plug to the top of the teeth.

2. Calculate the gear tooth caliper settings for measuring the following gears: (*a*) 37T, 6 mm module; (*b*) 40T 20 mm circular pitch.

3. A 5 mm module involute rack tooth is measured at its pitch line and found to be 7·99 mm wide. If the tooth spacing and angle are correct, what error has been made in the cutting of the teeth? (Pressure angle = 20°.)

4. A 30T replacement gear of 5 mm module is required, and the nearest cutter available for cutting the teeth is one of 5 diametral pitch, (inch series). If the blank is turned to the correct module dimensions, and the cutter sunk in to the depth marked on it, what will be the error in the tooth?

5. Determine the "constant chord" dimensions for the following gears: (*a*) 8 mm module, 20° pressure angle; (*b*) 25 mm circular pitch, 20° pressure angle.

6. Calculate the diameter of plug which will lie in the tooth space of a 5 mm module gear with its centre on the pitch circle. If the gear has 50T, find (*a*) distance over two such plugs spaced in opposite spaces, (*b*) distance over two plugs spaced 12 spaces apart ($v = 20°$).

7. Two plugs are placed in adjoining spaces of a 29T gear 20 mm circular pitch, and the gear is stood up resting on them. Calculate the distance from the face upon which these plugs are resting, to the top of a similar plug placed in the tooth space at the top of the gear. [Press. angle = 20°, and plug diameter is that which rests with its centre on the pitch circle.]

8. Determine the base pitch of the following gears: (*a*) 30T 8 mm module, $\psi = 20°$; (*b*) 30T, 25 mm circular pitch, $\psi = 20°$.

9. Two teeth of a 30T gear of 1·25 mm module, 20° pressure angle are projected to a magnification of 50. Calculate, to the nearest 0·5 mm the length on the projected image of the following measurements:

(*a*) base pitch,
(*b*) depth of tooth space,
(*c*) chordal thickness of tooth at pitch line,
(*d*) height from root of tooth to pitch line.

Stub teeth

For some purposes, particularly when gears are subject to shock and vibration, the tooth of standard proportions is apt to be weak and liable to break. In such cases stub teeth are often used.

For this type of tooth the size is indicated by a fraction. The numerator of the fraction expresses the module to which the circumferential proportions of the tooth conform, and the denominator determines the radial proportions of the tooth. Thus a $\frac{5}{4}$ stub tooth means one in which the pitch diameter is worked out on a basis of 5 mm module, and the tooth height on the proportions of 4 mm module. Since 5 mm module gives a larger normal tooth than 4 mm module, the result is a short stubby tooth, hence the name. Stub teeth are generally cut with a pressure angle of 20°, and the following are the pitches most commonly used:

$$\frac{5}{4}, \frac{6}{5}, \frac{8}{6}, \frac{10}{8}, \frac{12{\cdot}5}{10} \text{ and } \frac{15}{12{\cdot}5}$$

The same method is used when quoting stub tooth sizes in diametral pitches, but in this case the ratio produces a "proper vulgar fraction", i.e. with the numerator smaller than the denominator. Hence, if a stub tooth is denoted by a fraction in which the numerator is smaller than the denominator, the reader should appreciate that the sizes quoted refer to diametral pitches and not modules, and it will be necessary to state whether the diametral pitch is "millimetre series" or "inch series".

Example 4. Calculate the principal dimensions for a 45T gear having a $\frac{6}{5}$ stub tooth.

Here the pitch diameter will be worked out on 6 mm module and the heights on 5 mm module.

Pitch dia	$= mT = 6 \times 45 = 270$ mm
Addendum $= m$	$= 5$ mm
Top dia of gear	$= 270 + 2(5)$
	$= 280$ mm
Cutting depth	$= 2{\cdot}25 \times 5$
	$= 11{\cdot}25$ mm

Backlash in gearing

If a pair of gears were cut theoretically correct and assembled at the correct centre distance, a tooth on one gear would just fit hard into the tooth space of the other, because the pitch line width of the tooth and space would be equal. For freedom of action the above conditions would be unsuitable, and it is usual to allow a little play between the thickness of the tooth and the width of the space into which it fits. This play is called "backlash," and it is the backlash which allows one gear to be turned a fraction before the drive is taken up by the mating gear.

The amount of backlash to be allowed depends on the tooth size, and the following table gives an indication of suitable allowances:

Module (mm)	10	8	6	5	4	3	2·5	2	1·5
Backlash [in mm clearance between face of mating teeth]	0·4	0·4	0·4	0·3	0·2	0·15	0·15	0·1	0·1

Measurement of backlash

Two suitable methods of measuring backlash are (*a*) by means of feeler gauges between the teeth, (*b*) by measuring the distance that the centres of the gears may be moved nearer together from the standard distance before the teeth are in hard contact.

The first of the above methods is straightforward and needs no mathematical manipulation. For the second method it will be helpful for us to obtain an expression giving the backlash in terms of the amount the gears are capable of being moved together.

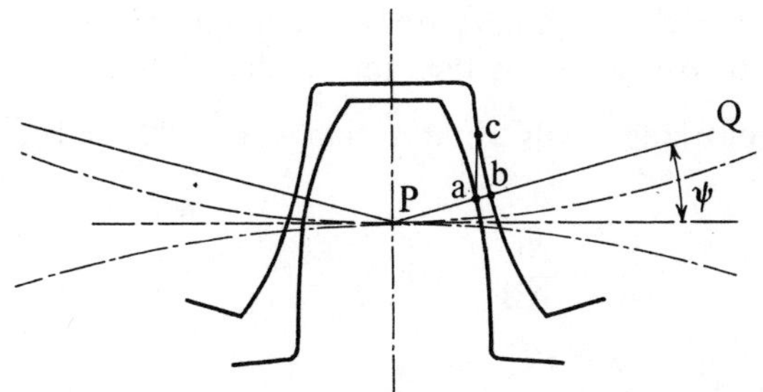

Fig. 76

In Fig. 76, *ab* is half the backlash and *P* is the pitch point.

If we consider the portion *cb* of the tooth as being a straight line, then triangle *abc* is rightangled at *b*, *ac* is the amount the gear centers may be moved together, $ab = \frac{1}{2}$ backlash and angle $acb = \psi$.

Let B = backlash = $2ab$
and D = amount the gear centres can be moved together = ac-

Then $$\frac{ab}{ac} = \sin \psi$$

$$\frac{\frac{B}{2}}{D} = \sin \psi \text{ and } B = 2D \sin \psi$$

or $$D = \frac{B}{2 \sin \psi}.$$

Helical (spiral) gears

The type of gear we have dealt with so far has been the spur gear, i.e. one in which the teeth are straight and parallel with the axis of the gear. In helical gears the teeth are not straight, but are cut on a helix. These gears are also called spiral gears, screw gears and skew gears.

A sketch of a portion of a helical gear is shown in Fig. 77, in which it will be noticed that the teeth slope at an angle σ (the helix (spiral) angle) to the axis of the gear, and in the gear shown, the teeth are cut RH helix. Teeth may, of course, be RH or LH.

Referring again to the figure, it will be seen that the pitch of the teeth may either be taken round the rim of the gear, or it may be taken perpendicular to the teeth. In the first case it is called the *circumferential* pitch (p_c), and in the second case it is known as *normal* pitch (p_n). Circular pitch is still considered as being taken along the surface formed by the pitch circle. The circular pitches p_n and p_c are shown in Fig. 77, and as will be seen, the relation between them is the same as the relation between the sides AC and AB of triangle ABC. In this triangle $\hat{C} = 90°$ and $\hat{A}$ = helix angle σ.

Hence $$\frac{p_n}{p_c} = \frac{AC}{AB} = \cos \sigma,$$

i.e. $$p_n = p_c \cos \sigma \tag{7}$$

or $$p_c = \frac{p_n}{\cos \sigma} = p_n \sec \sigma$$

It will be seen that if a section is taken through the teeth on a plane containing AC, we shall have the true shape of the tooth as it is cut. Hence the normal pitch (p_n), which is the one measured parallel to AC, is the pitch which governs the cutter to be used to cut the gear. Referring again to Fig.

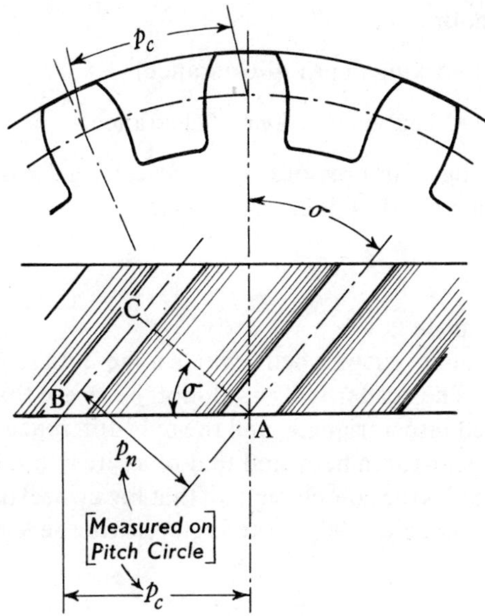

Fig. 77.

77, the pitch p_c, multiplied by the number of teeth, gives the pitch circumference. This pitch, then, governs the size of the gear, which does not depend on the number of teeth. The larger the helix angle σ, the greater will be the ratio $\frac{p_c}{p_n}$ and the larger the gear for a given number of teeth.

As well as circular pitch p_n and p_c we may, just as in the case of spur gears, express the pitch in the module form. The normal module (m_n) is the one which governs the true shape of the tooth, and since cutters are most commonly specified in terms of the module, this is important to us from the point of view of cutting the gear. The relation between m_n and p_n is the same as for spur gears.

i.e.
$$p_n = \pi m_n \tag{8}$$

For a spur gear we have $D = mT$
For a helical gear, since the circular pitch

$$p_c = \frac{p_n}{\cos \sigma}, \text{ then } m_c = \frac{m_n}{\cos \sigma} = \frac{m}{\cos \sigma}$$

$$\text{and } D = \frac{mT}{\cos \sigma} \tag{9}$$

Addendum of the tooth $= m$ (10)

and the cutting depth (working depth + clearance)

$= 2$ addendum + clearance $= 2\,m$ + clearance.

In modern practice, using a 20° pressure angle, the cutting depth has been standardised at (working depth + 0·25 addendum)
$= 2{\cdot}25\,m$ (11)

Helix (spiral) lead and angle

The teeth of a helical gear are cut on a helix, which is merely a screw thread with a very large lead. The reader will, no doubt, be aware that a screw thread can be developed into a triangle, and the only differences between the development of a gear-tooth helix and that of a screw thread are: (*a*) the helix angle of a thread is the complement of that for a wheel tooth (Fig. 78(*a*) [complement of an angle = 90° − the angle]; (*b*) the development is

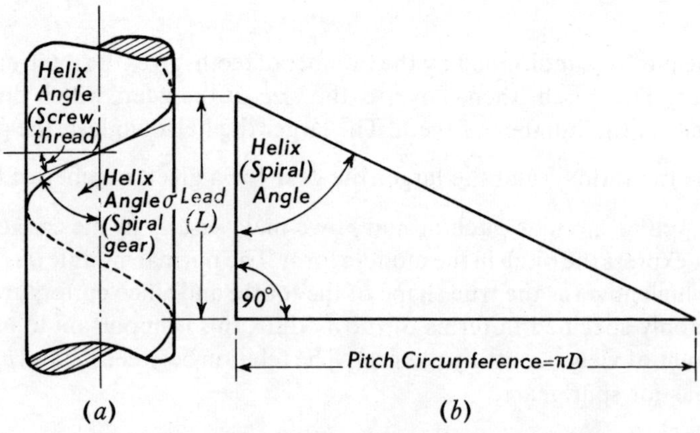

Fig. 78 Development of Helix.

based on the assumption that the helix makes one complete turn round the cylinder upon which it is cut. In a screw thread this is true, but the tooth of a gear only completes a small proportion of a complete turn. [The student may imagine a helical gear to be a short length of a very coarse thread having as many "starts" as there are teeth in the gear.] On the assumption noted under (*b*) above, the development of a helical gear tooth is shown in Fig. 78(*b*). From the diagram we have the following relationships

$$\tan \sigma = \frac{\text{Pitch circum}}{\text{Lead}} = \frac{\pi D}{L}$$

$$\text{or lead } L = \frac{\pi D}{\tan \sigma} = \frac{\pi m T \sec \sigma}{\tan \sigma} \qquad (12)$$

Cutter for helical gears

When cutting spur gears with a form cutter on the milling machine, the cutter is marked with the range of teeth for which it is suitable. For example, to cut a 30T gear, we should use a No. 4 cutter, which is suitable for a range of 26T to 34T. Due to the twist on the teeth of a helical gear this must be modified, and the size of cutter is given by

$$\frac{\text{No. of teeth } (T)}{(\cos \sigma)^3} \qquad (13)$$

Example 5. The pitch diameter of a helical wheel is to be approximately 120 mm, the helix angle is 30° and it is to be cut with a cutter of 4 mm module. Find the particulars of the nearest gear to this.

We have that the normal module = 4 mm and $\sigma = 30°$.

Hence, from (9) $$120 = \frac{4T}{\cos 30°}$$

and $$T = \frac{120 \cos 30°}{4}$$

$$= 30 \times 0{\cdot}866 = 25{\cdot}98$$

The nearest to this is $26T$

and $$D = \frac{mT}{\cos \sigma}, \quad \frac{26 \times 4}{\cos 30°} = \frac{104}{0{\cdot}866} = 120{\cdot}1 \text{ mm}$$

Top dia. $= 120{\cdot}1 + 2.\text{Add} = 120{\cdot}1 + 2(4)$
$= 128{\cdot}1$ mm

Cutting depth $= 2{\cdot}25m = 9{\cdot}00$ mm

From (12) Lead of helix $$= \frac{\pi D}{\tan 30°} = \frac{3{\cdot}142 \times 120{\cdot}1}{0{\cdot}577} = 654 \text{ mm}.$$

Thus the nearest gear has the following particulars: 26T. Pitch dia. 120·1 mm, Helix angle 30°, Lead of helix, 654 mm.

The cutter for this gear would be $\dfrac{26}{(0{\cdot}866)^3} = 40$, i.e. the same cutter as would be used for a 40T 4 mm module, spur gear.

Example 6. Two parallel shafts at 120 mm centres are to be connected by a pair of helical gears to give a speed ratio of 1:2. The helix angle of the wheels is to be approximately 20°. If the normal module is 2·5 mm, determine suitable wheels.

Since the shafts are parallel, the helix angles of the two wheels will be the same, but one will be RH helix, and the other LH

Centre distance $= 120$

Ratio of speeds $=$ ratio of pitch radii $= 1:2$

$r = \frac{1}{3} \times 120 = 40$ and $R = \frac{2}{3} \times 120 = 80$

Hence $D = 160$ and $d = 80$, also $m = 2{\cdot}5$ m

from (9) $D = \dfrac{mT}{\cos\sigma}$, $T = \dfrac{D\cos\sigma}{m} = \dfrac{160 \times 0{\cdot}9397}{2{\cdot}5} = 60{\cdot}13$

Since the ratio is to be 2:1 let us try 60T and 30T, and find a new value for σ.

Then for the wheel from $T = \dfrac{D\cos\sigma}{m}$

$$\cos\sigma = \frac{mT}{D} = \frac{2{\cdot}5 \times 60}{160} = \frac{150}{160} = 0{\cdot}9375$$

hence $\sigma = 20°22'$.

To obtain the leads of the helices of the wheels we have for the wheel:

Pitch circum $= 160\pi = 502{\cdot}7$ mm

and from (19) Lead $= \dfrac{502{\cdot}7}{\tan 20°22'} = \dfrac{502{\cdot}7}{0{\cdot}3712} = 1354$ mm

For the pinion Lead $= \dfrac{80\pi}{\tan 20°\,22'} =$ half of lead of wheel $= 677$ mm

The particulars of the gears are thus as follows:

Wheel. No. of teeth = 60
Pitch dia = 160 mm
Add = 2·5 mm
Top dia = 165 mm
Cutting depth = 2·25 m
= 5·625 mm
Helix angle = 20°22′.
RH helix.
Helix lead = 1 354 m

$$\text{Cutter to use} = \frac{60}{(0{\cdot}9375)^3}$$

= cutter as for 73T spur wheel.

Pinion. No. of teeth = 30
Pitch dia = 80 mm
Top dia = 85 mm
Cutting depth = 5·625 mm
Helix angle = 20°22′.
LH helix
Helix lead = 677 mm

$$\text{Cutter to use} = \frac{30}{(0{\cdot}9375)^3}$$

= cutter as for 36T spur wheel.

The reader will observe that the solution to these problems is arrived at by a compromise after a system of trial and error. With wheels of this type such a procedure is nearly always necessary before a practical set of working conditions can be arrived at. Generally, the conditions allow one or more of the gear elements to be varied to suit the problem.

Exercises 4c

1. Calculate the pitch diameter, top diameter and cutting depth for a 42T gear having $\frac{5}{4}$ stub teeth.

2. Find the gear-tooth caliper settings for checking the tooth of a 32T, $\frac{5}{4}$ stub-tooth gear.

3. A pair of gears are required to connect two shafts at 160 mm centres. If the speed ratio required is 3:5, and the gears are to have $\frac{5}{4}$ stub teeth, find their leading particulars.

4. A pair of gears consists of 27T and 63T gears of 4 mm module, 20° pressure angle. If the backlash allowance is 0·2 mm, what should be the centre distance between the two gears when the teeth are hard in contact?

5. A train of gears consists of the following: 30T driving 48T driving 48T driving 75T. The teeth are 4 mm module and the backlash allowance on all the teeth is 0·15 mm. If all the backlash is taken up in one direction, through what angle must the 30T gear be turned before the drive is taken up by the 75T wheel?

6. Calculate the following particulars for a 52T spiral gear of 4 mm normal module, 20° spiral angle: (*a*) pitch diameter, (*b*) top diameter, (*c*) cutting depth, (*d*) lead of spiral, (*e*) suitable cutter to use.

7. A helical gear is to have a helix angle of 30° (RH), and the normal module is 4 mm. The pitch diameter must be as near as possible to 125 mm. Calculate (*a*) the number of teeth, (*b*) the pitch, and top diameters, (*c*) the lead of the helix, (*d*) the correct cutter to use.

8. A spiral gear has 25 teeth, a helix angle of 45°, and an approximate pitch diameter of 75 mm. Calculate the nearest normal metric module. Find also the pitch diameter, top diameter, lead of spiral and cutting depth.

9. A pair of spiral gears are required to connect two parallel shafts 100 mm apart, with a gear ratio of 3:2. Working on a normal module of 2·5 mm, and an approximate helix angle of 20°, determine particulars of a suitable pair of wheels.

Worm gearing

A worm dirve is often used to connect two non-intersecting shafts which are at right-angles and a fair distance apart. The worm is the equivalent

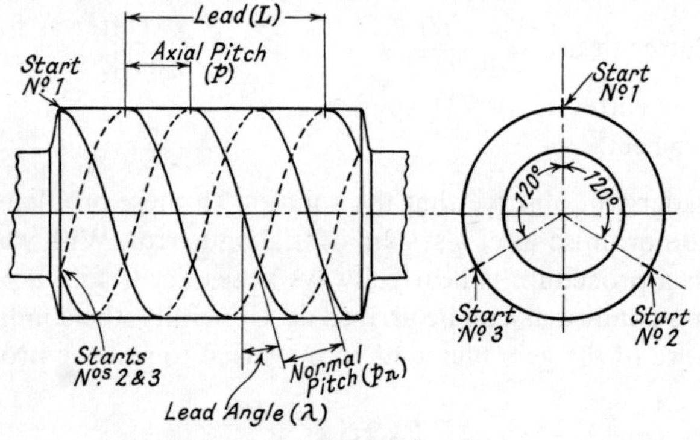

Fig. 79 Diagram of 3-Start Worm.

of a screw thread, the shape of a section of the thread on a plane through the axis of the worm, being the same as a rack tooth in the involute system. The action between a worm and wormwheel is equivalent to that of the wheel as a gear; rolling along the worm as a rack. As the worm is usually produced by turning, or by a milling process similar to turning, the pitch

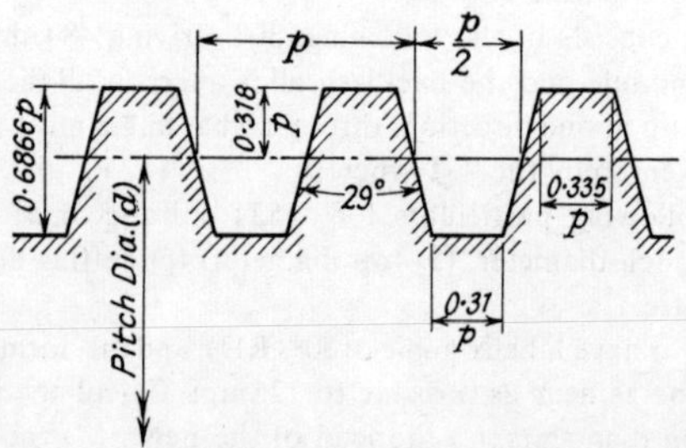

Fig. 80 Worm Thread Form for 14½° Pressure Angle.

most commonly used is the circular pitch (p). Fig. 79 shows the pitch, lead and lead angle for a worm, and Fig. 80 gives the proportions for the thread on a section through the axis for a tooth of $14\frac{1}{2}°$ pressure angle.

The relationships between the pitch, lead and lead angle are the same as for a screw thread.

$$\text{Lead } (L) = (\text{Axial pitch})(\text{No. of starts}) = pn$$

$$\tan \lambda = \frac{\text{Lead}}{\pi(\text{Pitch dia})} = \frac{L}{\pi d}$$

The pitch diameter of a worm is quite an arbitrary dimension, and a worm may be cut to any pitch diameter suitable to accommodate it to centre distance at which it is to engage with the wheel. In general, the pitch diameter should not be less than four times the pitch.

Worms with large lead angles

The efficiency of a worm drive increases with the lead angle up to a maximum at about 45°. In view of this, multi-start worms with large lead angles are to be preferred. Unfortunately, with such worms, interference difficulties occur in cutting and operation, and when the lead angle exceeds 20° it is usual to increase the pressure angle (i.e. the included angle of the worm thread is increased). The pressure angle may be taken up to 20° (40° incl. angle of thread), and in very quick start worms ψ is sometimes made 30°. For pressure angles other than $14\frac{1}{2}°$ the tooth proportions must be re-calculated on the basis of the new angle and will not be the same as those shown on Fig. 80. Also, when the lead angle exceeds 15°; it is more advantageous to base the tooth proportions on the normal pitch. For the case of the tooth shown in Fig. 80 these are modified as follows:

$$\text{Normal pitch} = (\text{axial pitch})(\text{cos of lead angle})$$

$$p_n = p \cos \lambda \text{ (as (7) above)}$$

Then

$$\text{Addendum of thread} = 0{\cdot}318p_n$$

$$\text{Depth of thread} = 0{\cdot}6866p_n$$

$$\text{Width of finishing tool at bottom} = 0{\cdot}31p_n$$

Worm wheel

For the best results the cross-section of the worm-wheel rim should be of the form shown in Fig. 81 (a). For light duty and moderate speeds, wheels as shown at 81 (b) will give satisfactory results. Teeth with curved bot-

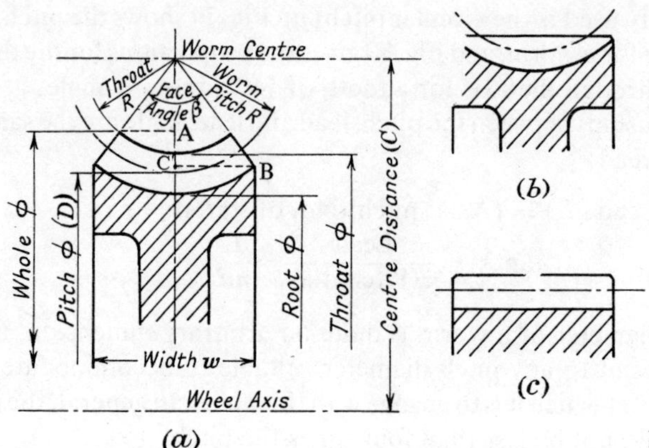

Fig. 81

toms should be cut with a hob or a flycutter; that at 81 (*c*) is really a helical gear and may be cut as such. The shape of the teeth of worm wheels is the same as for involute gears of the same pressure angle.

Worm wheel dimensions

These will be based on the circular pitch and for large worm lead angles the tooth proportions will be in terms of the normal pitch. In reading the following, Fig. 81 (*a*) should be referred to:

$$\text{Pitch dia } (D) = \frac{\text{Pitch circum.}}{\pi} = \frac{Tp}{\pi}$$

$$\text{Throat dia} = \text{Pitch dia} + 2 \text{ add} = D + 0{\cdot}63p$$

$$\text{Centre distance } (C) = \text{Pitch rad wheel} + \text{pitch rad worm}$$

$$= \frac{D}{2} + \frac{d}{2}$$

$$\text{Throat rad } (R_t) = C - \tfrac{1}{2}\text{ throat dia}$$

$$\text{Whole dia} = 2(C - OA)$$

$$= 2[C - R_t \cos(\tfrac{1}{2}\beta)]$$

$$\text{Width } (w) \text{ approx} = 2BC$$

$$= 2(\text{Top rad of worm})\,[\sin(\tfrac{1}{2}\beta)]$$

$$= (d + 0{\cdot}636p)\sin(\tfrac{1}{2}\beta)$$

In cases where tooth proportions are based on normal pitch, then in expressions (19) and (23) above, p_n should be used instead of p.

Speed ratio with worm gearing

If the wheel has T teeth, and the worm is single threaded (1 start), then the worm will turn T times for 1 turn of the wheel. A 2-start worm will turn $\frac{T}{2}$ times per revolution of the wheel, and so on. Hence for T teeth in the wheel and n starts on the worm:

$$\text{Speed ratio} = \frac{\text{Rev of worm}}{\text{1 Rev of wheel}} = \frac{T}{n}$$

Example 7. Determine the dimensions of a worm and wheel to operate at 120 mm centres and give a ratio of 16 – 1. Circular pitch 10 mm, pressure angle $14\frac{1}{2}°$, wheel face angle 75°.

For 10 mm pitch the minimum dia. of the worm should be 4 × 10 mm = 40 mm. This leaves 120 – 20 = 100 mm as the radius of the wheel. Dia of wheel = 200 mm. Circum = 200π = 628·4 mm.

At 10 mm circular pitch this gives 63 teeth.

If we make the worm 64T and use a 4-start worm, we shall obtain the 16 – 1 ratio required.

$$\text{Pitch dia wormwheel} = \frac{64 \times 10}{\pi} = \frac{640}{\pi} = 203{\cdot}7\,\text{mm}$$

$$\text{and pitch rad} = \frac{203{\cdot}7}{2} = 101{\cdot}85\,\text{mm}$$

$$\text{Throat dia} = 203{\cdot}7 + 0{\cdot}636p$$

$$= 203{\cdot}7 + 0{\cdot}636(10) = 210{\cdot}06\,\text{mm}$$

$$\text{Throat rad} = 120 - \tfrac{1}{2}(210{\cdot}06) = 14{\cdot}97\,\text{mm}$$

$$\text{Whole dia} = 2[120 - 14{\cdot}97 \cos 37\tfrac{1}{2}°]$$

$$= 2[120 - 14{\cdot}97 \times 0{\cdot}7949 = 216{\cdot}24\,\text{mm}$$

$$\text{Pitch rad worm} = \text{centre distance} - \text{rad wheel}$$

$$= 120 - 101{\cdot}85 = 18{\cdot}15$$

$$\text{and pitch dia} = 2 \times 18{\cdot}15 = 36{\cdot}30\,\text{mm}$$

$$\text{Top dia worm} = 36{\cdot}30 + 0{\cdot}636p = 36{\cdot}30 + 6{\cdot}36 = 42{\cdot}66\,\text{mm}$$

We may now find the approx. width of the wheel (w)

$w = (d + 0{\cdot}636p) \sin 37\frac{1}{2}° = 42{\cdot}66 \sin 37\frac{1}{2}° = 42{\cdot}66 \times 0{\cdot}6088$
$= 25{\cdot}97$ mm (say 26 mm)

$$\text{tan of worm lead angle} = \frac{\text{lead}}{\pi d} = \frac{4 \times 10}{\pi \times 36{\cdot}30} = 0{\cdot}3508$$

$$\lambda = 19°\ 20'$$

Whole depth of tooth = $0{\cdot}6866p$ = 6.87 mm

Width of threading tool at end = $0{\cdot}31p$ = 3·10 mm

This gives us all the data necessary for the worm and wheel.

As an exercise, the reader should make a full-size drawing of the pair.

Helical (spiral) gears to mesh with worms

Sometimes, as a compromise, and to avoid the delay and expense of ordering a new wormwheel, an ordinary straight-faced helical wheel is cut to replace a wormwheel. The main problem is to find, out of stock, a suitable cutter to give a satisfactory match-up.

If stocks of circular, diametral and module pitch cutters are available, it is often possible to arrive at a workable solution. Let us see what could have been done to match a helical wheel to the worm in Example 7 above:

$$\text{Normal circular pitch of wormwheel} = 10 \cos 19°20'$$
$$= 10(0{\cdot}9436) = 9{\cdot}436\,\text{mm}$$
$$\text{Normal module} = \frac{9{\cdot}436}{\pi} = 3{\cdot}003$$

This is very near a 3 mm module and a 3 mm module cutter would probably cut a satisfactory gear.

Bevel gears

Bevel gears are used to connect two shafts whose axes meet, and which are in the same plane. We saw in connection with spur gears that the motion of two gears was equivalent to that of two thin cylinders or discs rolling together, the diameters of the discs being the same as the pitch diameters of the gears. In the case of bevel gearing the fundamental conception of the motion is that of two cones rolling together.

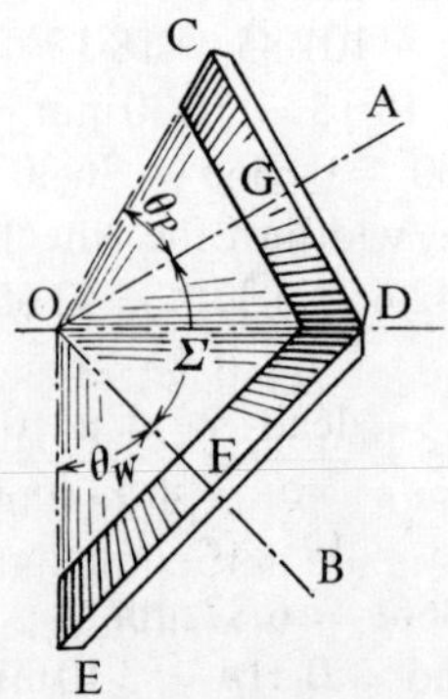

Fig. 82

In Fig. 82, OA and OB represent the axes of two shafts intersecting at O. COD and DOE are the two elemental cones, having OA and OB as their axes. The cones touch along the line OD, and if one is turned it will drive the other. In practice, the gears only consist of a narrow frustrum of the cones and are shown thickened. Metal is added at the back, as shown, to strengthen up the teeth in that region.

The two elemental cones are called the *pitch cones* and become the imaginary pitch surfaces of the gears. The angle θ_P is the *pitch angle* of the pinion, θ_W that of the wheel and Σ is the shaft angle. When teeth are cut in the gears, the number of teeth in each gear will be proportional to the pitch diameters CD and DE.

Hence if n = rev/min of wheel and N = rev/min of pinion

$$\frac{n}{N} = \frac{T}{t} = \frac{\mathrm{DE}}{\mathrm{CD}} = \frac{\sin\theta_W}{\sin\theta_P}$$

Note that $$\theta_P + \theta_W = \Sigma$$

Bevel gear calculations

In Fig. 83: $\widehat{\mathrm{AOB}} = \theta$ is the pitch angle.

AC = pitch dia (D).

$\widehat{\mathrm{DOA}} = \alpha$ is the *addendum angle*

$\widehat{\mathrm{AOF}} = \beta$ is the *dedendum angle*

$\widehat{\mathrm{EOB}} = \phi = \theta + \alpha$ is the *face angle*

$\widehat{\mathrm{FOB}} = \rho = \theta - \beta$ is the *root angle*

C is the *cone distance.*

L is the *tip distance.*

f is the face width and may be made about $= \dfrac{C}{3}$

D, L and C are given capital or small letters according to whether they refer to the wheel or to the pinion. The angles are generally given a suffix $_p$ or $_w$ to differentiate them. [p for pinion and w for wheel.]

The back face DAF is always made perpendicular to the pitch surface AO, and the size and shape of the teeth as developed round that face correspond to the proportions for the pitch of the teeth in the gear

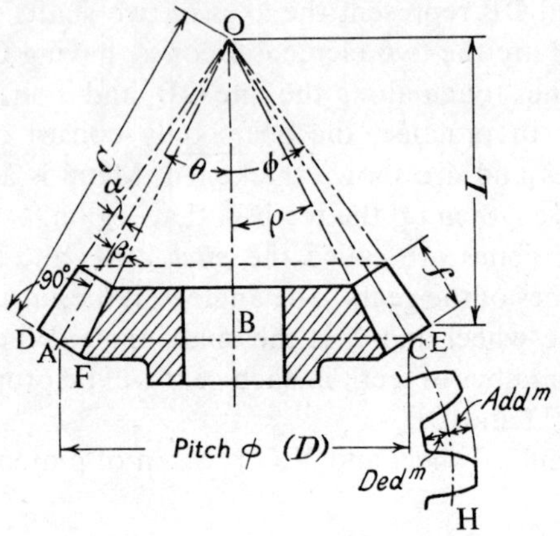

Fig. 83

(e.g. if the gear had teeth of 5 mm module, then the teeth at the surface DF (as shown developed round line CH) would be the correct size for that pitch). In travelling down the tooth from face DF towards O, every line on the tooth converges to O.

From Fig. 83:

$$\frac{D}{2} \div C = \sin\theta \text{ and } C = \frac{D}{2\sin\theta}$$

$$\tan\alpha = \frac{\text{Add}}{C} = \frac{m}{C} \text{ (where } m = \text{module)}$$

$$\tan\beta = \frac{\text{Ded}}{C} = \frac{1{\cdot}25m}{C}$$

Whole diameter (over corners DE) = pitch dia + 2AD cos θ

But $\quad AD = \text{Add} = m$

$$\text{Whole dia} = D + 2m\cos\theta$$

Examples 8. Two shafts at 90° are to be geared together by bevels. The speed ratio is to be 3:2 and the pinion pitch diameter is to be 120 mm. Determine the dimensions of 5 mm bevels.

Since the ratio is 3:2 and $d = 120$ mm

$$D = 120 \times \tfrac{3}{2} = 180\text{ mm} \quad T = 36 \text{ and } t = 24$$

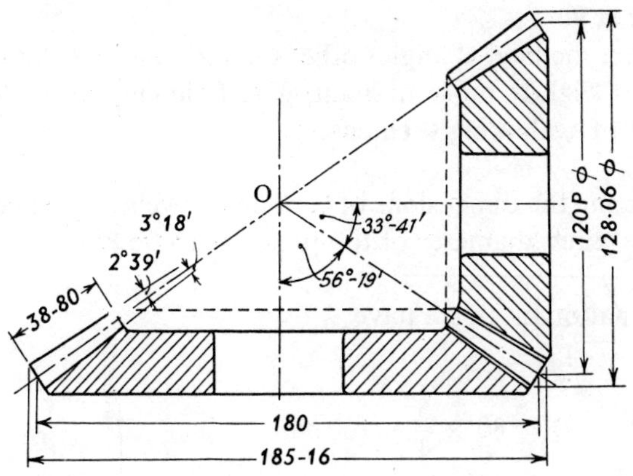

Fig. 84

Signifying the pitch angles by θ_W and θ_P.

$$\text{Then } \tan\theta_P = \frac{AB}{BO}\text{(Fig. 83).} = \frac{60}{90} = \frac{2}{3}$$

$$\theta_P = 33°\ 41' \text{ and } \theta_W = 90 - 33°\ 41' = 56°\ 19'$$

Add $= m = 5\,\text{mm}$ Ded $= 1{\cdot}25m = 6{\cdot}25\,\text{mm}$

$$OA = \sqrt{90^2 + 60^2} = 108{\cdot}10\,\text{mm}$$

$$\text{tan of add angle } \frac{5}{108{\cdot}1} = 0{\cdot}0463\ \alpha = 2°\ 39'$$

$$\text{tan ded angle } \frac{6{\cdot}25}{108{\cdot}1} = 0{\cdot}0578\ \beta = 3°\ 18'$$

Face angle wheel $\phi_W = 56°\,19' + 2°39' = 58°\,58'$
Face angle pinion $\phi_P = 33°\,41' + 2°\,39' = 36°\,20'$
Root angle wheel $P_W = 56°\ 19' - 3°\ 18' = 53°\ 1'$
Root angle pinion $P_P = 33°\ 41' - 3°\ 18' = 30°\ 23'$

Whole dia (wheel) $= D + 2m\cos\theta_W = 180 + 10(0{\cdot}5155) = 185{\cdot}16\,\text{mm}$
Whole dia (pinion) $= d + 2m\cos\theta_P = 120 + 10(0{\cdot}8056) = 128{\cdot}06\,\text{mm}$

$$\text{Face width (if made } \tfrac{1}{3}\text{C)} = \tfrac{1}{3}\frac{D}{2\sin\theta}$$

$$f = \frac{120}{6 \times 0{\cdot}5155} = \frac{20}{0{\cdot}5155} = 38{\cdot}80\,\text{mm}$$

A sketch of these wheels is shown at Fig. 84.

Shafts not inclined at 90°

When the shafts are inclined at angles other than 90° the calculation for the pitch angles is slightly more difficult. The following example will indicate a method of evaluating such cases.

Example 9. Determine the dimensions of 4 module bevels to connect two shafts at 70°. The pitch diameter of the pinion is to be 80 mm and the ratio 4:5.

From the information given we have

$$d = 80\,\text{mm}$$

$$D = 80 \times \frac{5}{4} = 100\,\text{mm}$$

$$T = \frac{100}{4} = 25 : t = \frac{80}{4} = 20$$

$$\Sigma = 70°$$

In triangles OAC and OAB (Fig. 85), AC = 50 and AB = 40

Also $$\frac{\text{AC}}{\text{OA}} = \sin\theta_W \text{ and } \frac{\text{AB}}{\text{OA}} = \sin\theta_P = \sin(70° - \theta_W)$$

Hence $$\frac{50}{\text{OA}} = \sin\theta_W \qquad (1)$$

$$\frac{40}{\text{OA}} = \sin(70° - \theta_W) \qquad (2)$$

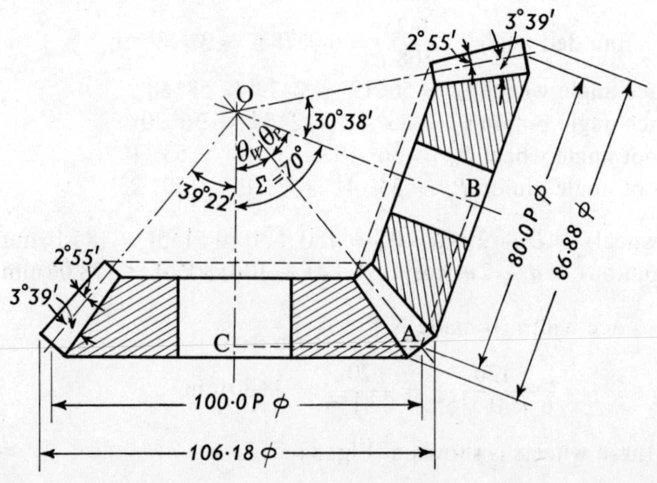

Fig. 85

Divide (2) by (1) $\quad \dfrac{40}{50} = \dfrac{\sin(70° - \theta_W)}{\sin \theta_W}$

$$= \frac{\sin 70° \cos \theta_W - \cos 70° \sin \theta_W}{\sin \theta_W} \text{ (see Appendix VI)}$$

$$= \frac{0{\cdot}9397 \cos \theta_W}{\sin \theta_W} - \frac{0{\cdot}342 \sin \theta_W}{\sin \theta_W}$$

$$= \frac{0{\cdot}937}{\tan \theta_W} - 0{\cdot}342$$

$\dfrac{4}{5} + 0{\cdot}342 = \dfrac{0{\cdot}937}{\tan \theta_W}$ from which $\theta_W = 30° \, 22'$

and $\quad \theta_P = 70° - \theta w = 70° - 39° \, 22' = 30° \, 38'$

$$OA = \frac{AB}{\sin 30° \, 38'} = \frac{40}{0{\cdot}5095} = 78{\cdot}48 \text{ mm}$$

Add = module = 4 mm

Ded = 4 × 1·25 = 5 mm

$$\tan \text{add angle} = \frac{4}{78{\cdot}48} = 0{\cdot}05107 \qquad \alpha = 2° \, 55'$$

$$\tan \text{ded angle} = \frac{5}{78{\cdot}48} = 0{\cdot}0638 \qquad \beta = 3° \, 39'$$

Face angle wheel $\theta_W = 39° \, 22' + 2° \, 55' = 42° \, 17'$

Face angle pinion $\theta_P = 30° \, 38' + 2° \, 55' = 33° \, 33'$.

Whole dia wheel $= D + 2m \cos \theta_W = 100 + 8 \cos 39° \, 33' = 106{\cdot}18$ mm

Whole dia pinion $= D + 2m \cos \theta_P = 80 + 8 \cos 30° \, 38' = 86{\cdot}88$ mm

The main dimensions are shown on Fig. 85.

Exercises 4c

1. Calculate the top diameter, root diameter and helix angle for a 2-start worm of 10 mm pitch and 40 mm pitch diameter.

2. If the worm in Question **1** drives a wheel, and the gear ratio is $17\frac{1}{2}$ to 1, calculate the centre distance, and full particulars for the worm wheel.

3. A worm is 60 mm pitch diameter, and 20 mm circular pitch. Find the number of starts in order that the lead angle may be approximately 30°, and state the actual lead angle. Calculate the normal thickness of the thread on the pitch line.

4. A worm drive operates at 150 mm centres and the ratio required is 15 to 1. Taking a circular pitch of 10 mm and a worm about 50 mm pitch diameter, find a suitable worm and wheel for the drive.

5. Two shafts at 90° are to be connected by equal bevel wheels. Determine the dimensions of one of these if the module is 2·5 mm, and the pitch diameter 60 mm.

6. Two shafts at 90° are to be connected by bevels to give a ratio of 3:2. If the pitch diameter of the smaller bevel is 130 mm and the module is 5 mm, determine the dimensions of the wheels.

7. A bevel gear has 20 teeth of 4 mm module and a pitch angle of 45°. Determine the top diameter and included angle of a taper pin, which will rest in a tooth space with its centre on the pitch cone, its large end level with the back face of the gear, and its curved surface making contact with the tooth sides for its whole length. (ψ = 20°).

8. Two shafts, inclined at 120°, are to be connected by bevel wheels to give a ratio of 4:3. The pitch diameter of the smaller gear is 90 mm and the teeth are 5 mm module. Determine particulars of the gears.

5 Milling and the milling machine

Milling Cutters

For the purpose of considering the calculations necessary in connection with milling cutters, we may divide them into three general types: (*a*) those with fluted teeth, (*b*) machine relieved, (*c*) inserted teeth. Sketches of these are shown in Fig. 86.

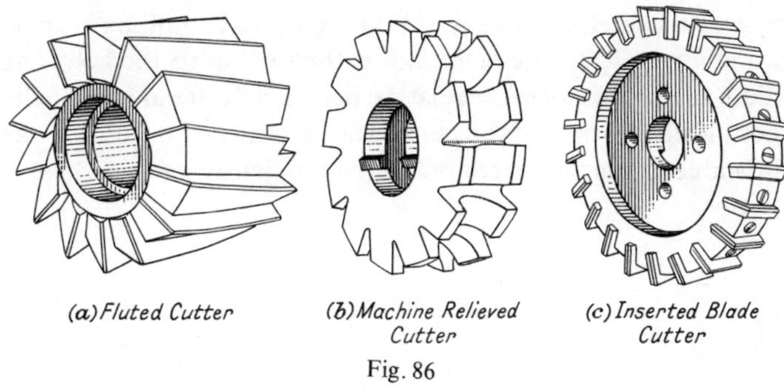

(*a*) *Fluted Cutter* (*b*) *Machine Relieved Cutter* (*c*) *Inserted Blade Cutter*

Fig. 86

Number of teeth

Milling cutters and milling conditions vary so widely that it is difficult to set hard and fast rules for determining the number of teeth to be put in a cutter.

For fluted and relieved cutters the rule $N = 2{\cdot}75\sqrt{D} - 5{\cdot}8$ gives a reasonably proportioned tooth [N = No. of teeth, D = Diameter of cutter].

The formula $N = \frac{D}{12} + 8$ gives a fairly coarse tooth for cutters over 60 mm diameter.

Take a 100 mm cutter, the first formula gives:

$$N = 2{\cdot}75\sqrt{100} - 5{\cdot}8 = 22 \text{ teeth}$$

whilst the second expression gives

$$N = \frac{100}{12} + 8 = 16 \text{ teeth.}$$

For an inserted-blade-face mill it is better to assess the number of teeth on the assumption of their being spaced a suitable distance apart on the periphery of the cutter. Thus if we take a 200 mm face mill and assume the blades to be spaced 30 mm apart, we have

$$\text{No of blades} = \frac{\text{Circumference of cutter}}{30} = \frac{200\pi}{30} = \text{approx } 20$$

Rake on cutter teeth

If a cutter has its teeth milled with their faces radial, and parallel to the cutter axis as shown in Fig. 87(*a*), the teeth have neither top nor side rake. If, however, the end view of the tooth is as shown in Fig. 87(*b*) the front rake is the angle α, since the tooth cuts relative to a radial line OA from the centre to its tip. Side rake is put on the tooth by milling it on a helix as shown at Fig. 87(*c*). The side rake is then equal to the helix angle β. When teeth are of this form the relation between the hand of the helix and the direction of rotation of the cutter is important, in order that the end thrust introduced may be accommodated efficiently.

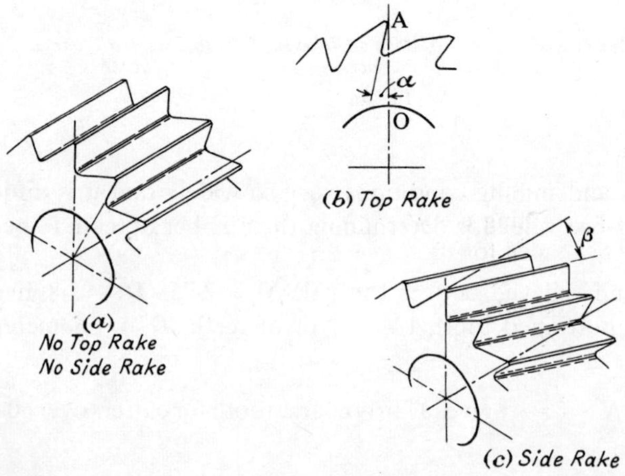

Fig. 87.

The calculation of the helix angle is discussed in the section on spiral milling.

Top rake can be put on the teeth by milling it off-set as shown in Fig. 88. Instead of the front of the tooth being milled on the centre line it is cut off centre by distance x. Then if R = radius of cutter and α the rake angle required we see that $\frac{x}{R} = \sin\alpha$ and $x = R\sin\alpha$.

Rakes up to 10° are advantageous, but above that angle they may cause the cutter to chatter.

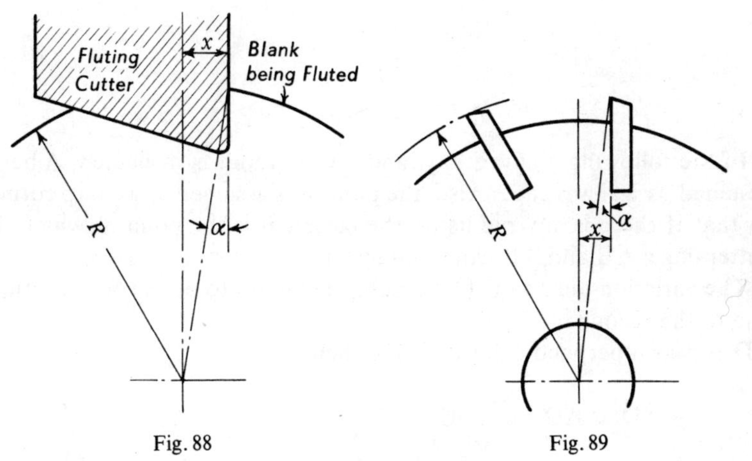

Fig. 88

Fig. 89

Example 1. Calculate the amount of offset to give 10° of rake on the tooth of a cutter 80 mm diameter.

In this case $R = 40$ and since $\sin 10° = 0{\cdot}1736$

$$\begin{aligned} x = 40 \sin 10° &= 40 \times 0{\cdot}1736 \\ &= 6{\cdot}944 \text{ (say 7 mm)} \end{aligned}$$

The case for an inserted-blade cutter is shown in Fig. 89, where if R = radius over blades, then

$$x = R\sin\alpha \text{ as before.}$$

Angle of fluting cutter

For milling the flutes in cutters the problem arises of determining the angle α of the fluting cutter to give the required depth (d) of the flute (Fig. 90).

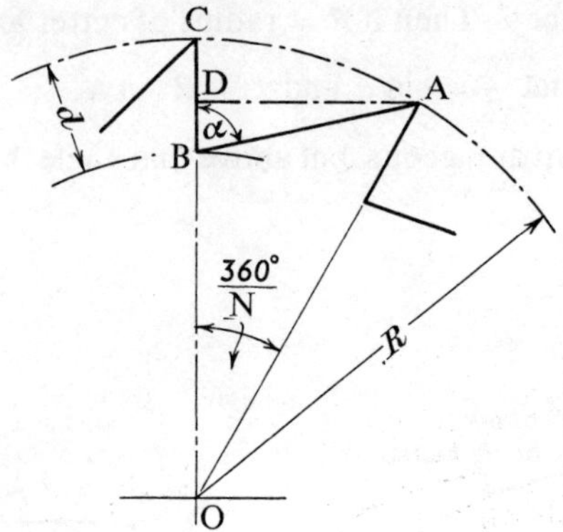

Fig. 90

In the following analysis any land on the tooth is neglected, A being assumed as a sharp edge. Also, the point B is assumed as a sharp corner, so that if there is any radius on the cutter, B is the point at which the cutter edges CB and AB would intersect.

The variation due to the first assumption tends to cancel out variations due to the second.

AD is drawn perpendicular to CBO, then

$$\begin{aligned} AD &= AO \sin \widehat{AOC} \\ &= AD \sin \frac{360}{N} \text{ [where } N = \text{No. of teeth in cutter]} \end{aligned}$$

and since AO = rad of cutter, R,

$$AD = R \sin \frac{360}{N}$$

Now $$\tan \alpha = \frac{AD}{DB} = \frac{AD}{CB - CD} = \frac{AD}{d - CD} = \frac{R \sin \frac{360}{N}}{d - CD}$$

But $$\begin{aligned} CD &= CO - DO = R - AO \cos \frac{360}{N} \\ &= R - R \cos \frac{360}{N} = R\left(1 - \cos \frac{360}{N}\right) \end{aligned}$$

Hence $$\tan \alpha = \frac{R \sin \frac{360}{N}}{d - R\left(1 \cos \frac{360}{N}\right)}$$

Example 2. Calculate the angle of fluting cutter required to mill 16 teeth, 6 mm deep in a cutter 80 mm diameter.

Here $R = 40$, $N = 16$ and $d = 6$

$$\tan \alpha = \frac{R \sin \frac{360}{N}}{d - R\left(1 - \cos \frac{360}{N}\right)} \qquad \frac{360}{N} = \frac{360}{16} = 22\tfrac{1}{2}^\circ$$

$$= \frac{40 \sin 22\tfrac{1}{2}^\circ}{6 - 40(1 - \cos 22\tfrac{1}{2}^\circ)}$$

$$= \frac{15{\cdot}31}{6 - 3{\cdot}044} = \frac{15{\cdot}31}{2{\cdot}956} = 8{\cdot}625$$

From which $\alpha = 81^\circ\ 25'$

The nearest cutter to use would probably then be an 80° cutter.

Clearance

The cutting clearance is put on the teeth at the time they are sharpened. The cutting edges may be ground either on the periphery of a disc wheel as shown at Fig. 91(*a*) or on the face of a cup wheel as at (*b*).

When the teeth are ground on the periphery of a disc wheel as at (*a*), the centre of the cutter is set below the centre of the wheel and the radial

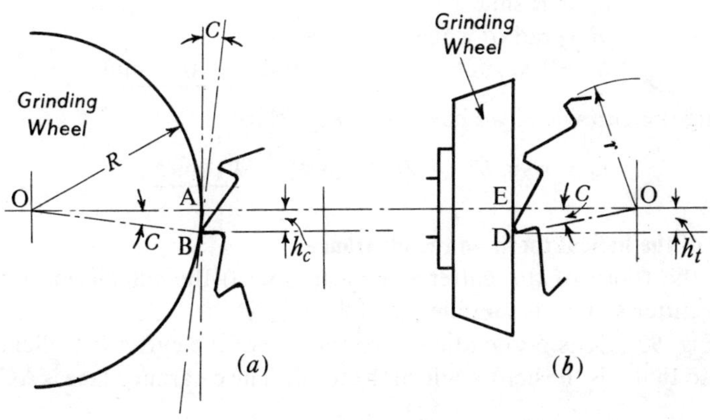

Fig. 91

line joining the tooth edge to the cutter centre is horizontal. The clearance angle obtained is shown as C, and in triangle OBA:

$$\frac{AB}{OB} = \sin C$$

But $\quad OB = \text{radius of wheel } (R)$

and $\quad AB = \text{offset } (h_c)$

Hence $\quad \frac{h_c}{R} = \sin C$

$$h_c = R \sin C$$

Using the face of a cup wheel as at (*b*), the position of the cutter centre relative to the wheel is immaterial, but the *tooth* is set below the cutter centre by the distance h_t and in triangle OED:

$$ED = h_t;\ OD = \text{rad of cutter } (r)$$

$$\frac{ED}{OD} = \sin C \text{ or } \frac{h_t}{r} = \sin C$$

and $\quad h_t = r \sin C$

Example 3. Calculate the settings for grinding the teeth of an 80 mm spiral mill. (*a*) Using the periphery of a 200 mm disc wheel and (*b*) using the face of a cup wheel. (Clearance required = 6°.)

The first condition is as shown at Fig. 91 (*a*)

and $\quad h_c = R \sin 6°$

$$R = \text{rad of wheel} = 100\,\text{mm}$$

$$\therefore h_c = 100 \sin 6° = 100 \times 0{\cdot}1045 = \underline{10{\cdot}45\,\text{mm}}$$

Using the cup wheel we have as in Fig. 91 (*b*)

$$h_t = r \sin 6° = 40 \times 0{\cdot}1045 = \underline{4{\cdot}18\,\text{mm}}$$

Effect of the helical tooth on the clearance

When the tooth of the cutter is helical (spiral) the calculation for the above cutter setting is modified as follows:

In Fig. 92 AK is perpendicular to the end of the cutter (parallel to its axis), so that β is the helix angle of the tooth. The clearance face is AC and $\widehat{BAC} = C_a$ is the clearance angle referred to the end of the cutter, or to a plane perpendicular to the cutter axis.

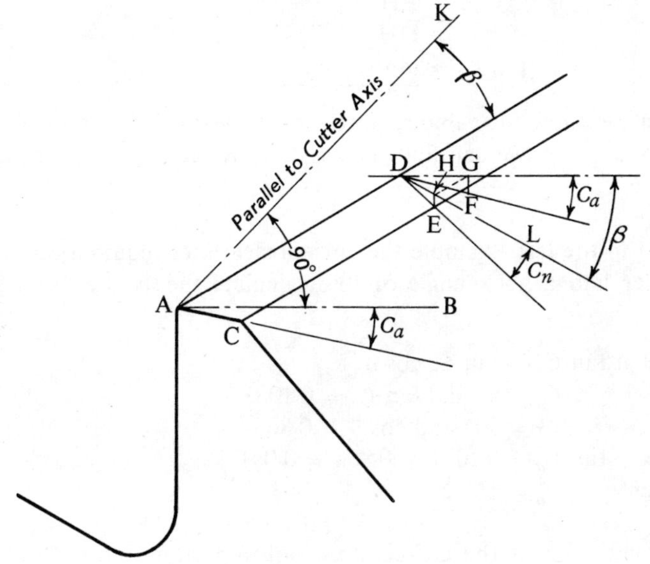

Fig. 92

DG is parallel to AB to DF to AC, so that $\widehat{FDG} = C_a$ as before.

DL is horizontal and perpendicular to the tooth face AD, and DE is also perpendicular to AD, but E is a point on the bottom of the clearance face. G and H are vertically above F and E respectively.

Hence $\widehat{EDH}$ is the clearance on the tooth referred to a plane perpendicular to its front. Call this normal clearance (C_n).

The axial clearance (C_a) is that put on by the grinding wheel, whilst the normal clearance (C_n) is the one effective when the cutter is in action. It is necessary, therefore, to grind such an axial clearance as will give us the required normal clearance, and for this purpose we require a relation between C_a and C_n. This may be obtained by considering triangles EHD, HDG and FGD, which are right-angled at H, H and G respectively.

$$\tan C_a = \frac{FG}{DG} = \frac{EH}{DG} \qquad \text{(since EH = FG)}$$

But
$$\frac{DH}{DG} = \cos\beta \text{ and } DG = \frac{DH}{\cos\beta}$$

Hence from above:
$$\tan C_a = \frac{EH}{DG} = \frac{EH}{\dfrac{DH}{\cos\beta}} = \frac{EH}{DH}\cos\beta$$

But $$\frac{EH}{DH} = \tan C_n$$

Hence $$\tan C_a = \tan C_n \cos \beta$$

Thus when we know the value required for the normal clearance (C_n) and the helix angle β, we can find the axial clearance angle C_a for the grinding setting.

Example 4. If in the last Example the normal clearance required was 6° and the cutter had a helix angle of 30°, calculate the axial clearance for setting.

We have that $\tan C_a = \tan C_n \cos \beta$

$$C_n = 6° \text{ and } \tan C_n = 0{\cdot}1051$$

$$\beta = 30° \text{ and } \cos \beta = 0{\cdot}866$$

$$\tan C_a = 0{\cdot}1051 \times 0{\cdot}866 = 0{\cdot}091$$

From which $$C_a = 5°\ 12'$$

For small helix angles the correction is not important, but it should be carried out on cutters with steep angles.

With the machine relieved cutter the clearance is put on at the time the tooth is form relieved and the tooth is sharpened by grinding its front with a saucer-shaped wheel. When this is carried out care should be exercised to ensure that if the front of the tooth was originally radial (on the centre), this position is preserved for it. If this is not done, the effect on the formed profile will be similar to that we discussed when considering the circular form tools on page 73, and the accuracy of the cutter form will be lost.

Exercises 5a

1. Calculate the following for an 80 mm diameter fluted cutter:

(*a*) a suitable number of teeth to give a coarse pitch,

(*b*) the off-set of the tooth front necessary to give 10° of front cutting rake,

(*c*) the setting for grinding the teeth on a cup wheel, to 300 mm give 7° of clearance.

2. 300 mm face mill is to be fitted with blades 6 mm thick. Estimate a suitable number of blades, and calculate the off-set of the blade necessary to effect 12° of top cutting rake.

3. The flutes of a 25 mm end mill are cut LH helix 500 mm lead. Assuming the flutes to be 4 mm deep, calculate the helix angle, based on the mean diameter of the flutes. If the end teeth follow this angle, is the rake on them positive or negative?

4. A spiral cutter is 60 mm diameter and the teeth are cut on a helix of 300 mm lead. If an apparent clearance of 8° is ground on these flutes, what is the true clearance?

5. Calculate the nearest angle of cutter to use for fluting a 60 mm diameter cutter with 12 flutes, 6 mm deep.

6. What depth of flute will be obtained by cutting 18 teeth in a 80 mm cutter with an 80° fluting cutter?

Speeds and feeds for milling cutters

The *cutting speed* for milling is found in the same way as for turning and drilling, so that if D mm = diameter of cutter, and N rev/min its speed,

$$\text{Cutting speed (m/min)} = \frac{\pi DN}{1000} \text{ and } N = \frac{1000\,S}{\pi D}$$

Cutting speeds should be as high as possible consistent with an economic cutter life before it needs re-grinding, and the speeds given for turning form a reasonable basis upon which to set the speed of a milling cutter.

The rate at which the work *feeds* beneath a milling cutter is sometimes expressed in millimetres per minute and sometimes in millimetres per revolution of the cutter. Neither of these methods gives a reliable indication of the cutter performance since both ignore the number of teeth in the cutter. The most equitable method of assessing milling feeds is in millimetres per tooth, since this gives an indication of the work each tooth is doing. From the feed per tooth, feed per revolution can be found by multiplying by the number of teeth, and a further multiplication by the rev/min gives feed per minute. The following table gives an indication of the feed per tooth possible with various types of milling cutters:

Table giving feeds for H.S.S. cutters.

Cutter	Feed per Tooth mm
Spiral (slab) mill (up to 30° helix angle of tooth)	0·1 to 0·25
Spiral mill (30°–60° helix angle)	0·05 to 0·2
Face mill and shell end mill	0·1 to 0·5
End mill	0·1 to 0·25
Saw	0·05 to 0·1
Slotting cutter	0·05 to 0·15
Form cutters	0·05 to 0·2

Example 5. Calculate a suitable speed and feed for a 80 mm spiral mill with 18 teeth to take roughing cuts on mild steel.

For roughing cuts we may take a moderately slow speed with a heavy feed.

Assume a speed of 20 m/min and a feed of 0·2 mm per tooth.

$$N = \frac{1000\,S}{\pi D} = \frac{1000 \times 22 \times 7}{80 \times 22} = 87{\cdot}5\,\text{rev/min}$$

A feed of 0·2 mm per tooth gives 0·2 × 18 = 3·6 mm per rev.
= 3·6 × 87·5 = 315 mm/min.

Power absorbed in milling

The conditions in milling are so variable that it is possible to attempt only a very rough computation of power requirements. From experimental work it has been found that the power requirements for milling are approximately as given in the table below. The figures should be taken only as a rough guide since the power varies with the amount of cut, the cutter, the cutting lubricant and other factors. However, even if the reader's results are not all they might be, the working out will provide useful mathematical practice.

ENERGY REQUIRED FOR MILLING*

Values given are Joules per cubic millimetre removed

Material being Cut	Cast Iron	Mild Steel	Hard Steel	Brass	Aluminium
J/mm^3	1·9	2·7	4·0 to 7·0	1·60	0·90

*For face milling the power may be taken as $\frac{2}{3}$ to $\frac{3}{4}$ of that given in table.

Using the values given in the table, the energy being absorbed is found by multiplying the tabulated energy by the volume of metal being removed per minute. This is found by multiplying the depth of cut, the width of cut and the feed length.

Thus if d = depth of cut; w = width of cut,

and f = feed

Volume = $d.w.f.$,

and Power = energy per second (watts)

To allow for frictional losses in the machine add approximately 30%.

Example 6. A spiral milling cutter is taking a cut 4 mm deep with a feed of 120 mm per min over a cast-iron block 80 mm wide. Estimate the power required to drive the machine.

Here the depth of cut (d) = 4 mm
width of cut (w) = 80 mm
feed = 120 mm/min = 2 mm/s

Volume of metal removed per second $= 4 \times 80 + 2 = 640\ \text{mm}^3$

From the table we have $1{\cdot}9\ \text{J/mm}^3$ for cast iron.

$\therefore$ Power for cutting $= 1{\cdot}9 \times 640\ \text{J/s} = 1216\text{W} = 1{\cdot}216\text{kW}$

Adding 30% for machine losses we have

$$1{\cdot}216 \times \frac{130}{100} = \underline{1{\cdot}58\text{kW}}$$

Exercises 5b

1. A 100 mm diameter spiral cutter has 18 teeth. Calculate the speed in rev/min and the feed in mm/min for this cutter to be operating at a cutting speed of 22 m/min and a feed of 0·15 mm per tooth per rev.

2. If a cutter in Question **1** was operating on a job 80 mm wide, with a cut 4 mm deep, calculate the volume of metal removed per minute, and estimate the power input to the machine if the material being cut is cast iron and frictional losses are equivalent to 30% of the cutting power.

3. If a milling machine is equipped with a 4 kW motor, estimate the deepest cut that may safely be taken on hard steel, when the work is 100 mm wide and the feed = 150 mm per min. (Take cutting power as 75% of motor rating.)

4. A face milling cutter is 300 mm diameter and has 28 teeth. If this is operating at a cutting speed of 33 m/min, and a feed of 0·2 m per tooth, how long will it take to travel over a cut 400 m long?

5. A certain job can be milled either with a 80 mm spiral mill, or with a 150 mm face mill. Each cutter has 16 teeth and the cutting speed to be employed is 22 m per min. If the feed for the spiral mill is 0·2 mm per tooth and for the face mill 0·25 mm per tooth, which is the most economical method of working?

6. A 25 mm end mill with 8 teeth is milling a slot 10 mm deep at a feed of 0·025 mm per tooth, and a speed of 600 rev/min. If the material being cut is brass, estimate the power input (assume 30% loss) and the time and power cost for milling a slot 300 mm long. Take power at 2*p* per B.O.T. Unit [1000 watt hours].

The dividing head

The dividing head, which is shown diagrammatically in Fig. 93 is used with the milling machine for the purpose of obtaining divisions of the

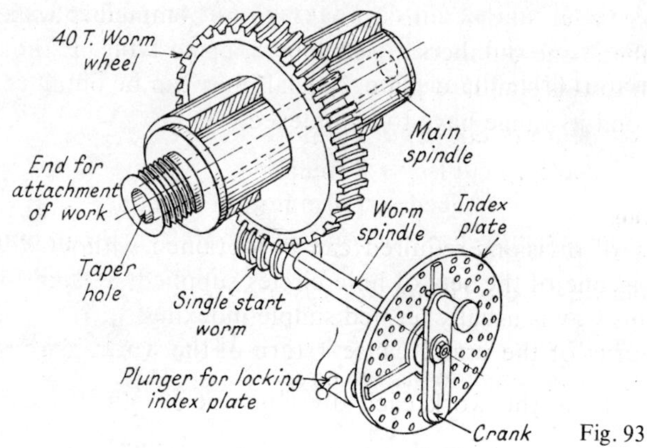

Fig. 93

circle. It consists essentially of the spindle to which is attached a 40-tooth wormwheel. Meshing with this is a single-threaded worm, to the spindle of which is attached the indexing crank. Adjacent to the indexing crank is the index plate containing several series of equally spaced holes arranged in circles on its face. A pin in the indexing crank can be adjusted so that its radius coincides with any of the hole circles, and an adjustable sector enables any proportion of the index plate circumference to be divided off.

Since the gear ratio in the head is 40–1, 40 turns of the crank cause the spindle (and the work attached to it) to make 1 turn, or 1 turn of the crank rotates the spindle $\frac{1}{40}$th of a turn. The object of the index plate with its holes is to subdivide further the turn of the crank, and the greater the range of hole circles available the greater will be the number of divisions possible without resource to special indexing methods.

The Brown and Sharpe dividing head is provided with three indexing plates having hole circles as follows:

Plate No. 1: 15, 16, 17, 18, 19, 20 holes.
Plate No. 2: 21, 23, 27, 29, 31, 33 holes.
Plate No. 3: 37, 39, 41, 43, 47, 49 holes.

The standard Cincinnati dividing plate is of larger diameter than those used on the Brown and Sharpe head and is reversible. It is provided with the following hole circles:

On one side: 24, 25, 28, 30, 34, 37, 38, 39, 41, 42, 43 holes.
On the reverse side: 46, 47, 49, 51, 53, 54, 57, 58, 59, 62, 66 holes.

This plate enables all divisions up to 60 to be obtained in addition to all even numbers, and numbers divisible by 5, up to 120.

In addition to this standard plate, special ones can be obtained when divisions beyond its range have to be indexed.

Simple indexing

The majority of divisions required can be obtained without difficulty by indexing in one of the sets of hole circles supplied. Straightforward working in this way is usually termed simple indexing.

Since 40 turns of the crank cause 1 turn of the work, if we require n equal divisions in the work each division will be $\frac{1}{n}$th of its circumference and the turns required of the crank will be $\frac{40}{n}$. It will help the reader to remember which way up this fraction should be if he remembers that when *more* than 40 divisions are required on the work the crank will have to rotate *less* than one complete turn.

Example 7. Calculate suitable indexing for the following numbers of divisions: (*a*) 6, (*b*) 10, (*c*) 15, (*d*) 22, (*e*) 28, (*f*) 37, (*g*) 48, (*h*) 62.

(*a*) 6 divisions.

$$\text{Indexing} = \tfrac{40}{6} = 6\tfrac{4}{6} = 6\tfrac{2}{3} = 6\tfrac{14}{21} \text{ or } 6\tfrac{16}{24}$$

= 6 whole turns + 14 holes in a 21 circle
or 16 holes in a 24 circle
or any combination giving $\frac{2}{3}$ of a turn

(*b*) 10 divisions.

$$\text{Indexing} = \tfrac{40}{10} = 4 \text{ complete turns}$$

(*c*) 15 divisions

$$\text{Indexing} = \tfrac{40}{15} = 2\tfrac{10}{15} = 2\tfrac{2}{3}$$

= 2 whole turns + $\frac{2}{3}$ of a turn [see (*a*) above]

(*d*) 22 divisions.

$$\text{Indexing} = \tfrac{40}{22} = 1\tfrac{18}{22} = 1\tfrac{9}{11} = 1\tfrac{27}{33} \text{ or } 1\tfrac{54}{66}$$

= 1 whole turn + 27 holes in a 33 circle
or 54 holes in a 66 circle

(*e*) 28 divisions.

$$\text{Indexing} = \tfrac{40}{28} = 1\tfrac{12}{28} = 1\tfrac{3}{7} = 1\tfrac{9}{21} \text{ or } 1\tfrac{18}{42}$$

= 1 whole turn + 9 holes in a 21 circle
or 18 holes in a 42 circle

(*f*) 37 divisions.

$$\text{Indexing} = \tfrac{40}{37} = 1\tfrac{3}{37}$$
$$= 1 \text{ whole turn} + 3 \text{ holes in a 37 circle}$$

(*g*) 48 divisions.

$$\text{Indexing} = \tfrac{40}{48} = \tfrac{5}{6} = \tfrac{15}{18} = \tfrac{20}{24}$$
$$= 15 \text{ holes in an 18 circle or 20 holes in a 24 circle}$$

(*h*) 62 divisions.

$$\text{Indexing} = \tfrac{40}{62} = \tfrac{20}{31}$$
$$= 40 \text{ holes in a 62 circle or 20 holes in a 31 circle}$$

Compound indexing

When a division is required which is beyond the capacity of the available hole circles, a method of compound indexing may be used.

The index plate is usually locked and prevented from turning by means of a plunger fitting in one of the circles of holes. The principle of compound indexing is to obtain the required division in two stages.

(1) By a movement with the crank in the usual way.

(2) By adding or subtracting a further movement by rotating the index plate and controlled by the plate locking plunger.

Suppose the crank is indexed 5 holes in a 20-hole circle and then the index plate, together with the crank, is indexed a further hole with the locking plunger registering in a 15-hole circle.

If both movements have been made in the same direction the total indexing will have been

$$\tfrac{5}{20} + \tfrac{1}{15} = \tfrac{15}{60} + \tfrac{4}{60} = \tfrac{19}{60} \text{ on the worm.}$$

If the plate had been turned *opposite* to the crank we should have had

$$\tfrac{5}{20} - \tfrac{1}{15} = \tfrac{15}{60} - \tfrac{4}{60} = \tfrac{11}{60}.$$

By compounding suitable hole circles in this way it is possible to obtain a large number of additional divisions.

If n is the number of divisions required on the work, then $\dfrac{40}{n}$ is the indexing required and the fractions representing the two movements to be used must give $\dfrac{40}{n}$, either when added or subtracted. Also the denominators of the two fractions must be numbers equal to available hole circles in the plate. Suitable hole circles must generally be determined by a method of trial and error and the following examples will illustrate the method.

Example 8. Determine suitable compound indexing for the following divisions: (*a*) 77, (*b*) 91.

(*a*) 77 divisions.

The indexing required is $\frac{40}{77}$ and we require two suitable fractions which give this when added or subtracted.

The method of trial and error may be assisted by the following working.

Put down the 77 above a line, the 40 below it, and factorise them.

$$\frac{77 = 11 \times 7}{40 = 2 \times 2 \times 2 \times 5}$$

The numbers representing hole circles are now required to be written below the 40 and factorised. Their difference, also factorised, must be written above the line. The numbers must be so chosen that all the factors above the line must cancel out with numbers below. [The reader should notice that since only one plate can be used, the numbers must be those of two hole circles on the same plate.]

Choosing 21 and 33 as the numbers, we have $21 = 7 \times 3$; $33 = 3 \times 11$ and the difference $12 = 2 \times 2 \times 3$.

Putting these numbers with their factors down we find that all the numbers above the line will cancel thus

$$\begin{array}{l} 77 = \cancel{11} \times \cancel{7} \\ 12 = \cancel{2} \times \cancel{2} \times \cancel{3} \\ \hline 40 = \cancel{2} \times \cancel{2} \times 2 \times 5 \\ 21 = \cancel{7} \times \cancel{3} \\ 33 = 3 \times \cancel{11} \end{array}$$

Hence 21 and 33 circles will be suitable and we require to find the respective number of holes to be indexed. Let these be *a* and *b*.

Then
$$\frac{a}{21} \pm \frac{b}{33} \qquad \frac{40}{77}$$
$$(7 \times 3) \quad (3 \times 11) \quad (11 \times 7)$$

Putting on a common denominator

$$\frac{11a \pm 7b = 3 \times 40}{7 \times 3 \times 11}$$

i.e. $11a \pm 7b = 120$

By trial and error we find that if $a = 9$, and $b = 3$; $99 + 21 = 120$.

Hence the indexing required is 9 holes in a 21 circle added to 3 holes in a 33 circle (i.e. both movements in the same direction).

(*b*) 91 divisions:

Testing for suitable hole circles as before we have:

$$\begin{aligned} 91 &= \cancel{13} \times \cancel{7} \\ 10 &= \cancel{5} \times \cancel{2} \\ \hline 40 &= 2 \times 2 \times \cancel{2} \times \cancel{5} \\ 39 &= \cancel{13} \times 3 \\ 49 &= 7 \times \cancel{7} \end{aligned}$$

This gives 39 and 49 as suitable sizes and

$$\underset{(13 \times 3)}{\frac{a}{39}} \pm \underset{(7 \times 7)}{\frac{b}{49}} = \underset{(13 \times 7)}{\frac{40}{91}}$$

Putting on a common denominator

$$\frac{49a \pm 39b = 40 \times 21}{13 \times 7 \times 7 \times 3}$$

i.e. $49a \pm 39b = 840$.

By trial and error:

If $a = 6$ and $b = 14$:

$$\begin{aligned} &49 \times 6 + 39 \times 14 \\ &= 294 \quad + 456 = 840. \end{aligned}$$

Hence 6 holes in a 39 circle added to 14 holes in 49 circle will be the indexing required.

Differential indexing

This is really an automatic method of carrying out compound indexing. The arrangement of the dividing head is shown in Fig. 94, from which it will be seen that the index plate is unlocked, and is geared back to the spindle. As the spindle is rotated via the crank and worm, the gear train causes the index plate to turn backwards or forwards, and the net result is the same as if the index plate were released and rotated by hand as in compound indexing.

Differential indexing is more straightforward and is capable of dealing with a wider range of divisions than compound indexing. The problem is

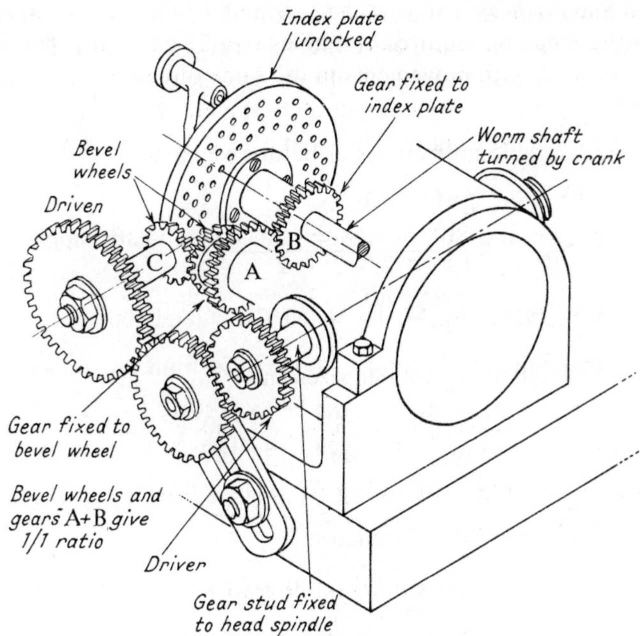

Fig. 94 Showing Arrangement of Gearing for Differential Indexing.

to calculate the indexing and the gear ratio necessary to obtain any given number of divisions on the work, and we will explain the method by working out a few examples:

Example 9. Calculate the differential indexing to give 107 divisions on the work.

The indexing required is $\frac{40}{107}$ turns of the crank per division, and when this indexing has been done 107 times the crank has turned $\frac{40}{107} \times 107 = 40$ times, i.e. the work has turned 1 complete circle as it should.

Since no 107 circle is available, let us take an approximately near indexing to the exact $\frac{40}{107}$ required.

$$\frac{40}{107} = \frac{8}{21} \text{ approximately (by approx cancellation by 5)}$$

If we take 107 moves of 8 holes in a 21 circle we obtain

$$\frac{107 \times 8}{21} = \frac{856}{21} = 40\tfrac{16}{21}$$

turns of the crank

But we have seen that the crank must make 40 turns only, during the 107 indexings, and we must therefore subtract $\frac{16}{21}$ of a turn. This is done by gearing up the plate, so that whilst the spindle makes 1 turn, the plate makes $\frac{16}{21}$ turn in the opposite direction to the crank.

Hence with an indexing of 8 holes in a 21 circle, the gear ratio from spindle to plate: $\dfrac{\text{Drivers}}{\text{Driven}} = \dfrac{16}{21}$

For the Brown and Sharpe dividing head, the gears supplied are as follows:

24(2), 28, 32, 40, 44, 48, 56, 64, 72, 86 and 100 teeth.

We may make up a train for the above ratio from this set as follows:

$$\frac{16}{21} = \frac{8 \times 2}{7 \times 3} = \frac{64}{56} \times \frac{32}{48} \frac{\text{Drivers}}{\text{Driven}}$$

In the above case the gears must be arranged so that the index plate revolves *opposite* to the crank.

Example 10. Calculate the differential indexing for 127 divisions.

$$\text{Exact indexing} = \tfrac{40}{127}$$

and roughly cancelling by 8 gives $\frac{5}{16}$ as the approximation.

Now 127 moves of 5 holes in a 16 circle gives $127 \times \frac{5}{16} = \frac{635}{16} = 39\frac{11}{16}$ turns of the crank.

But this is $40 - 39\frac{11}{16} = \frac{5}{16}$ short of what it should be.

Hence in 1 turn of the spindle the index plate must make $\frac{5}{16}$ turn in the *same direction* as the crank.

$$\text{Gear ratio: } \frac{\text{Drivers}}{\text{Driven}} = \frac{5}{16} = \frac{5 \times 1}{8 \times 2} = \frac{40}{64} \times \frac{24}{48}$$

With this ratio and an indexing of 5 holes in a 16 circle, the 127 divisions would be obtained.

Angular indexing

Very often, instead of a number of equal divisions, an angle must be indexed.

Since 1 turn of the crank rotates the spindle $\frac{1}{40}$ turn, the angle at the work centre equivalent to one turn of the crank is $\dfrac{360}{40} = 9°$ so that

$$\text{Turns of crank to give any angle} = \frac{\text{Angle required}}{9}$$

Example 11. Calculate the indexing for the following angles: (*a*) 41°, (*b*) 15° 30′, (c) 29° 30′.

(*a*) 41°. Indexing $= \frac{41}{9} = 4\frac{5}{9}$ turn of crank, say 4 whole turns and 30 holes in a 54 circle.

(*b*) 15° 30′. Indexing $= \dfrac{15\frac{1}{2}}{9} = 1\dfrac{6\frac{1}{2}}{9} = 1\frac{13}{18}$

= 1 whole turn and 13 holes in an 18 circle
or 39 holes in an 54 circle

(*c*) 29° 30′. Indexing $= \dfrac{29\frac{1}{3}}{9} = 3\dfrac{2\frac{1}{3}}{9} = 3\dfrac{\frac{7}{3}}{9} = 3\frac{7}{27}$.

= 3 complete turns and 7 holes in a 27 circle
or 14 holes in a 54 circle

Exercises 5c

1. Calculate suitable indexing to obtain the following divisions on the Brown and Sharpe head:
(*a*) 12, (*b*) 15, (*c*) 22, (*d*) 34, (*e*) 41, (*f*) 50, (*g*) 62, (*h*) 76 divisions.

2. Calculate suitable indexing on the Cincinnati head for the following:
(*a*) 13, (*b*) 17, (*c*) 25, (*d*) 36, (*e*) 45, (*f*) 54, (*g*) 65, (*h*) 82 divisions.

3. Find suitable indexing for the following angles on the Brown and Sharpe head:
(*a*) 15°, (*b*) 26°, (*c*) 33° (*d*) 52° 30′, (*e*) 63° 40′.

4. Determine appropriate indexing for the following angles on the Cincinnati head:
(*a*) 16° 30′, (*b*) 27° 45′, (*c*) 31° 20′, (*d*) 74° 15′, (*e*) 136° 30′.

5. A shaft, 50 mm diameter, is to have a groove milled along it. The sides of the groove are radial, it is 11·25 mm wide at the top and 6 mm at the bottom. The centre is to be cut with a cutter 6 mm wide, after which the shaft is to be indexed round and set over for milling the slot sides with the same cutter setting. Calculate the indexing and set over.

6. Determine suitable compound indexing for the following, using B. & S. plates:
(*a*) 51, (*b*) 63, (*c*) 87, (*d*) 189 divisions.

7. The crank of a dividing head is indexed N holes in a C circle, and then the plate is indexed in the opposite direction n holes in a c circle. Find an expression for the number of divisions obtained.

8. Determine suitable indexing and gears for obtaining the following by differential indexing:
(*a*) 97, (*b*) 53, (*c*) 101, (*d*) 131 divisions. [Use B. & S. plates and gears.]

9. The index plate of a dividing head is geared to the spindle in the ratio $\dfrac{\text{turns of spindle}}{\text{turns of plate}} = \dfrac{2}{1}$ (rotation opposite to crank). If the crank is now indexed 3 complete turns, + 15 holes in a 20 circle, through what angle has the spindle been rotated?

10. A round plate requires four notches, A, B, C and D, indexing in it spaced so that the angles between AB, BC, CD and DA are in the ratio 2:3:4:5. Using the same hole circle throughout, determine the indexing required.

Use of continued fractions for angular indexing

When an angle is required whose value involves obscure minutes and seconds, it is unlikely that an exact indexing for it will be possible. It is possible, however, by turning the ratio into a continued fraction, to obtain an indexing which is very near to the exact one. The method is illustrated by the following examples:

Example 12. Calculate the nearest indexing and the actual angle obtained for the following:

$$(a)\ 14^\circ\ 38',\ (b)\ 21^\circ\ 19'\ 35''$$

(*a*) The indexing will be $\dfrac{14^\circ\ 38'}{9} = 1\dfrac{5^\circ\ 38'}{9^\circ}$

Converting the fraction to minutes gives $1\frac{338}{540} = 1\frac{169}{270}$. We now convert $\frac{169}{270}$ to a continued fraction and find its convergents.

```
169)270(1
    169
    101)169(1
        101
         68)101(1
             68
             33)68(2
                66
                 2)33(16
                   32
                   1)2(2
```

The fraction is

$$\cfrac{1}{1+\cfrac{1}{1+\cfrac{1}{1+\cfrac{1}{2+\cfrac{1}{16+\frac{1}{2}}}}}}$$

The convergents are as follows:
1st $= \frac{1}{1}$; 2nd $= \frac{1}{2}$; 3rd $= \frac{2}{3}$; 4th $= \frac{5}{8}$; 5th $= \frac{49}{131}$; 6th $= \frac{169}{270}$

The 4th convergent is the last one we are able to make use of and $\frac{5}{8} = \frac{10}{16}$ or $\frac{15}{24}$.

Hence the indexing is 1 complete turn and 10 holes in a 16 circle or 15 holes in a 24 circle.

The actual angle obtained will be

$$9 \times 1\tfrac{5}{8} = 14\tfrac{5}{8}^{\circ} = 14^{\circ}\ 37\tfrac{1}{2}'\ \text{(an error of } -\tfrac{1}{2}'\text{)}.$$

(*b*) The indexing in this case will be $\dfrac{21^{\circ}\ 19'\ 35''}{9} = 2\dfrac{3^{\circ}\ 19'\ 35'}{9}$ and converting the fraction to seconds $= 2\frac{11975}{32400} = 2\frac{479}{1296}$

We now convert the $\frac{479}{1296}$ to a continued fraction

479)1296(2
958
338)479(1
338
141)338(2
282
56)141(2
112
29)56(1
29
27)29(1
27
2)27(13
26
1)2(2

The fraction is

$$\cfrac{1}{2+\cfrac{1}{1+\cfrac{1}{2+\cfrac{1}{2+\cfrac{1}{1+\cfrac{1}{1+\cfrac{1}{13+\frac{1}{2}}}}}}}}$$

and its convergents are 1st = $\frac{1}{2}$; 2nd = $\frac{1}{3}$; 3rd = $\frac{3}{8}$; 4th = $\frac{7}{19}$; 5th = $\frac{10}{27}$; 6th = $\frac{17}{46}$; 7th = $\frac{131}{625}$; 8th = $\frac{479}{1296}$.

If a 46-hole circle is available the 6th convergent may be used and the indexing will be 2 whole turns + 17 holes in a 46 circle, giving an angle of $9° \times 2\frac{17}{46} = 21\frac{15}{46}° = 21° 19' 33''$ (an error of $-2''$).

If a 46-hole circle cannot be used, then the 5th convergent must be indexed and this will be 2 whole turns + 10 holes in a 27 circle.

This will give an angle of $9° \times 2\frac{10}{27} = 21\frac{1}{3}° = 21° 20'$ (an error of $+25''$).

Spiral milling

For some reason unknown, the operation of milling a helix on a cylindrical piece of work has come to be known as spiral milling. Actually a spiral is a flat curve shaped like a clock spring. However, so long as we know the process and its principles, it matters little by what name we call it.

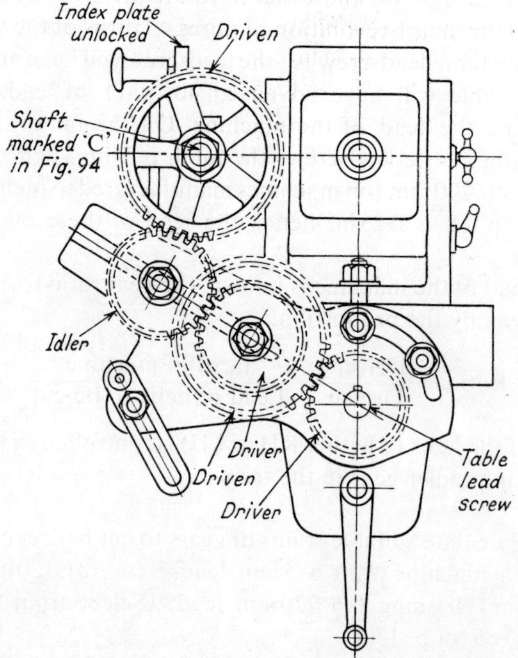

Fig. 95 End View of Dividing Head Geared to Leadscrew for Spiral Milling.

When the machine is set up for spiral milling the worm spindle of the dividing head is geared to the leadscrew of the machine table, so that when the leadscrew is turned the worm is turned also. This rotates the dividing head spindle, so that the longitudinal movement of the table is accompanied by a rotation of the work. A sketch of the machine set up is shown in Fig. 95.

The first calculation necessary for spiral milling is the gear ratio between the leadscrew and the dividing head worm-shaft to give the required lead of helix.

In order to do this we must first ascertain the "lead of the machine." The reader will recollect that the lead of a screw is the distance the screw advances along the cylinder whilst it makes one complete turn round it (Fig. 78a). The lead of the machine is the lead of the helix it would cut if the table leadscrew were connected to the dividing head worm by a $\frac{1}{1}$ gear ratio.

When this is the case we know that to rotate the dividing head spindle (and the work) through 1 revolution requires 40 turns of the worm. If the gear ratio to the table leadscrew is $\frac{1}{1}$ the leadscrew will have made 40 turns also, and the table will have advanced 40 (pitch of leadscrew). This distance will be the lead of the machine. On the majority of milling machines having metric leadscrews the pitch is 5 mm, hence the lead of these machines is 200 mm (on machines manufactured to inch dimensions the leadscrew pitch is 0·25 in, hence the lead of these machines is 10 inches).

When the lead of the machine is known, the gear ratio to cut a helix of any lead is given by the proportion:

$$\text{Ratio} = \frac{\text{Drivers}}{\text{Driven}} = \frac{\text{Lead of machine}}{\text{Lead of helix to be cut}}$$

The hand of the helix (whether RH or LH) is controlled by the presence or otherwise of an idler gear in the train.

Example 13. Calculate suitable trains of gears to cut helices of the following leads on a machine with a 5 mm leadscrew: (*a*) 120 mm lead, (*b*) 256 mm lead, (*c*) 480 mm, (*d*) 720 mm lead. [Select from the B. & S. set of gears given on p. 130.]

As the leadscrew is 5 mm pitch the lead of the machine will be $5 \times 40 =$ 200 mm.

(*a*) 120 mm

Ratio $\dfrac{\text{Drivers}}{\text{Driven}} = \frac{200}{120} = \frac{40}{24}$ and this is given by a 40 *T* driving a 24 *T*.

The train may be compounded as follows:

$$\frac{40}{24} = \frac{5 \times 8}{4 \times 6} = \frac{40}{32} \times \frac{64}{48} \frac{\text{Drivers}}{\text{Driven}}$$

(*b*) 256 mm lead.

$$\text{Ratio } \frac{\text{Drivers}}{\text{Driven}} = \frac{200}{256} = \frac{100 \times 2}{64 \times 4} = \frac{100 \times 24}{64 \times 48}$$

(*c*) 480 mm lead

$$\frac{\text{Drivers}}{\text{Driven}} = \frac{200}{480} = \frac{40}{48} \times \frac{5}{10} = \frac{40}{48} \times \frac{32}{64}$$

(*d*) 720 mm lead

$$\text{Ratio} = \frac{200}{720} = \frac{5}{9} \times \frac{40}{80} = \frac{40}{72} \times \frac{32}{64}$$

Helix angle

Before the helix can be cut it is necessary to set the cutter to the angle followed by the path of the curve. If this were not done a great deal of interference would take place and the shape of the groove would be nothing like the shape of the cutter working to produce it. Even with the cutter set into the helix angle some interference generally takes place and the shape of the groove varies from the profile of the cutter.

The helix angle is the angle σ on Fig. 78 (*b*), and if the helix is developed out into a triangle as shown, we see that

$$\frac{\text{circumference of cylinder}}{\text{lead of helix}} = \tan \sigma$$

When the helix angle has been determined, the cutter head or the machine table must be swung round so that the plane of the cutter lies at this angle, relative to the work. Care should be exercised to swing in the correct direction for RH or LH helix.

When grooves of appreciable depth are being cut, the circumference of the cylinder passing through the bottoms of the grooves will be much less than that of the cylinder in which they are being cut. This means that if the calculation for the helix angle is based on the outside diameter of the work, the inclination of the cutter will be correct at the top, but not at the bottom of the grooves. The reverse will be the case if the bottom diameter of the grooves is used when finding the cylinder circumference in the above expression.

When in doubt about which diameter to take for the calculation the reader is advised to take the mean between top and bottom of grooves. It may be that for grooves of certain shapes the top, or the bottom, might form the more suitable basis for the calculation, but only trial and experience can decide on the best compromise.

Example 14. Calculate the gears and setting for milling LH spiral flutes in a reamer 40 mm diameter. Lead of helix = 800 mm. Machine leadscrew 5 mm pitch. Reamer flutes 8 mm deep.

$$\text{Lead of machine} = 40 \times 5 = 200\,\text{mm}$$

$$\text{Gear ratio, table to head: } \frac{\text{Drivers}}{\text{Driven}} = \frac{200}{800} = \frac{1}{4} = \frac{1}{2} \times \frac{1}{2} = \frac{24}{48} \times \frac{32}{64}$$

To calculate the helix angle we will take the diameter at the mean depth of the flutes, i.e. 40 − 8 = 32 mm.

$$\text{Circum of cylinder} = 32\pi\,\text{mm}$$

$$\tan\sigma = \frac{\text{Circum}}{\text{lead}} = \frac{32\pi}{800} = \frac{\pi}{25} = 0{\cdot}1257$$

$$\text{From which } \sigma = \underline{7^\circ\,10'}$$

As the helix is LH the table of the machine must be swung with its LH end away from the operator.

Example 15. A spiral gear has a pitch diameter of 80 mm and a spiral angle of 30°. Calculate the gears for milling the teeth in it.

In this case we have to determine the lead of the helix in order to be able to solve the problem.

$$\text{The pitch circum} = 80\pi = 251{\cdot}3\,\text{mm}$$

$$\text{Also } \tan\sigma = \frac{\text{circum}}{\text{lead}}$$

$$\therefore \text{lead} = \frac{\text{circum}}{\tan\sigma} = \frac{251{\cdot}3}{\tan 30^\circ} = \frac{251{\cdot}3}{0{\cdot}5774} = 435{\cdot}2\,\text{mm}$$

$$\text{Gear ratio, leadscrew to dividing head} = \frac{200}{435{\cdot}2} = \frac{1000}{2176} = \frac{125}{272}$$

As this is an awkward fraction we will convert it to a continued fraction

```
125)272(2
    250
     22)125(5
        110
         15)22(1
            15
             7)15(2
               14
                1)7(7
                  7
```

The convergents are given by

$$\cfrac{1}{2+\cfrac{1}{5+\cfrac{1}{1+\cfrac{1}{2+\frac{1}{7}}}}}$$

and their values are:

$$1\text{st} = \tfrac{1}{2};\ 2\text{nd} = \tfrac{5}{11};\ 3\text{rd} = \tfrac{6}{13};\ 4\text{th}\ \tfrac{17}{37};\ 5\text{th} = \tfrac{125}{272}.$$

Taking the 3rd convergent and finding a suitable gear ratio we have

$$\frac{\text{Drivers}}{\text{Driven}} = \frac{6}{13} = \frac{30}{65} \times \frac{1}{1} = \frac{30}{65} \times \frac{40}{40}$$

The actual lead obtained will be $\frac{13}{6} \times 200\,\text{mm}$
$= 433{\cdot}3\,\text{mm}$ instead of the required $435{\cdot}2\,\text{mm}$

Cam milling on the dividing head

By employing a universal milling machine fitted with a swivelling vertical head, constant-rise cams may be cut on blanks held in the dividing head. The set-up is shown in Fig. 96, and the dividing head is geared to the table lead screw in the same way as for spiral milling.

The principle of the operation is that as the table moves to the right the axis of the end mill approaches nearer to the axis of the dividing head spindle. If, at the same time, the dividing head is geared so that its spindle rotates, the combination of the rotation and of the cutter approaching

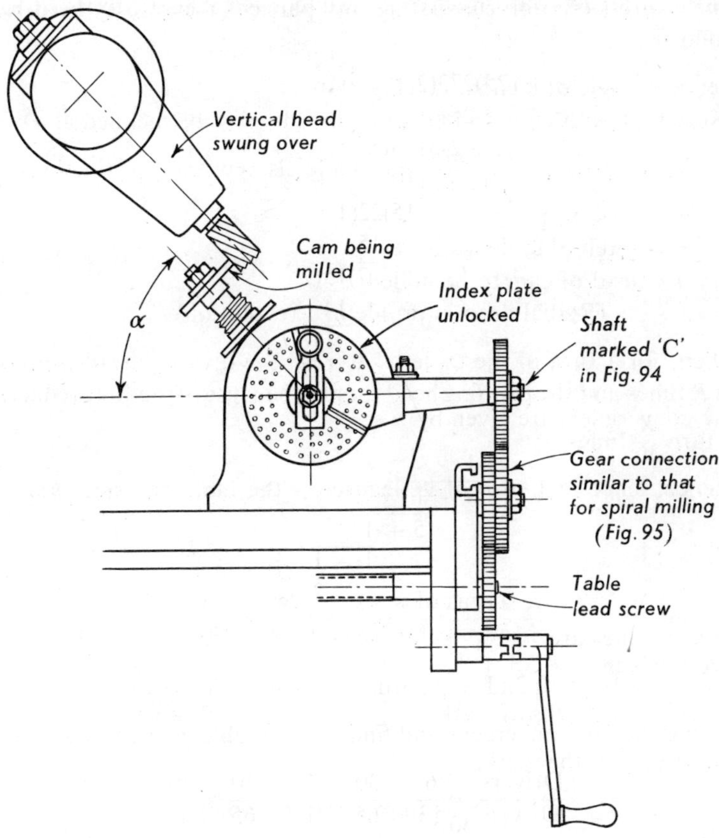

Fig. 96 Set-up for Cam Milling.

nearer to the centre, causes a cam to be cut on the blank held in the head. The rate at which the end mill approaches the dividing head axis is controlled by the angle α, and the reader will observe that if this is made zero (dividing head spindle horizontal), then, instead of a cam, a circular disc would be cut provided the end mill was long enough to do it. (It will be observed that as cutting proceeds, the blank gradually moves down the end mill so that a fairly long cutter is necessary.)

(As an alternative to the arrangement shown, the end mill axis may be located below the cam axis. Then the table must move to the left and the cam will move up the end mill as cutting proceeds.)

The expressions for calculating any particular case may be derived as follows:

Let α = angle of inclination (Fig. 96)
(Note that both cutter and dividing heads must be inclined at α)

R = Gear ratio $\frac{\text{Drivers}}{\text{Driven}}$ between leadscrew and dividing head worm

p = pitch of table leadscrew

l = lead of cam to be milled
(Radial drop in profile in 1 revolution)

Then, for 1 turn of the table leadscrew, the dividing head worm will turn R times and the dividing head spindle, because of the 40–1 reduction, will turn $\frac{R}{40}$ times

Hence, since in 1 turn of its leadscrew the table advances p mm we have:

$$\frac{\text{Turns of work}}{\text{Movement of table}} = \frac{\frac{R}{40}}{p} = \frac{R}{40p}$$

From which

$$\text{Turns of work} = \frac{R}{40p}(\text{movement of table})$$

For 1 turn of the work:

$$1 = \frac{R}{40p}(\text{movement of table})$$

and
$$\text{movement of table} = \frac{40p}{R}(\text{for 1 turn of work})$$

Now because of the inclination of the head and work, when the table has moved the distance cb (Fig. 97) the centre of the end mill has approached the centre of the work by the length ac.

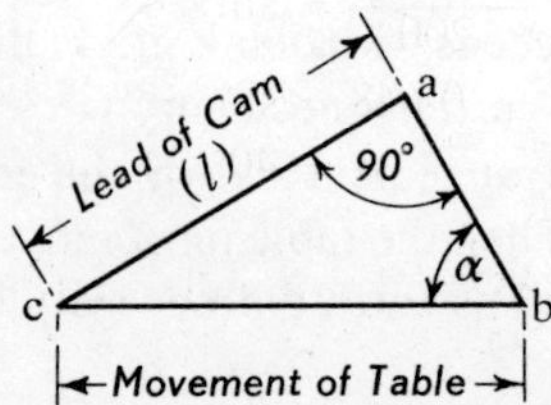

Fig. 97

Hence if *cb* represents the horizontal table movement for 1 turn of the work, *ac* will represent the lead of cam cut and from the triangle:

$$\frac{ac}{cb} = \sin \alpha \text{ or } \frac{l}{\text{table movement}} = \sin \alpha$$

Hence $$\text{Table movement} = \frac{l}{\sin \alpha}$$

If we substitute this in the expression for the table movement above we have:

$$\text{Table movement} = \frac{40p}{R}, \text{ i.e.} \frac{l}{\sin \alpha} = \frac{40p}{R}$$

and $$R = \frac{40p \sin \alpha}{l}$$

If $p = 5$ mm, as is usually the case, the expression reduces to

$$R = \frac{200 \sin \alpha}{l}$$

This expression controls the variables R and α, and in using it a value for one of them will have to be assumed before the other may be calculated. If a first trial gives unsatisfactory conditions, then one of the values may be changed to bring the other to reasonable dimensions.

Example 16. Calculate a suitable setting for milling a cam, the profile of which falls 12 mm in 100° of its angle. Leadscrew of machine has a pitch of 5 mm.

Here $p = 5$ mm, and if the cam profile falls 12 mm in 100°, its lead will be $12 \times \frac{360}{100} = 43{\cdot}2$ mm

Let us assume that $R = 3$

Then $$R = \frac{40p \sin \alpha}{l}: \quad 3 = \frac{200 \sin \alpha}{43{\cdot}2}$$

$$\frac{3 \times 43{\cdot}2}{200} = \sin \alpha$$

$$0{\cdot}648 = \sin \alpha$$

This gives $$\alpha = 40° \, 24'$$

Hence a gear ratio $\frac{\text{Drivers}}{\text{Driven}} = \frac{3}{1}$ and an angular setting of $\underline{\alpha = 40° \, 24'}$ will be suitable.

Exercises 5d

1. Calculate the nearest indexing for the following angles, using the standard Cincinnati plate, and determine the actual angle obtained for the indexing used:

(*a*) 10° 36′ 30″, (*b*) 41° 24′ 20″, (*c*) 75° 45′ 30″.

2. Determine the nearest indexing to divide an angle of 76° 30′ into 7 parts. Use hole circles available on B. & S. plates.

3. A plate is rectangular, 123 mm × 79 mm, with a hole in its centre. If this is on a mandril between dividing head centres, find the nearest indexing to rotate it through the angle contained by joining the end corners to the centre. [Angle contained by short side required.]

In the following exercises use the B. & S. gears (p. 130) and take the Lead of Machine as 200 mm.

4. Calculate suitable gear ratios to cut the following leads on a B. & S. machine: (*a*) 168 mm, (*b*) 288 mm, (*c*) 450 mm, (*d*) 640 mm.

5. A gear has a pitch diameter of 100 mm and the lead of the spiral is 410 mm. Determine a suitable gear ratio and find the helix angle for setting.

6. Calculate the gear ratio and angular setting for milling a 4-start thread of 35 mm pitch, on a worm of 100 mm pitch diameter.

7. A spiral milling cutter is 80 mm diameter and 120 mm long. Flutes are to be milled on it which make approx $\frac{1}{6}$ of their lead in the length of the cutter. Calculate suitable gears and angular setting for milling the flutes.

8. Slots having a lead angle of 30° are to be milled in a cylinder 45 mm diameter. Determine the gear ratio.

In the following examples take the table leadscrew pitch as 5 mm.

9. Calculate the lead of a cam which rises 10 mm in 50° of revolution, and determine a suitable setting and gear ratio for cutting it.

10. A cam which revolves at 2 rev/min has to move the roller in contact with it at a rate of 50 mm/min. Determine its lead, and find a suitable gear ratio and setting to mill its profile.

11. A cam is heart-shaped with uniform rise. The radius to the point of the heart is 60 mm, and to the corner where the curved portions meet the radius is 30 mm. Determine the lead and find a suitable gear ratio and setting to mill it.

The calculation of solid angles

Angular milling and shaping jobs often occur where a solid angle has to be calculated, the value of the angle depending upon the angles between other surfaces on the same work. Examples of such cases are likely to be varied, but the following worked cases may convey to the reader how any other example might be approached.

Example 17. Calculate the true angle between the sloping faces of the block shown in Fig. 98.

If we project a section through the angle, the section plane being taken at 90° to the sloping corner, we shall obtain the triangle ABD shown at the bottom of the diagram. The true angle we require will then be $\widehat{ADB}$.

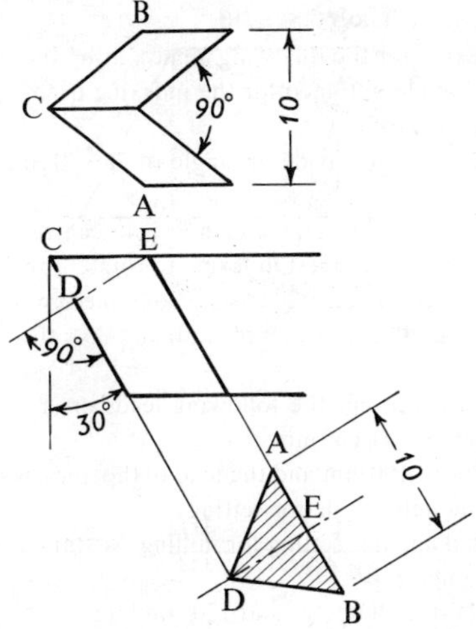

Fig. 98

Now $$DE = CE \cos 30°$$
and since triangle ABC is right angled at C and has 45° angles at A and B

$$CE = \tfrac{1}{2}AB = 5.$$

Hence $$DE = 5 \cos 30° = 4{\cdot}33 \text{ mm}$$

In triangle ADE (sectional view): $\dfrac{AE}{DE} = \tan \widehat{ADE}$

$$\frac{5}{4{\cdot}33} = \tan \widehat{ADE} = 1{\cdot}155$$

From which $$\widehat{ADE} = 49°\ 7'$$

$\widehat{ADB}$ which we require is twice $\widehat{ADE} = 2 \times 49°\ 7' = \underline{98°\ 14'}$

Example 18. Calculate the angle between the base and the sloping face of the block shown in Fig. 99.

The block is shown by full and plain dotted lines. Chain dotted lines are constructional only, for the purpose of explanation.

If AB is perpendicular to AG and BE, and BC perpendicular to BE (BC being a line on the base), then the angle we require is angle ABC.

FC is parallel to EB, and BD to FE

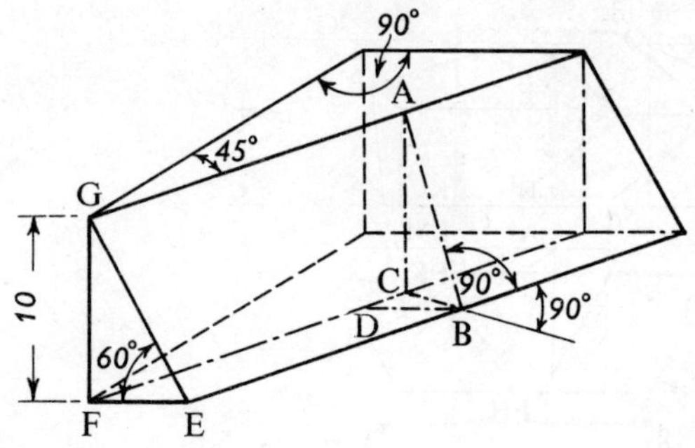

Fig. 99

Then in triangle BDC:

$$BD = FE = \frac{10}{\tan 60^\circ} = \frac{10}{1{\cdot}732} = 5{\cdot}774$$

$\widehat{BDC} = 45^\circ$ so that $BC = BD \sin 45^\circ = 5{\cdot}774 \times 0{\cdot}7071 = 4{\cdot}083$

But $\frac{AC}{BC} = \tan$ of $\widehat{ABC}$ and $AC = 10$

$$\therefore \tan \widehat{ABC} = \frac{10}{4{\cdot}083} = 2{\cdot}453$$

$$\underline{ABC = 67^\circ\ 49'}$$

Example 19. Calculate for the tool shown in Fig. 100.

(*a*) The true angle between the cutting edge AB and the line AC

(*b*) The inclination of the top cutting face, perpendicular to AB

(*c*) The true angle between the top cutting face and the front clearance face.

Lines FE on the cutting face and EG on the clearance face are perpendicular to the edge AB.

FA is on the cutting face and is perpendicular to AC

FH and EK are vertical lines and angles FHG and EKG = 90°

In Fig. 100 (*b*), EM and FS are horizontal, LM vertical and EL is perpendicular to AC.

(*a*) True angle between AB and AC

If we call this angle α, then $\frac{EL}{AL} = \tan \alpha$

Now $\frac{EM}{EL} = \cos 25^\circ$ and $EL = \frac{EM}{\cos 25^\circ}$

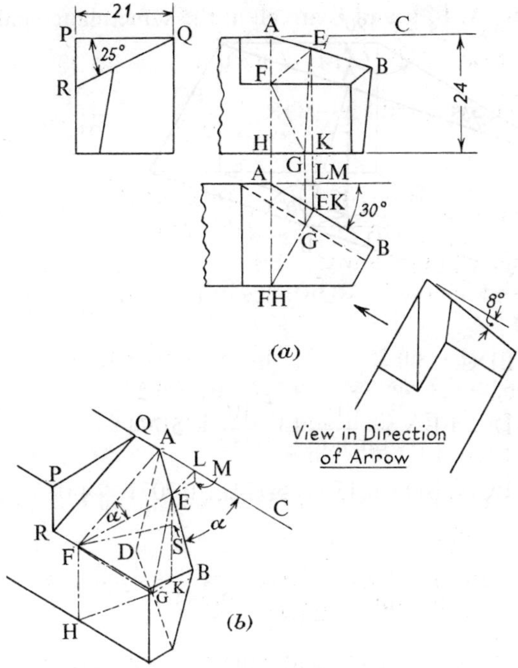

Fig. 100

Also $$\text{AL} = \text{Projected length AM}$$

and $$\frac{\text{EM}}{\text{Projected AM}} = \frac{\text{EM}}{\text{AL}} = \tan 30^\circ$$

and $$\text{AL} = \frac{\text{EM}}{\tan 30^\circ}$$

Hence $$\tan \alpha = \frac{\text{EL}}{\text{AL}} = \frac{\dfrac{\text{EM}}{\cos 25^\circ}}{\dfrac{\text{EM}}{\tan 30^\circ}} = \frac{\text{EM}}{\cos 25^\circ} \times \frac{\tan 30^\circ}{\text{EM}}$$

$$= \frac{\tan 30^\circ}{\cos 25^\circ} = \frac{0{\cdot}5774}{0{\cdot}9063} = 0{\cdot}6371$$

Hence $$\underline{\alpha = 32^\circ\ 30'}$$

(*b*) Inclination of top face perpendicular to edge AB
This will be the inclination of line FE

Now since points A, F, E and L are all in the same plane, and

$$\widehat{FAL} = \widehat{FEA} = 90°; \widehat{AFE} = \widehat{EAL} = \alpha = 32° 30'$$

$$FE = FA \cos \alpha \text{ and } FA = QR = \frac{PQ}{\cos 25°} = \frac{21}{\cos 25°}$$

Hence

$$FE = \frac{21}{\cos 25°} \cos \alpha = \frac{21 \cos 32° 30'}{\cos 25°} = \frac{21 \times 0{\cdot}8434}{0{\cdot}9063} = 19{\cdot}54 \text{ mm}$$

The vertical distance of F below E = ES

= Distance of F below A − Distance of E below A

= PR − LM

$= PQ \tan 25° - EL \sin 25° = 21 \tan 25° - EL \sin 25°$

$= 21 \times 0{\cdot}4663 - EL \sin 25° = 9{\cdot}79 - EL \sin 25°$

But $EL = EA \sin \alpha$ and $EA = FE \tan \alpha$

$\therefore EL = FE \tan \alpha \sin \alpha$

Hence $EL \sin 25° = FE \tan \alpha \sin \alpha \sin 25°$ which, since FE = 19·54, and $\alpha = 32° 30'$

$$= 19{\cdot}54 \times 0{\cdot}6371 \times 0{\cdot}05373 \times 0{\cdot}4226 = 2{\cdot}83$$

$$PR - LM = 9{\cdot}79 - 2{\cdot}83 = 6{\cdot}96 = ES.$$

The inclination of the top cutting face in a plane perpendicular to AB = Angle EFS

and $$\frac{ES}{FE} = \sin \widehat{EFS} = \frac{6{\cdot}96}{19{\cdot}54} = 0{\cdot}3563$$

From which $$\widehat{EFS} = \underline{20° 52'}$$

(*c*) True angle between top face and front clearance face.

This will be $\widehat{FES} - 8°$

$$= 90° - 20° 52' - 8° = 90 - 28° 52' = \underline{61° 8'}$$

Exercises 5e

1. Determine the angle, when measured perpendicular to the clearance face, of a tool for cutting acme threads (29° on its top face). Clearance angle on tool = 15°.

2. The angle of the vee in the block at Fig. 101 is to measure 60° on the front face as shown. Calculate the angle of the vee when measured along its slope (i.e. the angle to which it would be milled).

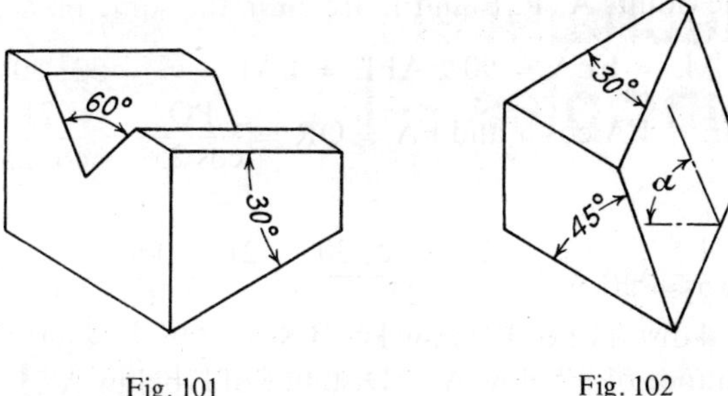

Fig. 101 Fig. 102

3. Find the true angle α between the sloping face and the base of the block shown in Fig. 102.

4. A square pyramid is 40 mm high and has a base 30 mm square. Calculate (*a*) the angle at the apex between two opposite faces, (*b*) the angle between two adjoining faces as measured perpendicular to the sloping edge bounding them.

5. A piece of sheet steel 240 mm × 120 mm is bent as in Fig. 103. Determine the base, height and vertical angle of a triangular piece of material which will fit into the angle as shown dotted.

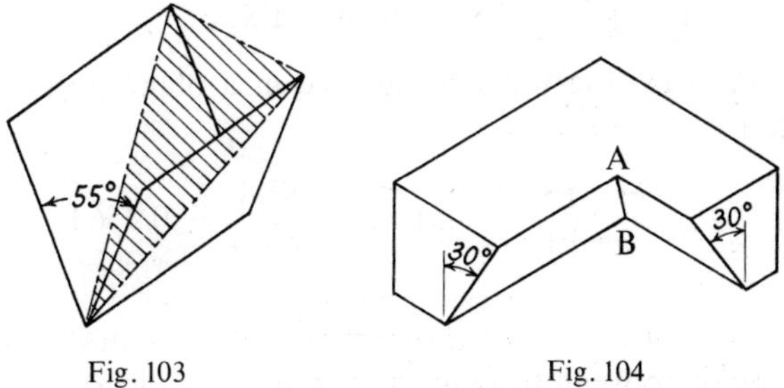

Fig. 103 Fig. 104

6. In Fig. 104 calculate (*a*) the angle between the corner AB and the top face of the block, and (*b*) the angle between the two sloping faces as measured perpendicular to AB.

6 Mechanical principles – I

Vectorial representation

We are familiar with the numerical representation of quantities and with the processes to which we have to submit our calculations to obtain the desired result. In the study of some parts of mechanics it is an advantage to be able to express certain quantities in the form of vectors. When anything has amount and direction it can be represented by a vector, and a vector is a line, the length of which represents the amount of the quantity being represented, and whose direction indicates which way the quantity is acting. Thus in Fig. 105, *ab* represent a vector $3\frac{1}{2}$ units long directed in an

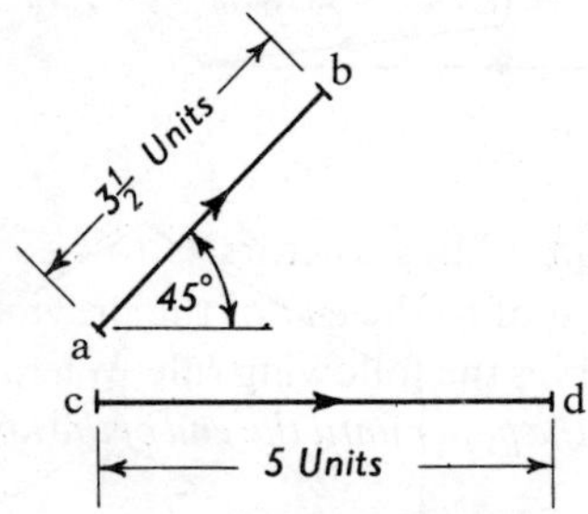

Fig. 105

upward direction at 45° to the horizontal; *cd* represents a vector 5 units long directed horizontally from left to right.

Addition and subtraction of vectors

When we add or subtract numerical quantities we merely add or subtract the numerical amounts, the result being a numerical sum or difference, as the case may be. When adding or subtracting vector quantities, however, we have to take into account not only their numerical value but also their direction. This is achieved if we observe the following rules:

Adding

To add two or more vectors, draw the first in the direction of its arrow, continue the second one on the end of the first, the third on the end of the second, and so on. The sum of the vectors is the vector joining the beginning of the first to the end of the last in the series. The arrow on the sum vector must be in the same general direction as those on the vectors being added. This will be understood from the vectors shown added in Fig. 106.

Draw *ab* equal and parallel to vector *A*; on the end *b* draw *bc* equal and parallel to *B* and from *c* draw *cd* equal and parallel to *C*. The sum of *A*, *B* and *C* is the vector *ad*, and its arrow is as shown.

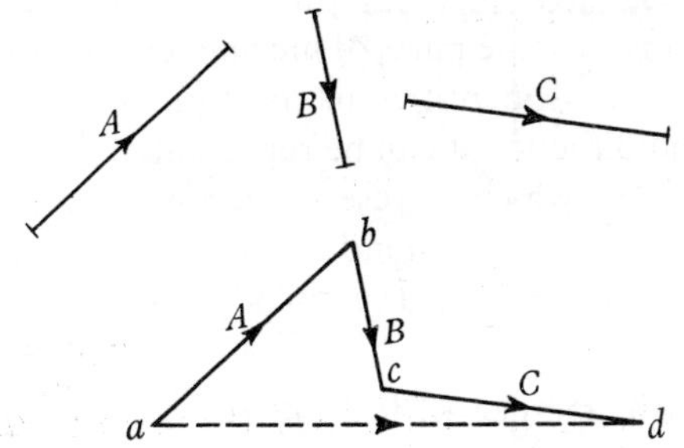

Fig. 106

The chief mistake made in adding vectors is to add the succeeding vector to the *beginning* instead of to the *end* of the previous one. This can be avoided if the reader observes the following rule: When adding vectors, *do not remove the pencil from the paper until the end of the last one is reached*.

Subtracting

We know that $A - B$ is the same as $A + (-B)$. Hence to subtract a vector *B* from another one *A* we may *add* $-B$ to *A*. A minus vector is a positive one with the direction of its arrow reversed.

This if *a* ——>—— *b* is a vector representing $+ A$, then *b* ——<—— *c* will represent $-A$.

The following example will illustrate the subtraction of vectors:

Example 1. Subtract a vector of 5 units horizontal L to R, from a vector of 4 units directed at 45° to the NE, and then add a vector of 6 units vertical downwards.

The vectors are shown at Fig. 107 (*a*), and the problem is

$$\mathrm{B} - A + C$$

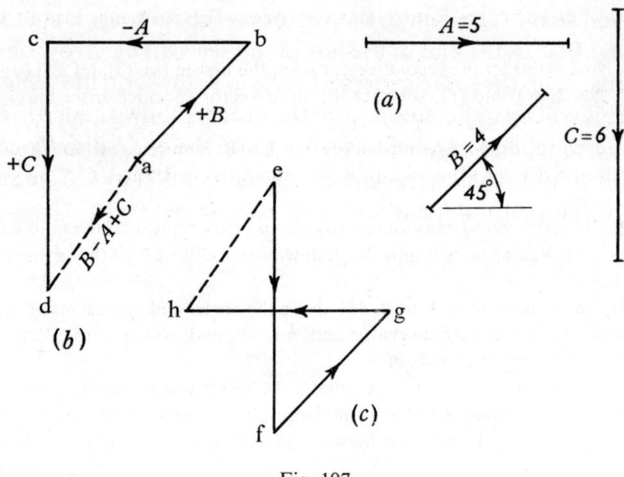

Fig. 107

It does not matter in which order we deal with the vectors, providing we observe the rules for their addition or subtraction.

In this case we have to reverse the arrow of A and then add them all together. This is shown at (*b*) and the result is the vector *ad*.

To convince the reader that the result is unaffected by the order in which the vectors are drawn, the diagram has been re-drawn at (*c*), where the vectors have been taken it the order $C\ B\ A$ instead of $B\ A\ C$, as at (*b*). The result is the same for each case, since *eh* and *ad* are equal in length and direction.

Exercises 6a

[Where an angle is specified, it refers to the angle made with the horizontal or vertical line drawn to the beginning end of the vector.]

1. Draw vectors to represent the following: (*a*) 7 units, vertically upwards; (*b*) 8·5 units horizontal L to R; (*c*) 3 units upwards at 30° to L of vertical; (*d*) 6·4 units downwards 15° to R of vertical; (*e*) 7·2 units R to L at 30° above horizontal; (*f*) 5 units L to R at 45° below horizontal.

2. Add together the following vectors:

(*a*) 6 units vertically upwards, to 4 units horizontal L to R.
(*b*) 8·2 units horizontal R and L, to 7·1 units vertically downwards.
(*c*) 4·5 units downwards, 10° to R of vertical, to 6·5 units vertically downwards.
(*d*) 7·2 units R to L 20° above horiz, to 6·5 units L to R, 45° below horiz.
(*e*) 6·3 units vert upwards to 6 units horiz L to R to 6 units R to L, 30° below horiz.

(*f*) 5 units horiz L to R, to 5 units vert, downwards, to 8 units L to R, 30° above horiz.

3. In Ex. No **2**, subtract the second vector from the first in (*a*), (*b*), (*c*) and (*d*).

4. In Ex. No **2**, (*e*) and (*f*), subtract the third vector specified from the sum of the first two.

5. A horizontal vector, *ab*, 8·6 units long, arrow L to R, represents the sum of two vectors, *ac* and *cb*, where $\widehat{acb} = 90°$. If *ac* is L to R, 40° above the horizontal, find the values of *ac* and *cb*.

6. A vertical vector, *ab*, 10 units long, arrow downwards, represents the difference of two vectors (*ac* − *cb*). Vector *ac* is 8 units long, downwards, 30° to R of the vertical. Find the value of vector *cb*.

7. A vector *ab*, 15 units long, L to R, 45° above the horizontal, represents the sum of two vectors, *ac* and *cb*. The angle between *ac* and *cb* is 30°, and *ac* is upwards, 30° to R of the vertical. Find the values of *ac* and *cb*.

8. When two vectors, *ab* and *bc*, are added, the result is a horizontal vector 10 units long, L to R. When *bc* is subtracted from *ab* the result is an upward vector, 30° to the R of the vertical, 10 units long. If the angle between *ab* and *bc* is 90°, find their values.

Applications of vectors

We will now consider some of the examples which occur in practice, requiring the use of vectors for their solution.

Forces

In order to specify a force completely we must know its amount, its line of action and its direction. Force may be represented vectorially since the length of the vector may represent the amount of the force, the inclination of the vector may represent its line of action and the arrow head will show the direction. When problems arise where a number of non-parallel forces are acting at a point, the solution can be arrived at vectorially, since this method takes into account the angular effect as well as the magnitude of the forces. A simple example will probably make this clear. Suppose that a pin is being driven into a hole by a force *F*, applied on an angle as shown in Fig. 108 (*a*). We know from experience that if *F* were large enough it would eventually drive the pin home, although it would not do so as well as if it were acting vertically. We also know that if *F* were sloping too far over towards the horizontal, it would bend the pin. We may say, therefore, that *F* is equivalent to the combination of a vertical force and a horizontal one, and Fig. 108(*b*) shows the forces acting on the pin: *Q* is the pressure of the side of the hole and *R* is the resistance tending to prevent the pin from entering the hole. By drawing a vector diagram we may find *Q* and *F*

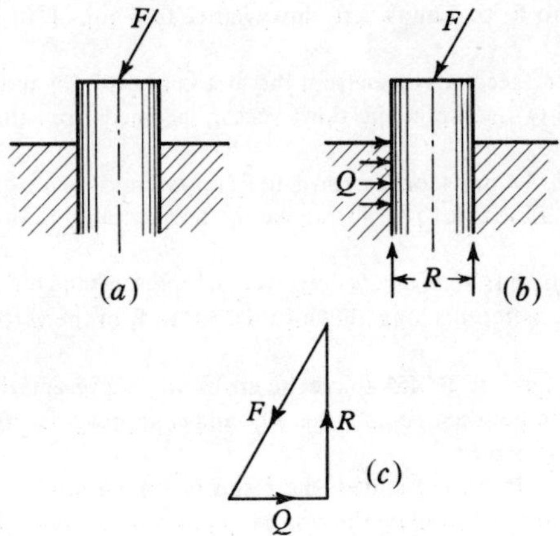

Fig. 108

if we know the amount and direction of F, because we know that $F = Q + R$. The diagram is shown in Fig. 108(c). The vector for F is drawn parallel to F and equal to its amount to some scale. Since only 3 forces are acting, the diagram is a triangle, and this is completed by making one side parallel to Q and the other parallel to R, Q, being drawn from one end of F and R from the other. R represents the driving in effect, and Q and bending effect of F.

The reader will observe that here the arrows follow round the diagram, whereas when we were discussing the addition of vectors they did not. Here we are dealing with vectors representing a set of forces which are in *balance* amongst themselves, whilst before we were finding a vector which represented the *resultant* of a number of others. If F were representing the *resultant*, or the net effect of Q and R, its arrow would point upwards, but as it represents a force which *balances* the other two, then its direction must be reversed. The only difference between the resultant of a number of forces and the single force that will balance them is that the balancing force is opposite in direction to the resultant.

Example 2. A round bar of metal which exerts a vertically downward force of 100 N is resting in a 90° vee block. Find the load on the sides of the block.

In all problems of this type, a clear conception of the forces acting should be gained before attempting the vectorial solution. Also, in all

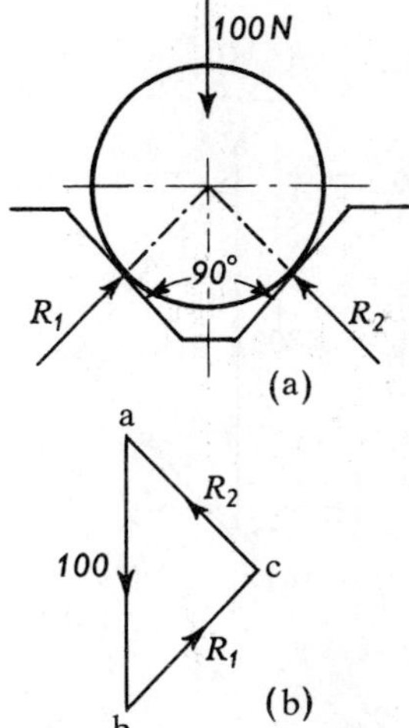

Fig. 109

vectorial problems, the data or details must be drawn out to scale in order that the vectors may be drawn parallel to the quantities they represent.

In this case the weight of the bar (100 N) acting vertically downwards is being balanced by the forces R_1 and R_2 exerted *on the bar* by the vee block. As the vee block is symmetrical about the centre line, the forces R_1 and R_2 will be equal. The bar, of course, exerts equal and opposite forces, R_1 and R_2, on the block (Fig. 109*a*).

In drawing the vector diagram, first draw a vertical vector to represent the weight of the bar acting downwards. From each end of this draw vectors parallel to the balancing forces acting. The lengths of these will represent the magnitude of the forces. This is shown in Fig. 109(*b*).

It will be seen that in the vector triangle *abc*, since each side of the vee block slopes at 45°, the angles *abc* are each 45°.

Hence

$$\begin{aligned} bc &= R_1 = ac = R_2 \\ &= ab \sin 45° = 0{\cdot}707\,ab \\ &= 0{\cdot}707 \times 100 = \underline{70{\cdot}7 \text{ N}} \end{aligned}$$

Example 3. A casting whose weight exerts a downward force of 1000 N is slung by chains as shown in Fig. 110(*a*). Find (*a*) the tension in the chains, (*b*) the least angle α between the chains and the casting if the tension in the chains is not to exceed 1600 N.

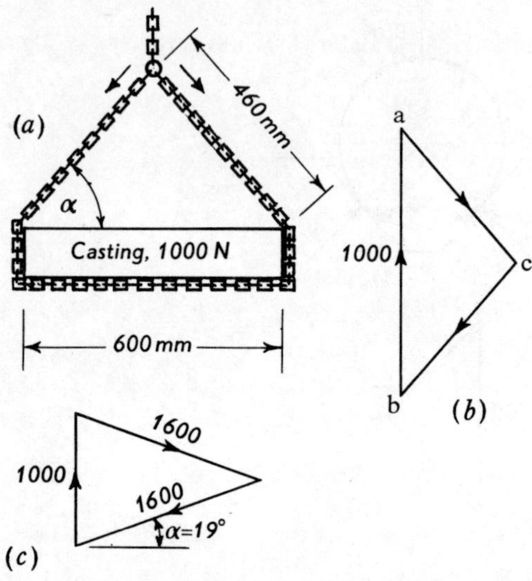

Fig. 110

(*a*) The forces acting at the ring where the chains meet are (1) lifting chain pulling upwards, (2) sling chains pulling in their directions. These forces are shown by the arrows.

The diagram must be set out to scale so that vectors may be drawn parallel to their forces; this has been done for Fig. 110(*a*) to save an additional diagram.

We may now draw the vector diagram, and this is shown in Fig. 110(*b*). *ab* is the vertical vector for the upward pull of the lifting chain, whilst *ac* and *bc* are drawn parallel to the sling chains.

Upon measurement, *ac* and *bc* are found to have a length representing 700 N, which is the force in the chains.

(*b*) If the tension in the chains is 1600 N, the vector diagram will be as shown in Fig. 110(*c*), and by measurement the angle α is found to be 19°.

The reader will observe that the smaller the value of α, the greater will be the load on the sling chains.

Exercises 6b

1. The leadscrew of a lathe is threaded 5 mm lead, and is connected to the spindle by a $\frac{1}{4}$ gear ratio. The feed shaft is set to give a feed of 1 mm per rev to the cross-slide. If the nut and the cross-slide feed (outwards) are engaged at the same time, determine the actual movement of the tool point.

2. A fitter holds a chisel at an angle of 40° to the horizontal, and strikes it a 50 N blow with a hammer. Find the force tending to drive the chisel horizontally, and that tending to drive it vertically into the metal.

3. A bar of steel, which exerts a vertically downward force of 300 N, rests symmetrically on a pair of 90° vee-blocks.

(*a*) Determine the reaction between the bar and the block at an area of contact

(*b*) If contact takes place on an area of size 50 mm × 0·08 mm, what is the contact pressure in N/mm²?

4. A wheel, 60 mm diameter, rolls along a flat surface at 0·06 m/s. Determine the actual speed and direction of a point on its circumference, and level with its centre.

5. A bar of steel 2 m long and 31 kgf (304 N) weight, is lifted by a chain attached to its ends. The total length of the vee formed by the chain is 2·5 m. Determine the tension in the chain.

6. A casting weighing 20 kgf (196 N) is suspended by a chain and is being pulled to one side by another chain attached to it. If, when the first chain is inclined at 30° to the vertical, the angle between the chains is 105°, find the tension in the chains.

7. A casting of weight equivalent to 2000 N is raised by driving 4 wedges under it. If the angle of each wedge is 25° and the weight is equally distributed between them, find the force tending to push the wedge out, and the pressure perpendicular to the wedge surface. [Neglect friction between the wedge and casting.]

Conditions for equilibrium

For a body to be in equilibrium under the action of 3 forces, the forces acting upon it must satisfy *one* of the following conditions:

(*a*) They must be parallel, or

(*b*) If not parallel they must meet at a point, and their vectors, when drawn, must form a closed figure.

As we shall be dealing with parallel forces later, we will consider case (*b*).

It is not always obvious, upon the examination of a problem, in which direction all the forces are acting. Generally the points which they are being applied can be picked out easily, as can the directions of at least two of them. When we know that to be in equilibrium, non-parallel forces must meet at a point, we can generally find this point by using what information we have, and employ it to help in the solution of the problem.

In this connexion we might remind the reader of the following:

(*a*) The weight of a body always acts vertically downwards through its Centre of Gravity, and if the mass is m kilogrammes, the weight can be taken as $9{\cdot}81\,m$ newtons.

(*b*) When friction is neglected the pressure between two bodies acts at the point of contact and in a direction perpendicular to a tangent drawn to the surfaces in contact.

Example 4. A bar of metal, mass 15 kg (147 N weight), is rested on its end and leaned against a wall so that it is inclined at an angle of 60° to the floor. If the friction between the end of the bar and the wall is neglected, find the force on the floor and against the wall.

The forces acting on the bar are (1) The gravitational pull of its weight, acting downwards through its centre; (2) the reaction of the wall acting horizontal (since friction is neglected); (3) the reaction of the floor. Of these we know the amount, direction and line of action of (1), the direction and line of action of (2), and the point of application of (3).

If lines representing (1) and (2) are drawn on the diagram they meet at O [Fig. 111(*a*)]. Obviously, if the forces acting must meet at a point, the third force must pass through O, and since it must also act at the end B of the bar, its line of action is OB. Having thus determined the directions of all the forces acting, and knowing that they must form a closed vectorial figure, we may now draw the vector diagram.

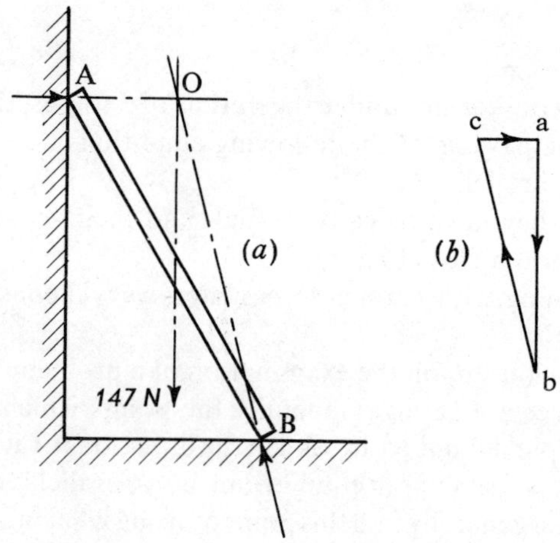

Fig. 111

Draw *ab* to represent the weight of the bar, *bc* parallel to OB, and *ca* parallel to AD.

From the diagram we find that reaction of floor (*bc*) = 153 N and load on wall (*ca*) = 40 N.

Example 5. A bell crank lever ABC is pivoted at B and the forces acting at A and C are as shown in Fig. 112(*a*). Find the force on the pivot B.

If the lines of action of the forces at A and C are continued they meet at D [Fig. 112(*b*)], so that the third force acting on the lever must pass through D. Since the lever is supported at B, this force must also pass through B, so that the forces acting on the lever are as shown by the arrows.

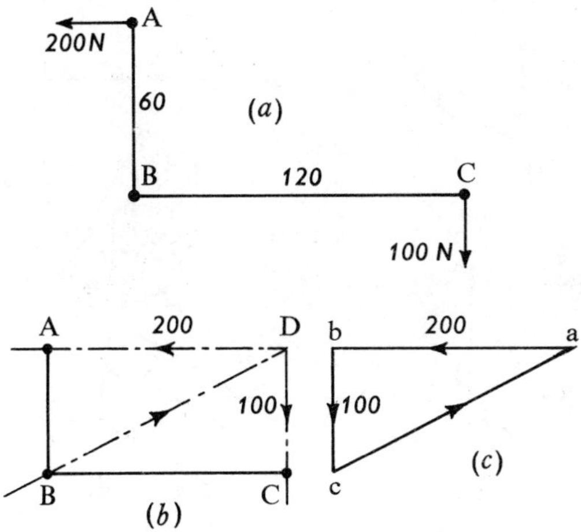

Fig. 112

The vector diagram of forces is shown at Fig. 112(*c*) and from it we see that force acting at B $= ac$

$$= \sqrt{200^2 + 100^2}$$

$$= \underline{224\,\text{N}}$$

Forces acting on a cutting tool

We have noticed previously that when a lathe tool is cutting there are three perpendicular forces acting on it. These are shown diagrammatically in Fig. 113(*a*), where C is the vertical cutting force, F the feeding force, and H the horizontal pressure of the work. By means of vector diagrams we may determine the resultant of these forces.

Since the forces are acting in two planes we must solve the problem in two stages. Let us find the resultant of F and C first. This is shown by the vector diagram *abc* at (*b*), and R_{FC}, represented by *ac*, is the resultant, acting in the vertical plane containing F and C. We may now imagine the tool being acted upon by the forces R_{FC} and H, acting in a plane inclined at θ to

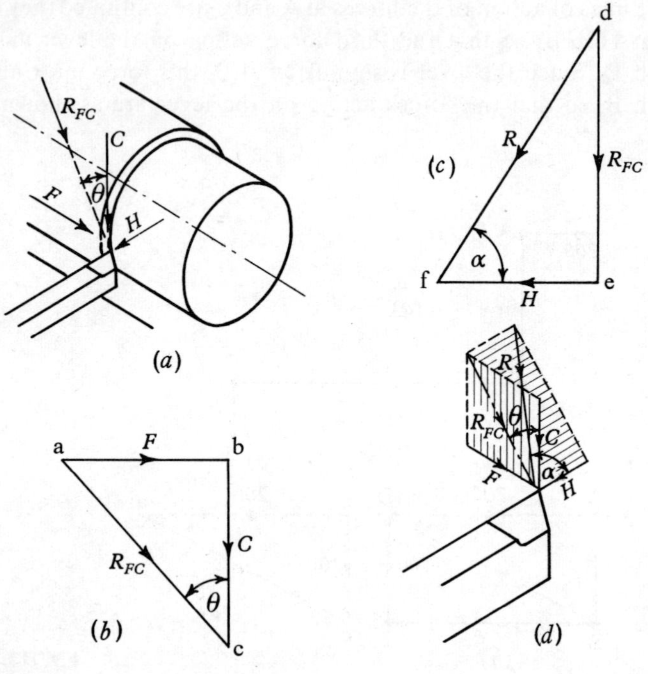

Fig. 113

the vertical as shown at (*a*). Combining these in a second vector diagram, we obtain the final resultant force on the tool (R) as shown at (*c*). R lies in a plane sloping at θ to the vertical and its line of action is inclined at α to the line of H. A diagrammatic sketch of the forces and their resultants is shown at (*d*).

The reader will observe that we might solve this problem by calculation alone, since from Fig. 113(*b*) $F^2 + C^2 = R_{FC}^{\ 2}$, and $\dfrac{F}{C} = \tan\theta$; and from (*c*) $R^2 = R_{FC}^{\ 2} + H^2$ and $\tan\alpha = \dfrac{R_{FC}}{H}$

In all such cases, however, it is advisable to be able to visualise the conditions and not to calculate a result blindly from a formula.

Example 6. The forces acting on a lathe tool are $C = 1000$ N, $F = 100$ N and $H = 400$ N [Fig. 113(*a*)]. Find the resultant force on the tool.

As we have discussed the problem diagrammatically, we will solve this problem by calculation.

Referring to Fig. 113(*b*), (*c*) and (*d*).

$$R_{FC}^2 = F^2 + C^2 = 700^2 + 1000^2$$

$$R_{FC} = \sqrt{700^2 + 1000^2} = 1220\text{N}$$

$$\tan\theta = \frac{F}{C} = \frac{700}{1000} = 0{\cdot}7$$

from which $\theta = 35°$.

$$R^2 = R_{FC}^2 + H^2 = 1220^2 + 400^2$$

$$R = \sqrt{1220^2 + 400^2} = 1285\text{N}$$

$$\tan\alpha = \frac{R_{FC}}{H} = \frac{1220}{400} = 3{\cdot}05$$

from which $\alpha = 71°\ 51'$

Hence the resultant is a force of 1285N, and the angles α and θ in Fig. 113(*d*) are 71° 51′ and 35° repectively.

The balancing of work on lathe face-plates

When a mass is rotating at a certain distance from the centre of rotation the disturbing effect due to its being out of balance is proportional to the mass and to its distance from the centre of rotation. Furthermore, the disturbing effect is always directed from the centre to the masses. Thus if Fig. 114 represents a rotating plate carrying rotating masses m_1 and m_2 at radii r_1 and r_2, the out-of-balance forces are proportional to m_1r_1 and m_2r_2 and are directed from the axis (O), through the mass centres.

We are thus able to deal with such problems vectorially, provided we draw our vectors equal in length to the product *mr*.

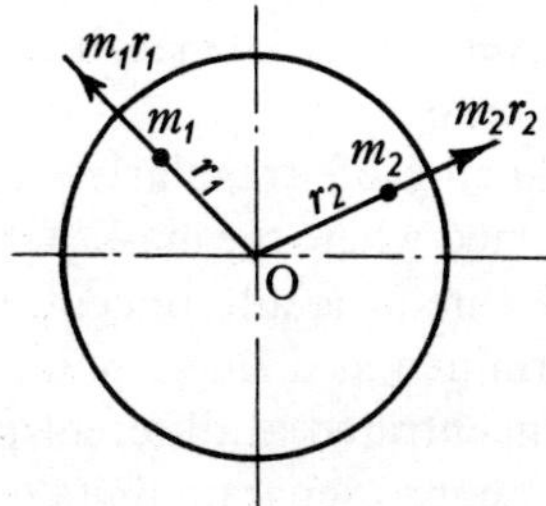

Fig. 114

Example 7. A rotating plate carries masses of 15 kg and 20 kg placed at radii 80 mm and 100 mm respectively. The angle between the masses is 120°.

Find where a 22 kg mass must be placed to balance the system.

The two masses are shown at Fig. 115(*a*).

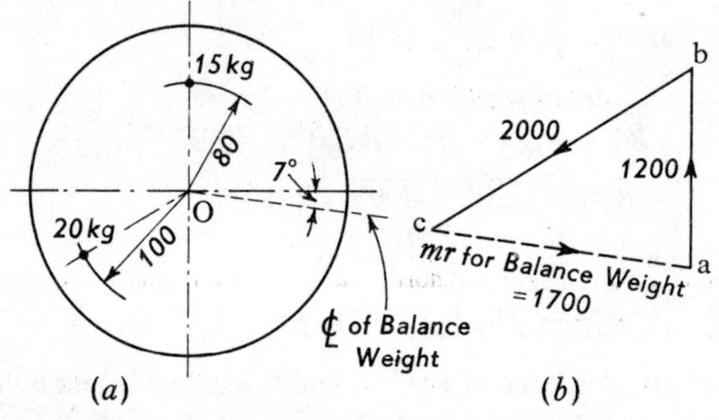

(*a*) (*b*) Fig. 115

The products of their mass and radii are

$$15 \times 80 = 1200$$
$$20 \times 100 = 2000$$

The vector diagram is now drawn with the vector lengths proportional to 1200 and 2000, the directions of the vectors being parallel to radii joining the centre O to each respective weight. This is shown at *abc* in Fig. 115 (*b*) and *ca* is the vector representing the product *mr* for the balancing mass. From the diagram the length of *ca* is 1700 units, and since for the balance weight $m = 22\,\text{kg}$, $r = \frac{1700}{22} = 77\,\text{mm}$.

The position of the balance weight relative to the other two is found by drawing a line through O parallel to *ca*. This is shown dotted on Fig. 115(*a*). Hence to balance the masses given, the 22 kg mass must be fixed at 77 mm radius, and 97° from the 15 kg mass.

When working out the balancing of irregularly shaped castings, the point or points must be determined where the mass of the casting is acting (the Centre of Gravity). If the metal is all concentrated together, the centre of gravity may be determined as a single point, but if the casting consists of lumps of metal concentrated at different positions, a better method would be to estimate them as separate units of mass.

Exercises 6c

1. The forces acting on a lathe tool are 1200 N vertical, 800 N along the axis of the work and 500 N outwards, perpendicular to the axis of the work. Find the amount and direction of the resultant force.

2. If the tool in question **1** is 20 mm deep, how far back from its point does the line of action of the resultant force intersect its base?

3. The helix angle of the tooth of a spiral milling cutter is 20°. When the tangential cutting force perpendicular to the cutter axis is 850 N, find the end thrust and the force acting perpendicular to the tooth face.

4. The arms of a bell crank lever are 60 mm and 40 mm long. When the long arm is inclined at 45° to the upwards vertical, the short arm is below the centre line, and with the lever in this position a vertical upwards force of 120 N at the end of the long arm is balanced by a horizontal force of 180 N at the end of the short arm. Find the force acting on the lever pivot.

5. A bar of steel weighing 31 kgf (304 N) rests with one end in the corner between a wall and the floor and is inclined at 30° to the horizontal. It is held in this position by a rope attached to the outer end, the rope making an angle of 90° with the bar. Find the tension in the rope and the force where the bar rests in the corner.

6. A countershaft is driven by a horizontal belt and the down belt makes an angle of 75° with the top one. When the tension in each side of the driving belt is 200 N and in each side of the down belt 120 N find the resultant force on the shaft.

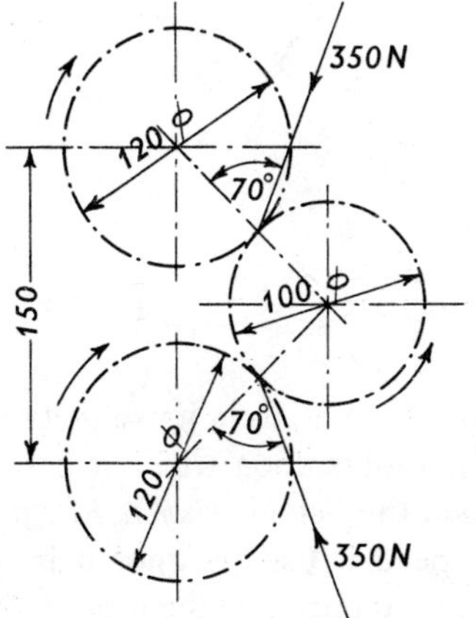

Fig. 116

7. Fig. 116 is a diagrammatic sketch of a gear drive, and forces of 350 N act on the teeth of the 100 mm gear as shown. Find the resultant thrust on the bearings of this gear.

8. A toggle press mechanism is as shown in Fig. 121. When the horizontal force at C is 250 N and the angle CA_2D is 5°, find the vertical force at the ram.

9. A casting is bolted to a lathe face-plate, the total mass being equivalent to masses of 50 kg at 200 mm radius and 60 kg at 260 mm radius. The angle between these is 120°. Find the radius and position of a 50 kg mass which will give balance.

10. For the mechanism shown at Fig. 126, if a pressure of 10 kN acts vertically downwards at E, what is the thrust in link BC?

11. A large CI pulley has two out-of-balance bosses on it each 60 mm diameter and 40 mm thick. Their radii are A = 260 mm and B = 360 mm, and the angle between radii drawn to A and B is 110°. Find the volume and position of a lead balance weight to be attached to the pulley at 360 mm radius.

[Density CI = 7200 kg/m³ lead = 11 kg/m³],

Vector diagrams of velocity

Velocity, as well as force, may be represented by a vector since it has amount, line of action and direction. The application of vector velocity diagrams is very useful when studying the speeds of points in machine mechanisms, and for that reason it is worthy of consideration.

Before going further into the subject it will be well to impress certain fundamental points on the reader's mind, as the success or otherwise of his further study will depend upon his appreciation of them.

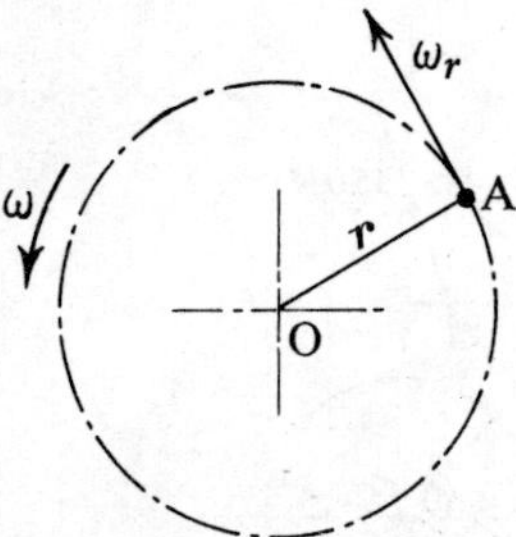

Fig. 117

(1) When an object is rotating in a circle its velocity at any instant is directed perpendicular to the radius upon which it lies. If ω rad/s is the speed and r is the radius, then the velocity is ωr. For most engineering applications the rotational speed is usually quoted in rev/min and the radius in millimetres. For general purposes the most convenient unit for velocity is metres per second, and hence if

$$N = \text{speed in rev/min}$$

and $$r = \text{radius in millimetres}$$

then $$v = \frac{2\pi rN}{60\,000} = \frac{\pi dN}{60\,000} \text{ metres/second}$$

(2) Whatever may be the motion of a rigid rod, the only velocity that one end may have relative to the other is perpendicular to the rod. (The "relative" motion of one body to another is the motion the first would appear to have to an observer situated at the second one.)

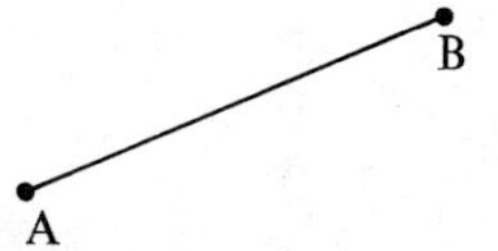

Fig. 118

In Fig. 118, AB is a rod having any motion whatsoever. To an observer at A, B can only appear to move perpendicular to AB. If it could move in any direction other than this, it must either approach nearer to A or recede from it. Both of these are impossible since AB is rigid and of fixed length.

(3) When a part of a machine is guided in slides it can only move parallel to the slides.

We will discuss vector velocity diagrams by working one or two problems, and the reader is advised to take particular note of the system of lettering adopted.

Example 8. ABC is a slider crank mechanism. Find the speed of C for the position and values given (Fig. 119).

$$\text{Speed of B} = \frac{2\pi rN}{60000} = \frac{2 \times 22 \times 60 \times 500}{7 \times 60000}$$
$$= 3{\cdot}142 \text{ m/s}$$

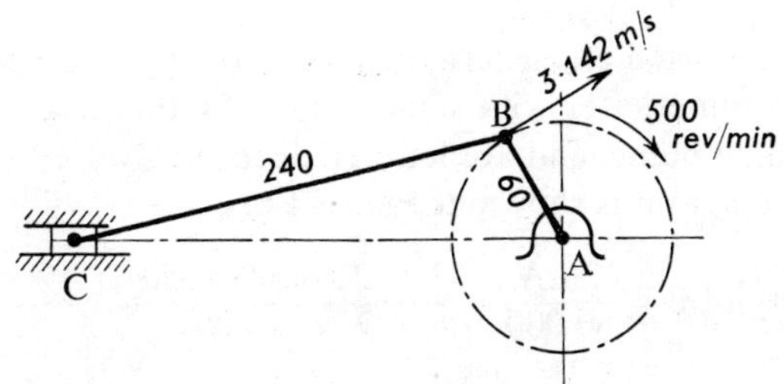

Fig. 119

From the diagram we know the following:

(1) B is moving perpendicular to AB at 3·142 m/s per sec,
(2) Relative to B, C can only move perpendicular to BC,
(3) Relative to A, C can only move horizontal.

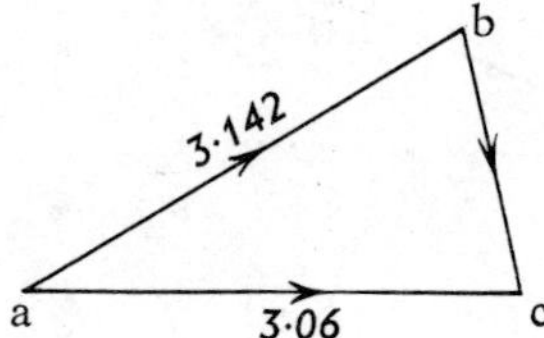

Fig. 120

The velocity diagram is shown at Fig. 120 and the explanation of its construction is as follows:

(Arrows are shown on the vectors, but in practice these are omitted.)

ab represents the velocity of B relative to A (*i.e. the velocity B would appear to have to an observer at A*). The relative velocity of C to B is perpendicular to BC, hence from *b* a line is drawn perpendicular to BC, and *c* must lie somewhere on that line. But relative to A, C can only move horizontal, hence *c* must lie somewhere on a horizontal line through *a*. The point *c* is therefore given by the intersection of the two lines drawn, and *abc* is the velocity diagram. For the given position C is moving towards A at a speed of 3·06 m/s, scaled off from *ac*.

[Note in the lettering of velocity diagrams that *ab* = velocity of B relative to A and *not* of A relative to B as might have been expected. Similarly for *ac*, *bc*, etc.]

Example 9. The mechanism of a toggle press is shown in Fig. 121 (*a*). Find the speed of the ram for the position shown. The figure is drawn to scale.

When the frame (the fixed element) appears in more than one place it should be given the same letter with small figures. In this case A_1 and A_2 are both fixed frame points and are lettered accordingly.

The vector velocity diagram is shown at Fig. 121 (*b*).

$$\text{Velocity of B} = \frac{2\pi rN}{60\,000} = \frac{2 \times 22 \times 60 \times 50}{7 \times 60000}$$
$$= 0{\cdot}314 \text{ m/s}$$

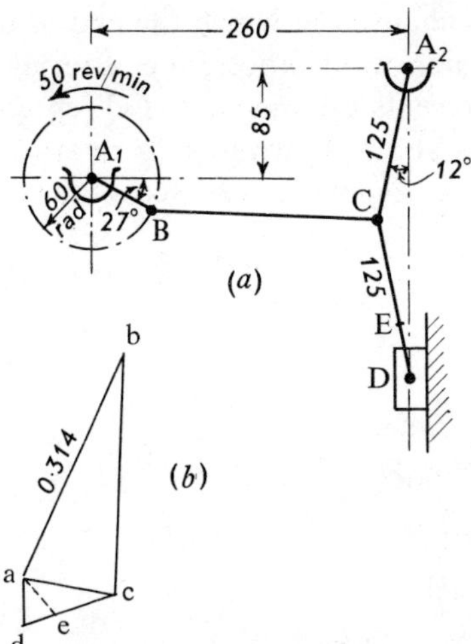

Fig. 121

Draw *ab* perpendicular to A_1B to represent the velocity of B relative to A_1. From *b* draw a line perpendicular to BC, and from *a* draw perpendicular to A_2C. The intersection of these lines gives the point *c*. From *c* draw a line perpendicular to CD and from *a* draw a vertical line (velocity of D relative to A is fixed as vertically). The intersection of these gives point *d*.

The vector *ad* represents the relative velocity of D to A (the frame). This is shown to be downwards and scales off from the diagram to be 0·052 m/s. If the speed and direction of a point on any lever is required, it can be found immediately from the vector diagram, since lines on the vector diagram are images of corresponding ones on the mechanism. Thus for a point E, $\frac{2}{3}$ the distance from C to D, locate the point *e*, $\frac{2}{3}$ from *c* to *d*, and *ae* represents the velocity of E.

There are one or two additional points to be explained in connection with velocity diagrams, and these will be covered by the next example.

Example 10. The mechanism for a slotted-link shaping machine quick-return motion is shown drawn to scale in Fig. 122 (*a*). Determine the speed of the ram for the position shown.

The crank A_1B rotates, and the block B moves up and down in the slotted lever A_2D. This lever is thus made to oscillate about its pivot A_22, and through the link DE drives the ram of the machine.

When dealing with a mechanism in which the end of one lever slides in or on another lever which itself moves, the lettering up should be arranged as shown. B represents the block, and C represents a point *on the lever* A_2D. B is rotating about A_1 whilst C is rotating about A_2. The reason for doing this will be seen when we discuss the velocity diagram.

$$\text{Velocity of B} = \frac{2 \times 22 \times 80 \times 40}{7 \times 60000} = 0{\cdot}335\,\text{m/s}$$

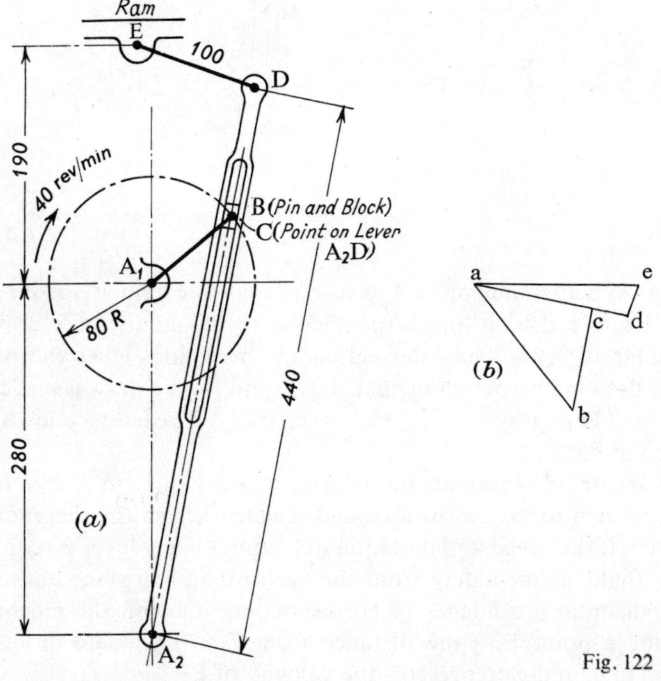

Fig. 122

In Fig. 122 (*b*) *ab* represents the velocity of B relative to A. Now the velocity of C relative to B (or B to C) is along the lever A_2D. From *b* draw a line parallel to A_2D and from *a* draw a line perpendicular to A_2D (since relative to A, C is moving perpendicular to A_2D). The intersection of these gives the point *c*. The line *ac* now represents the relative velocity of C to A. The velocity of D relative to A will be a continuation of *ac* to *d* such that $\frac{ac}{ad} = \frac{A_2C}{A_2D}$ because C and D are on the same lever and their movements are proportional to their respective radii. (For this purpose C is assumed to be coincident with B, as it is only an imaginary point introduced for this purpose of the construction.)

When *d* is thus located, draw a line through it perpendicular to DE, to represent the velocity of E relative to D and draw a horizontal line through *a* to represent the relative velocity of E to A. The intersection of these gives the point *e*. From the lettering it will be seen that E is moving to the right and the scaled length of *ae* gives its speed to be 0·353 m/s. The speed at which the block B is sliding in lever A_2D is given by the length *bc* on the velocity diagram.

Forces acting in a mechanism

The vector velocity diagram for a mechanism may be used to estimate the force acting at a certain point when the force at another point is known. Let us assume that for a mechanism we have the velocity of two points A and E, and the force acting at A. If v_A and v_E are the velocities, and F_A and F_E the forces, respectively, then assuming A to be the energy input point and E the point of output, the input rate of work at A will be $F_A v_A$ and if the machine is 100% efficient, this will equal the output rate $F_E v_E$.

We can assume an efficiency η and then we shall have

$$\eta = \frac{\text{Output}}{\text{Input}} = \frac{F_E v_E}{F_A v_A}$$

or, since we know F_A, v_A and v_E,

$$F_E = \frac{\eta(F_A v_A)}{v_E}$$

Example 11. If the torque input to the toggle press in Example 9 is 100 Nm and the efficiency of the mechanism is 60%, estimate the pressure on the ram for the position shown.

Since torque = (Force)(radius), and r = 60 mm = 0·06 m
100 = (Force)(0·06) and the force at the end

$$\text{of the crank} = \frac{100}{0{\cdot}06} = 1670\,\text{N}$$

Here we have that $v_B = 0{\cdot}314$ m/s, $v_D = 0{\cdot}052$ m/s, and $F_B = 1670$ N

Hence

$$\text{efficiency} = \frac{F_D v_D}{F_B v_B}; \quad 0{\cdot}6 = \frac{F_D \times 0{\cdot}052}{1670 \times 0{\cdot}314}$$

$$\text{From which } F_D = \frac{0{\cdot}6 \times 1670 \times 0{\cdot}314}{0{\cdot}052} = 6000\ \text{N}$$

Exercises 6d

1. In a slider-crank engine mechanism similar to Fig. 119 the crank AB is 60 mm long and the connecting-rod BC is 220 mm. Find the speed of C when AB is rotating at 1000 rev/min and (*a*) the angle BAC is 45°, (*b*) angle BAC = 120°.

2. For the problem in Question **1**, find the velocity of the mid-point of BC, when angle ABC = 90°.

3. Fig. 123 shows a quick return shaping machine drive in which cutting takes place when C moves to the left. Find (*a*) The ratio $\frac{\text{cutting time}}{\text{return time}}$. (*b*) The speed of B in rev/min if C is to have a velocity of 0·24 m/s when at the mid-point of its cutting stroke.

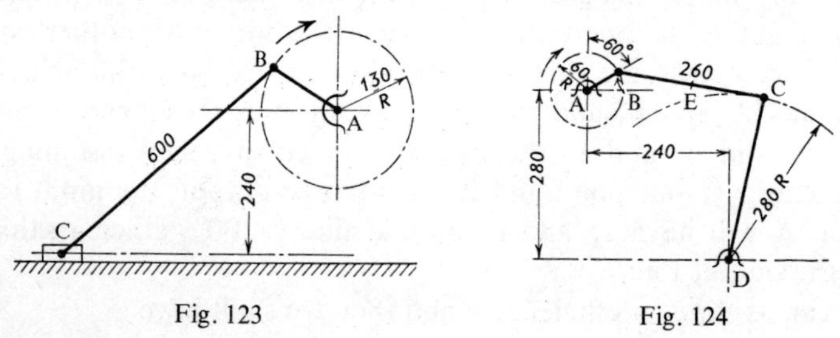

Fig. 123 Fig. 124

4. In Fig. 124 crank AB revolves at 200 rev/min and CD is caused to rock backwards and forwards. When AB is at 30° to the horizontal as shown, find the speed of C and of E, the mid-point of BC.

5. In Fig. 125 A and B are two blocks which slide in slots at right angles. If AB = 240 mm and AC = 80 mm, find the speed and direction of C when angle OBA = 40° and A is moving downwards at 0·24 m/s.

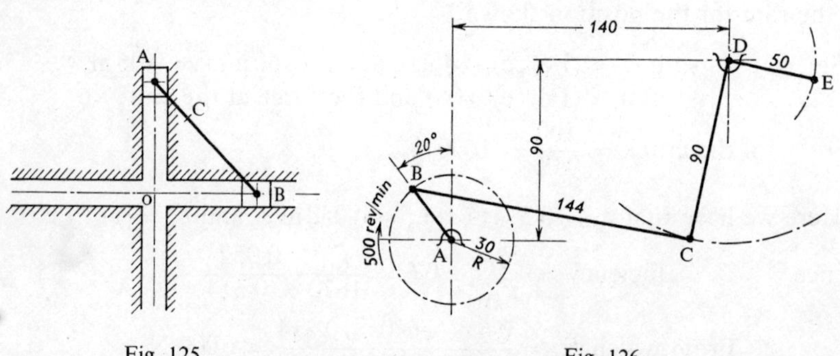

Fig. 125 Fig. 126

6. In Fig. 126 crank AB rotates as shown and CDE is a solid bell crank lever. Find the speed of E when AB is at 20° to the vertical.

7. In a toggle press mechanism similar to Fig. 121, A_1B = 40 mm, BC = 240 mm, A_2C = CD = 160 mm. The vertical centre lines are 280 mm apart and the centre line of A_1 is 120 mm below the centre line of A_2.
When B is rotating at 60 rev/min and angle CA_2D is 10°, find the speed of D.

8. In the last problem if the torque on A_1B is 100 Nm, find the pressure at D if the overall efficiency is 60%.

9. In the press mechanism shown in Fig. 127, find the speed of E when D is moving upwards at 0·02 m/s (A_1E is horizontal). If in this position the pressure at D is 4000 N, what force can E exert if the overall efficiency is 50%? [CA_1E is a solid lever.]

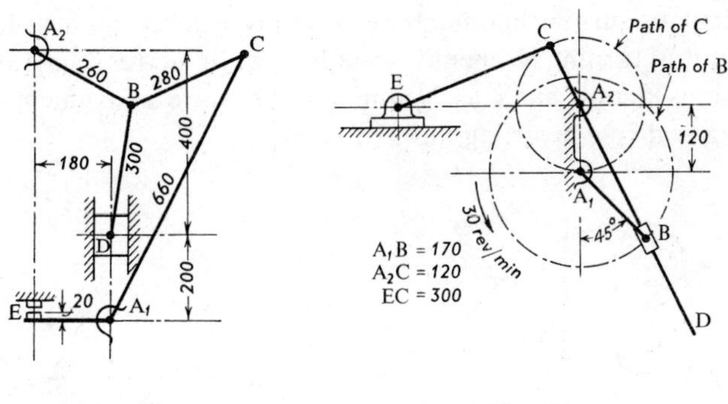

Fig. 127 Fig. 128

10. In the Whitworth quick-return mechanism sketched in Fig. 128, B rotates about A_1 and slides along the lever CD. CD is pivoted at A_2.

Find (*a*) the ratio $\dfrac{\text{Time of outer stroke}}{\text{Time of inner stroke}}$ for E, and (*b*) the speed of E when A_1B is at 45° as shown.

11. In Fig. 129 AB is a door hinged at A. CD is a spring-loaded arm for closing the door and hinged at C. If B is moving at 0·36 m/s, find the speed at which D is sliding along the door when the door has opened 45°.

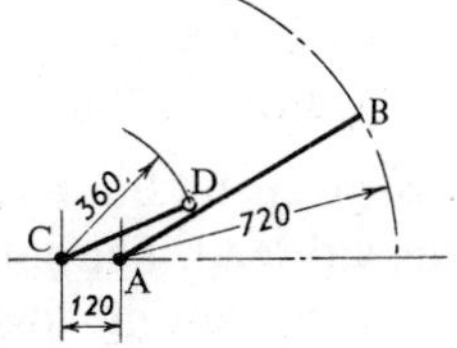

Fig. 129

The moment or turning effect of a force

If a force acts on a body, and the effect of the force is considered relative to some point not on its line of action, the tendency is for the force to rotate the body about the point. This tendency is called the *moment* of the force about the point. Thus in Fig. 130, if the effect of the force F is considered relative to the point 0, F tends to rotate the body about O. The numerical value of the moment of F about O is found by multiplying F by the *perpendicular distance* from O to its line of action. Thus the moment of F about O $= Fx$. If F were rotated to act in some other direction (e.g. as shown dotted), then its moment would be F_1(perpendicular distance) $= F_1y$.

To calculate turning moment we multiply a force by a distance so that the unit of turning moment is usually newton metres (Nm) (although on occasions a unit such as Nmm may be more convenient to save converting and re-converting units of length).

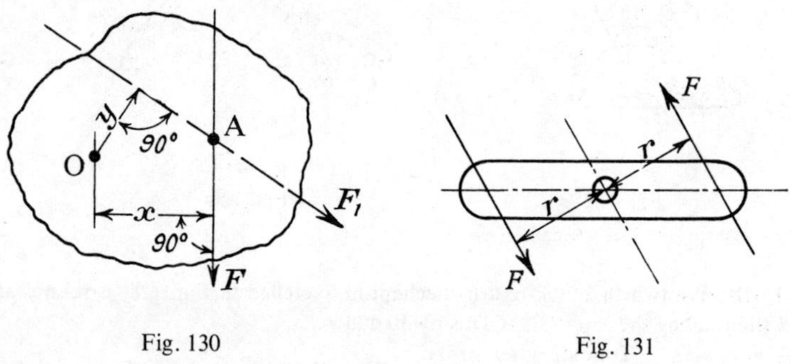

Fig. 130 Fig. 131

When two equal and opposite forces act on either side of a pivot they constitute what is called a *Couple*, and the turning moment exerted by a couple is given by one of the forces multiplied by the perpendicular distance between their lines of action (Fig. 131).

$$\begin{aligned}\text{Total moment of forces } P &= Fr + Fr \\ &= 2Fr = F(2r) \\ &= F(\text{perp distance between forces}).\end{aligned}$$

A good example of a couple is given by the forces applied to a tap wrench or die stocks when cutting a thread. The couple applied is equal to the turning moment resistance at the cutting edges of the tap or die.

Moment of a force about a point on its line of action

Since moment = (Force)(distance), if the distance is zero, then the moment will be zero if the point lies on the line of action of the force. Thus in Fig. 130 the moment of F about $A = F \times O = 0$.

Conditions for equilibrium with moments acting

The reader will have observed that a moment may be directed clockwise or contra-clockwise.

The condition for a body to be in equilibrium is that *the sum of the clockwise moments about any point must be equal to the sum of the contra-clockwise moments.* When this condition is satisfied there will be no unbalanced turning effort causing the body to rotate.

Example 12. A shaft is 7·5 m long between the bearings and carries 3 pulleys spaced at 2 m, 3 m and 6 m from the LH bearing. The downward force on the pulleys due to the belt drives is 300 N, 250 N and 350 N respectively. Calculate the load on each bearing (Fig. 132).

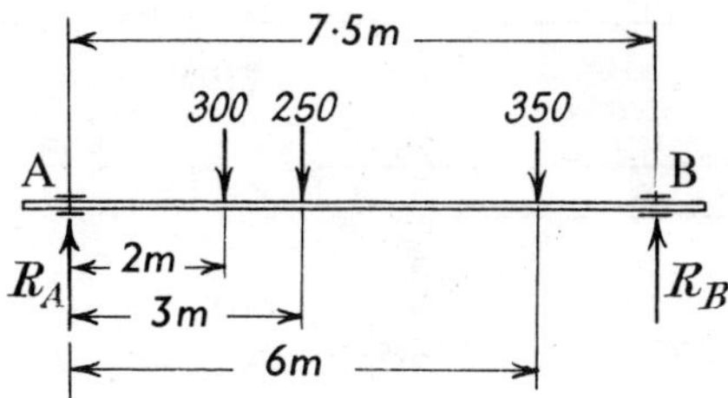

Fig. 132

Since the loading on the shaft by the pulleys is downwards the forces exerted *on the shaft* by the bearings will be upwards. Call these R_A and R_B.

We thus have the shaft acted upon by a system of parallel forces, and since it is in equilibrium, the conditions to be satisfied are:

(1) Total upward forces = Total downward forces.
(2) Clockwise moments = Contra-clockwise moments.

If we take moments about the bearing A, we can neglect the force acting there since it will have no moment about that point.

Hence by moments about A

$$\text{Clockwise moments} = 300 \times 2 + 250 \times 3 + 350 \times 6$$
$$= 600 + 750 + 2100 = 3450\,\text{N m}$$
$$\text{Contra-clockwise} = R_B \times 7{\cdot}5\,\text{Nm}$$

These must be equal

$$\therefore 7{\cdot}5\,R_B = 3450 \text{ and } R_B = \frac{3450}{7{\cdot}5} = \underline{460\text{ N}}$$

Also, since upward forces = downward forces:

$$R_A + R_B = 300 + 250 + 350 = 900\,\text{N}$$
$$R_A = 900 - R_B = 900 - 460 = \underline{440\text{ N}}$$

Example 13. A system of levers is shown in Fig. 133. Calculate what load hung at W may be balanced by a force of 10N at A. [Neglect friction and the weight of the levers.]

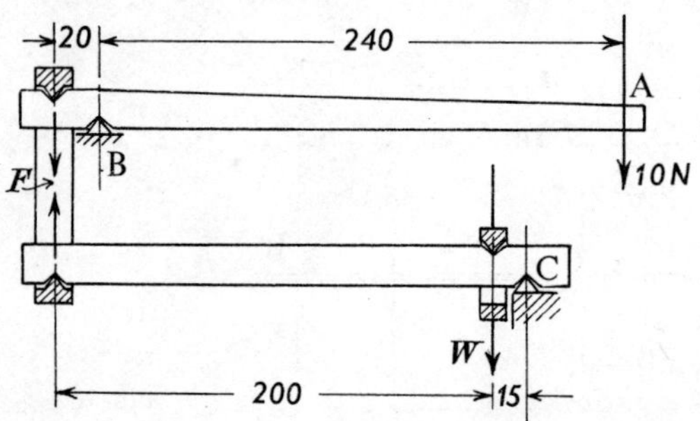

Fig. 133

First let us consider the top lever, which will be balanced by the force F in the connecting link and the 10N at A.

Taking moments about B, and working in units of N and mm, we have

$$\text{Clockwise} = 10 \times 240 = 2400 \text{ and contra-clockwise} = 20F$$

Hence $\quad 2400 = 20F$ and $F = 120\text{N}$

This will pull down on the top, and upwards on the bottom lever.
Now consider the bottom lever and take moments about C.

$$\text{Clockwise} = F \times 215$$
$$\text{Contra-clockwise} = W \times 15$$

These must be equal, and since $F = 120$

$$120 \times 215 = 15W$$

$$W = \frac{120 \times 215}{15} = \underline{1720\,\text{N}}$$

The actual value of W would be affected by friction, the weight of the levers and of the stirrup. If the lever weight is appreciable it can be allowed for by assuming the weight of each lever to be acting as a downward force approximately at the lever centre. For example, if each lever weighs 10N and the weight is assumed at the lever centre, we have for the top lever:

$$\begin{aligned} 20 \times F &= 10 \times 240 + 10 \times 110 \\ &= 2400 + 1100 = 2500 \\ F &= 175\,\text{N} \end{aligned}$$

For the bottom lever

$$\begin{aligned} F \times 215 &= 15W - 10 \times 107{\cdot}5 \text{ and since } F = 175\,\text{N} \\ 175 \times 215 &= 15W - 1075, \\ 15W &= 37\,625 + 1075 = 38\,700 \\ W &= \frac{38\,700}{15} = \underline{2580\,\text{N}} \end{aligned}$$

To obtain an exact calculation, the centre of gravity of the levers could be found by balancing on a knife-edge. The weight is then taken as acting through the centre of gravity.

Example 14. If in Example 6, p. 158, the work is 240 mm long between centres, and the cutting tool is 60 mm from the tailstock centre, calculate the forces acting on the centres.

The forces acting on the *work* are as follows:

(1) Vertical upwards force of 1000N.

(2) Horizontal force of 400N directed away from the tool.

(3) Longitudinal dorce of 700N towards the headstock.

These are shown in Fig. 134 (*a*).

Let us consider the vertical force first. This will cause an upward force on each centre and an equal and opposite downward force on the work by the centre.

Taking moments about centre A, and working on units of N and mm we have

Clockwise moment = (vert force at B) 240

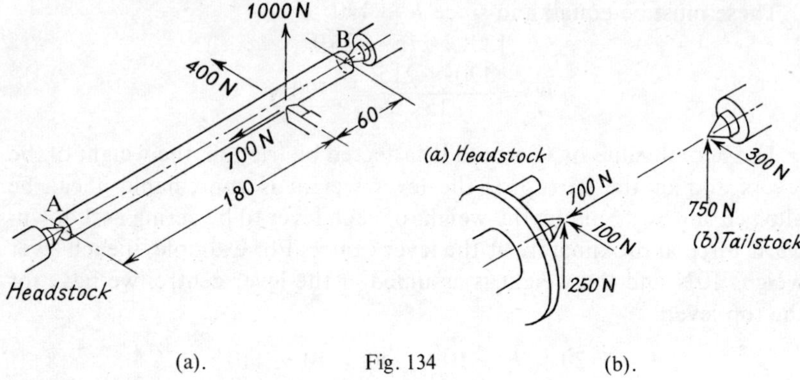

(a). Fig. 134 (b).

$$\text{Contra-clockwise moment} = 1000 \times 180 = 180\,000$$

$$\text{Hence} \qquad 240(\text{vert force at B}) = 180\,000$$

$$\text{Vert force at B} = \frac{180\,000}{240} = 750\,\text{N}$$

$$\text{Vert force at A} = 1000 - 750 = 250\,\text{N}$$

In the same way we have that the 400N force is balanced by horizontal forces of 300N at B and 100N at A.

The 700N longitudinal thrust is transmitted through the bar entirely to A.

We thus have forces acting on the two centres as shown by Fig. 134 (b), and as an additional exercise the reader should combine these vectorially to find the resultants.

Exercises 6e

1. A bell crank lever has equal arms of 120 mm at 90°. When the lever is pivoted with one arm vertically upwards, a weight of 120N is hung on the end of the horizontal arm. What force, inclined at 45°, must be applied to the end of the upper arm to balance the lever?

2. A 20 mm hand reamer is being operated by hand pressure at each end of a lever 480 mm long. The hole is 20 mm long and each of the 6 teeth is taking a cut of 0·04 mm If the cutting pressure at the teeth is 80N per sq mm of cut, estimate what force must be applied at each end of the 480 mm wrench.

3. A bar is 240 mm long between lathe centres. When the tool is 90 mm from the tailstock the vertical cutting pressure is 850N. Find the vertical force on each centre due to this.

4. A piece of material is held in a lathe chuck and at the point at which cutting takes place overhangs from the centre of the front bearing by 125 mm. If the vertical pressure due to the cut is 1200N, and the bearings are 360 mm apart, estimate the force on each bearing. [Assume point contact at each bearing and neglect weight of spindle and chuck.]

5. The bearings of a countershaft are 900 mm apart. The horizontal force due to the top belt is 450 N at 240 mm from the LH hanger and the vertical force due to the down belt is 400 N at 720 mm from the LH hanger. Find the load on each bearing.

6. A clamp is 120 mm long between the centres of the clamping and supporting points. If the bolt is 45 mm from the clamping point, to what tension must it be tightened up in order to apply a clamping load of 1000 N? What will be the reaction at the support?

7. A casting is being raised by a 720 mm crowbar which is supported at 40 mm from the end where it takes the weight. If the casting has a mass of 612 kg (6000 N weight), and half this is taken by the crowbar, what force must be applied at the end of the bar in order to raise the casting?

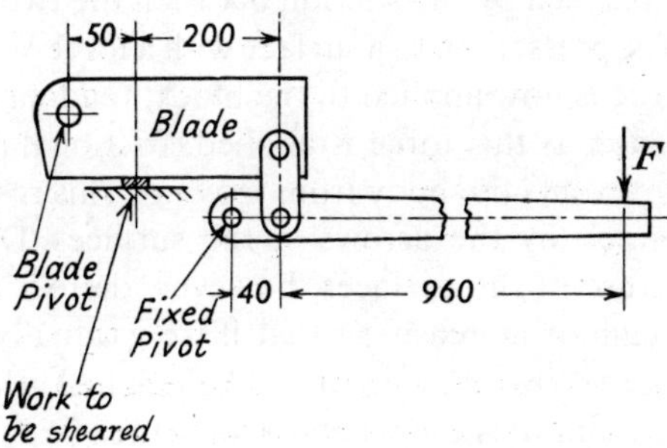

Fig. 135

8. A bench shearing machine is shown diagrammatically at Fig. 135. If the shearing strength of steel is 400 N/mm², what force F must be applied to shear a piece of material 10 mm × 2·5 mm?

7 Mechanical principles – II

Friction

Friction plays such an important part in a workshop that the calculations connected with it are worthy of some consideration. If we press two surfaces together and attempt to slide one over the other, a resistance is encountered, and this is caused by the friction between the two surfaces.

Let us consider a block pressed on to a surface with a force W as shown in Fig. 136. Another force is now applied to the block, tending to slide it from left to right. As soon as this force is applied, frictional resistance comes into action and prevents the body from moving. This resistance is denoted by f and indicated by the arrows at the surfaces. Depending upon W, and on the nature of the surfaces, however, there is a limiting value beyond which f cannot increase, so that if we gradually increase the force tending to slide the block, a point will be reached at which the block will just be on the point of sliding. Let the force then be F, and since the block is just about to slide $F = f$, the frictional resistance. The block at this point is being acted upon by three forces: (1) W downwards, (2) F horizontal, (3) the reaction of the other surface (say R). The vector diagram is shown drawn in Fig. 136 at *abc*.

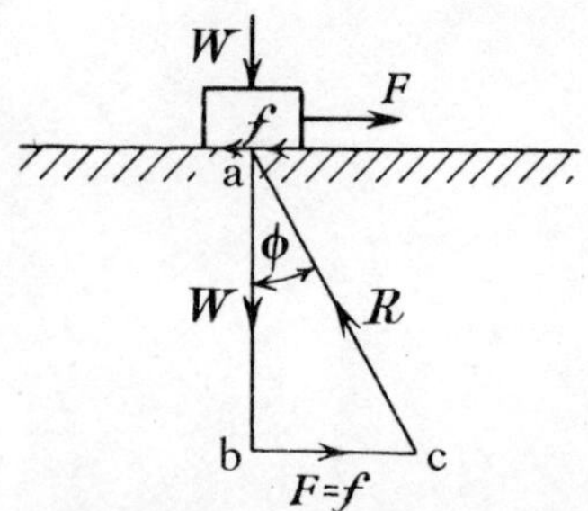

Fig. 136

We mentioned earlier, that when friction is neglected the reaction between two surfaces is normal to their common tangent or along *ab* in Fig. 136. It will now be seen that when friction is allowed for, the reaction moves round so as to oppose motion, and its line makes an angle ϕ with the normal line to the surfaces.

This angle ϕ is called the Friction Angle and it will be noticed that

$$\tan \phi = \frac{F}{W} = \frac{\text{Frictional force}}{\text{Pressure between surfaces}}$$

The ratio $\frac{F}{W}$ is called the Coefficient of Friction and is usually denoted by μ.

$$\mu = \frac{F}{W}$$

Thus if $\frac{F}{W} = \tan \phi$ and also $= \mu$

then

$$\mu = \tan \phi.$$

[The reader will appreciate the fact that the reaction R between the surfaces moves round to some angular position, and is directed in such a way as to oppose motion, if he considers where and in which direction it would act in the event of a definite step being raised in front of the block.]

Approximate Values for the Coefficient of Friction

Nature of surfaces in contact		μ (Coefficient).
Cast iron on cast iron	(dry)	0·15
Steel on cast iron	(dry)	0·20
Steel on brass	(dry)	0·15
Cast iron on oak	(dry)	0·49
Steel on leather	(dry)	0·56
Steel on leather	(greasy)	0·23
Oak on oak	(dry)	0·40
Leather on oak	(dry)	0·33
Ferodo bonded asbestos on steel		0·3– 0·4

[Values of μ depend to some extent upon the pressure between the surfaces and upon the speed of sliding.]

Clamping of work

Almost all methods of clamping in the shop depend for their hold upon the frictional resistance between the two surfaces being clamped. This applies to work clamped to machine tables, in lathe chucks, work held in vices, and so on.

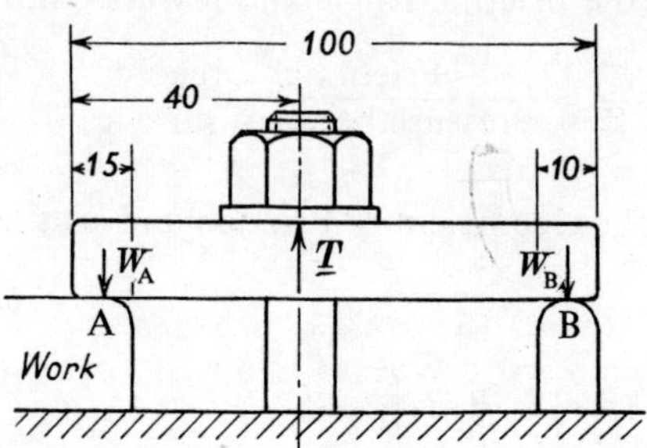

Fig. 137

Example 1. A casting is clamped to a shaping machine table by 4 clamps arranged as shown in Fig. 137. If the cutting pressure at the tool causes a thrust of 4500N against the work and if the coefficient of friction between the work and the table is 0·15, what is the least tension to which the bolts be tightened in order that the job may not move under the pressure of the cut.

If the sliding force to be resisted is 4500N and $\mu = 0{\cdot}15$, the surfaces must be pressed together with a force of $\dfrac{4500\,\text{N}}{0{\cdot}15} = 30\,000\,\text{N}$

Each clamp must therefore exert a pressure of $\dfrac{30\,000}{4} = 7500\,\text{N}$

In Fig. 137 the forces exerted by the clamp are shown and T = tension in bolt, W_A and W_B = Pressure exerted on work and packing respectively.

We will assume that W_A and W_B act at the centre of the length being clamped as shown. Then from W_A to the centre of the bolt will be $40 - 7{\cdot}5 = 32{\cdot}5$ mm and from W_B 60 mm − 5 mm = 55 mm.

Taking moments about B and working in units of N and mm, we have

$$\text{Clockwise moment} = T \times 55$$
$$\text{Contra-clock moment} = W_A(55 + 32{\cdot}5) = 87{\cdot}5\, W_A\,.$$

But W_A must be 7500N from above, so that putting in this value and equating the moments we have

$$55T = 87{\cdot}5 \times 7500$$
$$T = \frac{87{\cdot}5 \times 7500}{55} = \underline{12\,000\,\text{N}}$$

Example 2. A milling cutter is tightened up between the collars on the arbor and is driven by the friction between itself and the collars. If the

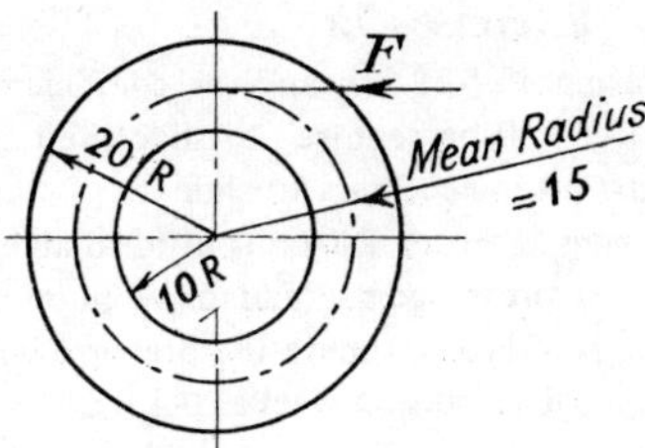

Fig. 138

collars are 20 mm bore and 40 mm outside diameter, calculate the tightening force necessary if the cutter is not to slip when 3·3 kW is being absorbed at 70 rev/min [Coeff of friction = 0·15.]

If T newton metres is the torque to tbe transmitted, we have

$$\text{Power} = T \text{ newton metres/second} = T\omega \text{ Watts}$$

also $$\text{Power} = 3{\cdot}3\,\text{kW} = 3300\,W,$$

Now $$N = 70 \text{ rev/min}$$

so that $$\omega = \frac{70 \times 2\pi}{60} = \frac{22}{3} \text{ rad/s}$$

$$T = \frac{\text{Power}}{\omega} = \frac{3300 \times 3}{22} = 450\,\text{Nm}$$

This torque must be transmitted by the friction between the collars and the cutter, and slip when it takes place, must occur at two faces:

Hence torque transmitted per face $= \dfrac{450}{2} = 225\,\text{N m}$

This torque will be developed by a tangential frictional force F which we will assume to act at the mean radius of the collars (Fig. 138).

Hence $$\text{Mean radius} = \frac{30\,\text{mm}}{2} = 15\,\text{mm} = 0{\cdot}015\,\text{m}$$

$$T = Fr,\ F = \frac{T}{r} = \frac{225\,\text{N}}{0{\cdot}015\,\text{m}} = 15\,000\,\text{N}$$

Now if W = Force between the collars

$$\frac{F}{W} = \mu, \text{ i.e. } \frac{15\,000}{W} = 0{\cdot}15$$

$$W = \frac{15\,000}{0{\cdot}15} = 100\,000\,\text{N}$$

Exercises 7a

1. The tailstock of a lathe has a mass of 21.5kg and the coefficient of friction at the slides is 0·122. What horizontal force will be required to slide the tailstock? Determine the amount and direction of the *least* force necessary to slide it.

2. A disc 240 mm diameter has a ring of ferodo 240 mm outside diameter and 20 mm wide riveted to one face. This is made to press against and drive another steel disc. If the turning moment to be transmitted is 33 N m estimate the pressure with which the discs have to be pressed together. [Take μ for ferodo on steel as 0·4.]

3. A planing machine is taking a cut on a casting bolted directly to the table. The force of the cut is 7400N and the job is clamped by four clamps. If the coefficient of friction between the casting and the machine table is 0·15, what force must be exerted on the work by each clamp to prevent the work from sliding under the force of the cut?

4. A 300 mm diameter brake drum is attached to a shaft the driving pulley of which is 200 mm diameter. When two leather-faced brake blocks are pressed against opposite sides of the drum with a force of 200N what force must be applied to the rim of the pulley to turn the shaft. [Take μ for leather on cast iron as 0·45.]

5. The table of a planing machine with weight equivalent to 5000N is supporting a casting which exerts a similar force of 2000N. If the average speed of the table is 0·2 m/s and for half the time a downward cutting force of 800N is acting, calculate the average power required to overcome friction at the table slides. [Take μ = 0·08.]

6. A block is clampted between the jaws of a milling-machine vice, the force at the jaws being 12 000N. If the cutter operating on this is 80 mm diameter and its speed 52·5 rev/min, calculate the approximate power being absorbed when the work is caused to slip in the jaws of the vice by the force of the cut. [Take μ at the vice jaws as 0·15.]

Machines and efficiency

A machine is a contrivance for receiving energy in some form and converting it into energy of a type more suitable for the purpose required. Most of the energy available in a machine shop is in the form of rotational energy (line shafting, rotation of driving motors, etc.). A machine, such as a shaper, receives some of this rotational energy at its pulley, and converts part of it into the energy contained in the backwards and forwards movement of the ram and part into the various other movements required to transverse the tool across the work.

Each element of a machine may be regarded as a little machine in itself. For example, in the mechanism for elevating the knee of a milling machine a torque is applied to the handle, and this torque is converted into the rotation of a nut or screw. This in its turn raises or lowers the table and cross-slide on the vertical slides. An electric motor is just as much a machine as any other, for it takes in electrical energy from the mains and converts it to rotational energy at its driving pulley.

For mechanical machines:

the *Effort* is the force applied at the input end of the machine,
and the *Load* is the resistance overcome at the output end.

The ratio $\frac{\text{Load}}{\text{Effort}}$ is called the *Mechanical Advantage* of the machine and the ratio $\frac{\text{Distance moved by Effort}}{\text{Distance moved by Load}}$ in the same time, is called the *Velocity Ratio* of the machine.

If we called the effort E, and the load W:

The work input will be E (Distance moved) and the output in the same time $= W$ (Distance moved).

The *Efficiency* of the machine will be $\frac{\text{Output}}{\text{Input}}$

$$= \frac{W\,(\text{Distance moved})}{E\,(\text{Distance moved})}$$

But $$\frac{W}{E} = \text{Mechanical Advantage}$$

and $$\frac{\text{Distance moved by } W}{\text{Distance moved by } E} = \frac{1}{\text{Velocity Ratio}}$$

Hence $$\text{Efficiency} = \frac{\text{Mechanical Advantage}}{\text{Velocity Ratio}}$$

If the efficiency were unity, the Mechanical Advantage would be the same as the Velocity Ratio. Actually the efficiency is always less than 1 due to frictional losses, so that the Mechanical Advantage is always less than the Velocity Ratio.

Example 3. The knee, cross-slide and table of a milling machine have a total mass of 600 kg, and it is found that a force of 60 N must be applied at the end of the 210 mm elevating handle to raise the knee. One turn of the handle raises the knee 2 mm.

Calculate the Mechanical Advantage, Velocity Ratio and Efficiency of this mechanism.

$$\text{Effort } (E) = 60\,\text{N}$$
$$\text{Load } (W) = mg = 600 \times 9{\cdot}81 = 5886\,\text{N}$$
$$\text{Mech Advantage} = \frac{5886}{60} = 98$$

$$\text{Velocity Ratio} = \frac{\text{Distance moved by effort}}{\text{Distance moved by load}}$$
$$= \frac{2\pi \times 210\,\text{mm}}{2\,\text{mm}} = 660$$
$$\text{Efficiency} = \frac{\text{Mech. Adv.}}{\text{Vel. Ratio}} = \frac{98}{660} = 0{\cdot}148 = 14{\cdot}8\%$$

Example 4. When disengaged from the operating mechanism a grinding machine table can be pushed along by a force of 40 N. With the mechanism engaged, a torque of 0·35 N m at the traversing wheel is required to move it. One turn of the wheel moves the table a distance of 10 mm. Find the efficiency of the traversing mechanism.

The load on the mechanism = resistance of the table = 40 N

If 1 turn of the handwheel moves the table 10 mm work done on the load in 1 turn

$$= 40\,\text{N} \times 10\,\text{mm} = 40\,\text{N} \times 0{\cdot}010\,\text{m}$$
$$= 0{\cdot}4\,\text{N m} = \text{output}$$

Work done by a torque of 0·35 N m in 1 turn

$$= 2\pi \times 0{\cdot}35\,\text{N m} = 2{\cdot}2\,\text{N m} = \text{input}$$
$$\text{Efficiency} = \frac{\text{Output}}{\text{Input}} = \frac{0{\cdot}4}{2{\cdot}2} = 0{\cdot}182 = 18{\cdot}2\%$$

The inclined plane

We have seen in previous work (Fig. 78a) that a screw thread is an inclined plane wrapped round a cylinder. In order to study the mechanics of the screw, therefore, we must give some attention to the inclined plane. We find that in doing this friction plays an important part and its effects must be allowed for.

Tightening up

When a nut is being tightened up under a load W, the conditions are equivalent to pushing a weight W up an inclined plane sloping at the helix angle of the screw. The force F which is pushing W is the tangential force at the mean radius of the screw and is being applied in a horizontal direction. This is shown in Figs. 139 and 140.

Now if there were no friction between the block and the plane the

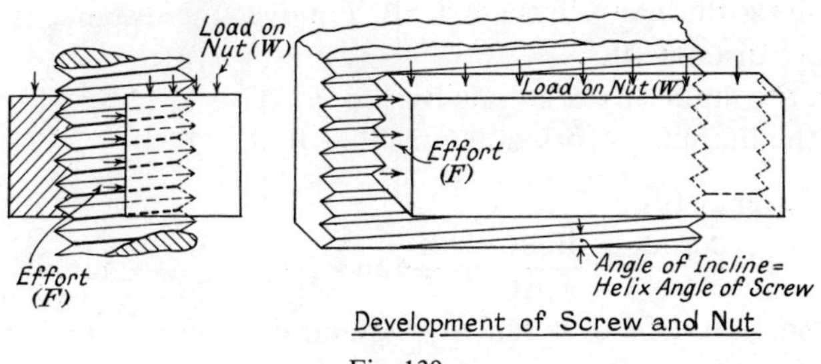

Fig. 139

vector diagram for the forces acting on the block would be as *abc*; *ab* = weight of block acting downwards, *bc* = *F*, the force to pushing it up the plane and *ca* = the reaction between the plane and the block. We have seen, however, that when friction is present, the reaction *R* is no longer perpendicular to the surfaces, but is rotated round through the friction angle ϕ in the direction to oppose motion. Hence the vector for *R* will be rotated round to *ad*, and the force *F* required to push the block up the plane will become = *bd*.

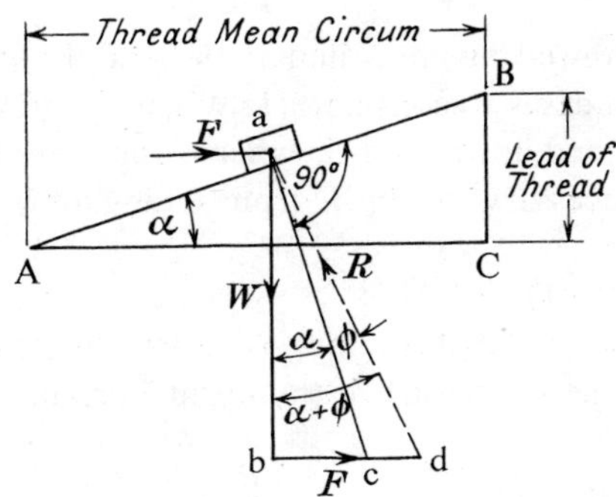

Fig. 140

$$\text{Now } \frac{bd}{ab} = \tan \widehat{bad} = \tan(\alpha + \phi)$$

$$\therefore \frac{F}{W} = \tan(\alpha + \phi) \text{ and } F = W \tan(\alpha + \phi) \qquad (1)$$

In pushing the block from A to B, F moves the distance AC and W is raised to distance BC.

Hence the input = work done by F = F.AC
and the output = work done on W = W.BC

The efficiency (η)

$$= \frac{\text{output}}{\text{input}} \quad \frac{W.\text{BC}}{F.\text{AC}} = \frac{W}{F}\tan\alpha \quad \left[\text{since } \frac{\text{BC}}{\text{AC}} = \tan\alpha\right]$$

But from above: $F = W\tan(\alpha + \phi)$ and if we substitute this for F we have

$$\eta = \frac{W}{F}\tan\alpha = \frac{W\tan\alpha}{W\tan(\alpha + \phi)}$$

$$= \frac{\tan\alpha}{\tan(\alpha + \phi)} \qquad (2)$$

$$\alpha = \text{Helix angle of screw, i.e. } \tan\alpha = \frac{\text{Lead}}{\text{Mean circum}}$$

$$\phi = \text{Friction Angle. } \operatorname{Tan}\phi = \mu$$

This is an expression for the efficiency of a screw when tightening up and is in terms of μ and the helix angle of the screw.

Loosening

When a nut is being unscrewed it is equivalent to the load W moving down the plane. There are two cases to consider: (1) When ϕ is greater than α and the load must be pushed down, and (2) when α is greater than ϕ and a push *up* the plane is necessary to stop W from sliding down of its own accord.

(1) ϕ greater than α (Fig. 141).

As motion is now taking place in the opposite direction, the reaction line *ad* swings round to the other side of the normal *ac*, and the vector

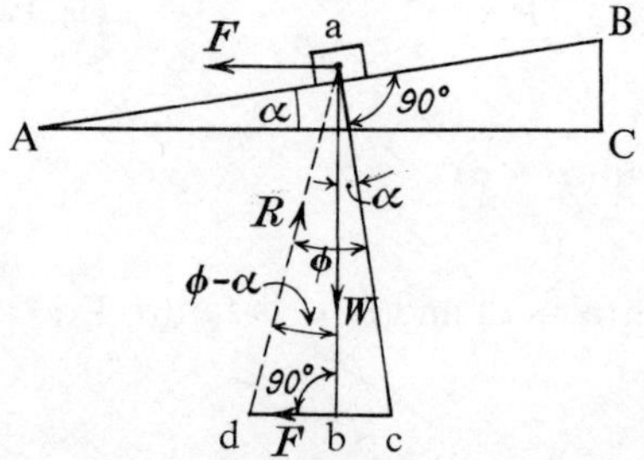

Fig. 141

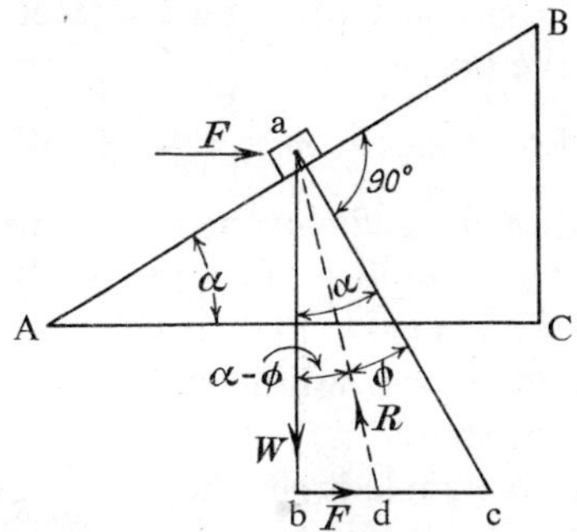

Fig. 142

diagram is *abd*. In this case since ϕ is greater than α, *ad* swings round to a position to the left of *ab*.

Force required at mean radius to unscrew nut

$$= F = db = ab \tan \widehat{bad}$$
$$= W \tan (\phi - \alpha) \quad (3)$$

(2) α greater than ϕ (Fig. 142).

In this case a force = *bd* will be required to hold the nut from unscrewing.

$$F = bd = \text{ab} \tan(\alpha - \phi)$$
$$= W \tan(\alpha - \phi) \quad (4)$$

Vee threads

The above reasoning for screw threads assumes that W is the normal load on the thread surfaces. Whilst this is true for a square thread [Fig. 143 (*a*)], when a vertical load W is applied to a vee thread the force is resolved into components as shown by the vector diagram *abc* shown at (*b*).

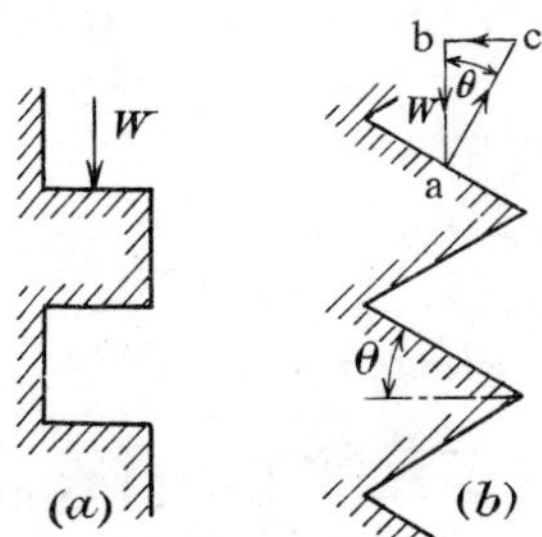

Fig. 143

The normal load on the thread surface is now the length *ac*, whilst *bc* is the force tending to burst the nut.

Hence normal load on thread face $= ac = \dfrac{W}{\cos\theta} = W\sec\theta$.

As the frictional resistance depends on the normal pressure we may modify our previous formulae to apply it to vee threads by modifying the value of the coefficient of friction (μ).

If, instead of taking μ we take for it a value equal to $\mu\sec\theta$, we may use the previous formulae as they stand.

For a metric thread, the vee-angle is 60°, hence $\theta = 30°$ and $\sec\theta = 1{\cdot}155$.

Hence for a metric thread take a modified value for the coefficient of friction equal to $1{\cdot}155\mu$.

Friction at a nut face

In addition to the friction at the threads, friction at the nut face must be allowed for.

Let $W =$ load on nut
$\mu =$ coefficient of friction
$r =$ mean radius of nut.

Then frictional force at nut face $= \mu W$.

Torque necessary to overcome this $=$ (force)(radius) $= \mu Wr$

Example 5. A screw-operated arbor press has a square-threaded screw 50 mm dia 5 mm pitch single start. If the coefficient of friction at the threads is 0·10, what load may be applied by the press when an effort of 200 N is applied at the end of a handle 200 mm long attached to the screw.

Since $\tan\phi = \mu$; $\tan\phi = 0{\cdot}1$ and the friction angle $(\phi) = 5°43'$

The mean circumference of the thread $= \pi(50 - 2{\cdot}5) = 47{\cdot}5\pi = 149{\cdot}2$ mm

If α is the helix angle of the thread

$$\tan\alpha = \frac{\text{Lead}}{\text{Circum}} = \frac{5}{149{\cdot}2} = 0{\cdot}0335$$

from which $\alpha = 1°55'$

The mean radius of the screw $= \dfrac{47{\cdot}5\text{ mm}}{2} = 23{\cdot}75$ mm so that a force of

200 N at 200 mm radius will be equivalent to a force $\frac{200 \times 200\,\text{N}}{23{\cdot}75}$ at 23·75 mm radius = 1684 N. This is the force F up the inclined plane.

Now
$$F = W\tan(\alpha + \phi)\text{(Fig. 140)}$$
$$= W\tan(1°55' + 5°43')$$
$$= W\tan 7°38' = W \times 0{\cdot}1340$$
$$W = \frac{F}{0{\cdot}1340} = \frac{1684}{0{\cdot}134} = \underline{12\,600\,\text{N}}$$

Example 6. A machine slide weighing 255 kgf (2500 N) is elevated by a 2-start acme thread (29° thread angle) 40 mm dia, 4 mm pitch. If the coefficient of friction is 0·12, calculate the torque necessary (*a*) to raise the slide, (*b*) to lower it. The end of the screw is carried on a thrust collar, 32 mm inside and 56 mm outside diameter.

$$\text{Mean dia of thread} = 40\,\text{mm} - 2\,\text{mm} = 38\,\text{mm}$$
$$\text{Mean circum} = 38\pi = 119{\cdot}4\,\text{mm}$$
$$\text{Lead} = 2 \times 4\,\text{mm} = 8\,\text{mm}$$

If α = helix angle $\tan\alpha = \frac{8}{119{\cdot}4} = 0{\cdot}0670$
$$\alpha = 3°\,50'$$

Since the thread half angle = $14\frac{1}{2}°$ we have to use a modified coefficent of friction = $0{\cdot}12 \sec 14\frac{1}{2}°$

$$= 0{\cdot}12 \times 1{\cdot}033 = 0{\cdot}124$$
$$\tan\phi = 0{\cdot}124 \text{ and } \phi = 7°\,4'$$

To raise the load we have if F = force at the mean radius
$$F = W\tan(\alpha + \phi) = 2500\tan(3°\,50' + 7°\,4')$$
$$= 2500\tan 10°54' = 2500 \times 0{\cdot}1926 = 481{\cdot}5\,\text{N}$$

The torque will be F (radius at which it acts)
$$= F \times \frac{38\,\text{mm}}{2} = F \times 0{\cdot}019\,\text{m} = 481{\cdot}5\,\text{N} \times 0{\cdot}019\,\text{m} = 9{\cdot}15\,\text{N m}$$

To this torque must be added the friction torque at the thrust collar.

$$\text{Frictional force} = 2500\mu = 2500 \times 0{\cdot}12 = 300\,\text{N}$$
$$\text{Frictional torque} = 300 \text{ (mean rad of collar)}$$
$$= 300 \times \frac{44\,\text{mm}}{2} = 300\,\text{N} \times 0{\cdot}022\,\text{m} = 6{\cdot}6\,\text{N m}$$
$$\text{Total torque to raise slide} = 9{\cdot}15\,\text{N m} + 6{\cdot}6\,\text{N m} = \underline{15{\cdot}75\,\text{N m}}$$

$$\text{To lower the load } F = W\tan(\phi - \alpha) \text{ (Fig. 141)}$$
$$= 2500\tan(7°4' - 3°50')$$
$$= 2500\tan 3°14' = 2500 \times 0{\cdot}0565 = 141{\cdot}25\,\text{N}$$
$$\text{Torque} = 141{\cdot}25\,\text{N} \times 0{\cdot}019\,\text{m} = 2{\cdot}68\,\text{N m}$$

Adding the friction torque at the collar we have
Total Torque to lower the slide = 2·68 N m + 6·6 N m = 9·48 N m.

Friction of sliding keys

It is often necessary in machine-tool construction to slide a collar or wheel along a shaft at the same time as the wheel is being driven by the shaft through one or two sliding keys. The force required to slide the collar or wheel along the shaft is worthy of consideration as it is affected by the disposition of the keys.

In Fig. 144(*a*) the key is fixed in the shaft which rotates in the direction of the arrow and drives the outer part. Clearances have been exaggerated and it will be seen that the torque is transmitted by a force F at the key and a similar force W acting at the circumference of the shaft. If r is the radius to the centre of the key as shown, and T is the torque being transmitted, then $T = Fr$ and $F = \frac{T}{r}$

The force required to slide the outer member along the shaft will be $F\mu + W\mu = 2F\mu$ (since $F = W$).

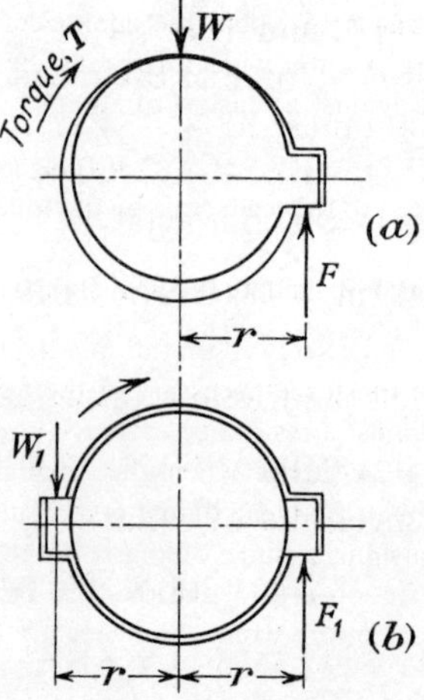

Fig. 144

In Fig. 144 (*b*) there are two keys, and if they are well fitted so that each takes an equal share of the load, the torque is given by $T = F_1r + W_1r = F_1(2r)$ [since $F_1 = W_1$].

Hence $F_1 = \frac{T}{2r}$, which is half the force for the case of Fig. 144 (*a*).

Force to slide outer member along the shaft $= F_1\mu + W_1\mu = 2F_1\mu$, which is half of that for the case of Fig. 144 (*a*).

Exercises 7b

1. In a hand crane a 20T gear attached to the handle drives an 85T gear on the rope drum. The radius of the drum to the centre of the rope is 35 mm. If the handle is 300 mm long, calculate the velocity ratio. If the efficiency is 75%, what force must be applied to the handle to raise a load of 250 kg on the rope?

2. A chain conveyor carries goods up an incline of 28° at a speed of 0·2 m/s. If the average mass of the articles carried is 20 kg, and they are spaced at 300 mm centres, calculate the power necessary to drive the loaded conveyor if its efficiency is 75%, the incline carries 60 articles, and 0·4 kW is necessary to overcome friction.

3. The saddle of a lathe is equivalent to a weight of 1600 N and 1 turn of the traversing wheel moves it 100 mm along the bed. If the efficiency of the traversing gear is 0·7 and the coefficient of friction at the slides 0·10, calculate the force necessary at the rim of a 140 mm wheel to move the saddle.

4. A flypress has a screw of 50 mm lead, the efficiency of which is 60%. Neglecting the weight of the screw and top arm, what force must be applied at the end of and perpendicular to the level of 280 mm radius to put a force of 2500 N on the ram?

5. Calculate the efficiency of a 20 mm square-threaded screw of 5 mm pitch 2 start if the coefficient of friction at the threads is 0·080. What tension may be exerted on this screw by a nut if 120 N is applied at the end of a 350 mm spanner? [Neglect friction at the nut face.]

6. The efficiency of a screw and nut is 15%, and the coefficient of friction at the nut face is 0·1. If the lead of the thread is 2 mm what force must be applied to the end of a 240 mm wrench to pull up the nut against a tension of 8000 N? [Mean radius of nut = 15 mm.]

7. The spindle of a lathe is connected to the leadscrew by the following gears: $\frac{\text{Drivers}}{\text{Driven}} = \frac{30}{50} \times \frac{20}{45}$. If the leadscrew is 5 mm pitch, calculate the velocity ratio between the carriage and a point on the rim of an 160 mm chuck screwed on the spindle. If the overall efficiency of the arrangement is 10%, calculate the force necessary at the rim of the chuck to turn the lathe and traverse the carriage against a resistance of 200 N.

8. Calculate the efficiency of a M24 thread when the coefficient of friction at the threads is 0·08. [For the M24 thread take the mean diameter as 22 mm and the pitch 3 mm.]

9. Calculate the work done in pushing a slide of mass 100 kg up an inclined plane sloping at 30°, if the coefficient of friction is 0·15, the plane is 3 m long, and the push is applied horizontally. What horizontal effort would be necessary to hold the slide from moving down the plane?

10. A wheel slides along a shaft and is driven by a sliding key. If the shaft is 45 mm diameter and the key projects 5 mm from the circumference, calculate the force necessary to slide the wheel along the shaft when 6·6 kW is being transmitted at 315 rev/min and $\mu = 0{\cdot}15$.

12. If the shaft in the last example were fitted with two opposite keys projecting the same amount as before, calculate the torque being transmitted when an axial force of 60 N is required to slide the outer member along the shaft. [$\mu = 0{\cdot}15$.]

Bearings

The main function of a bearing is to hold and line up the shaft it carries and support the load to which the shaft is subjected. Bearings are generally designed on the basis of the load carried per unit of projected area, and if the length and diameter of a bearing are l and d respectively, the projected area will be $l \times d$ (Fig. 145).

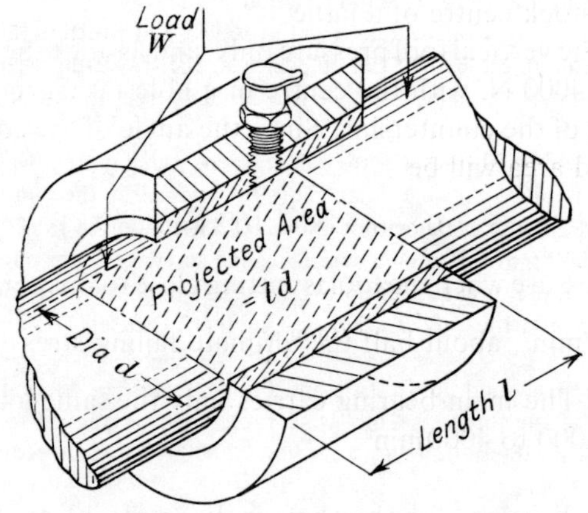

Fig. 145

If the load on the shaft = W, the intensity of bearing pressure (p) will be $\frac{\text{Load}}{\text{Area}}$

$$p = \frac{W}{ld}$$

The pressure to which bearings may be subjected in practice depends upon various factors, including the speed, method of lubrication, duration of full load operation, materials in contact, and so on.

The following table conveys an idea of bearing pressures used:

Table of Bearing Pressures

Type of Bearing	Allowable Pressure N/mm^2
Line-shafting (bronze lined)	0·7– 1·0
High-speed engines: Main bearings	1·0– 2·0
Crank pins	2·0– 4·0
Gas engines: Main bearings	3·5– 5·0
Crank pins	10 –12·5
Punching and shearing machines (low speed intermittent loading)	15 –30
Horizontal turbines	0·3– 0·5

Probably the most severely loaded bearing in the whole of engineering practice is the tailstock centre of a lathe.

Let us consider the vertical tool pressure only, and assume the moderate case of a load of 4000 N, with the centre in a hole measuring 5 mm at the large diameter of the countersink. Since the angle of the countersink is 60° the projected area will be

$$\tfrac{1}{2} \times 5 \times 0{\cdot}866 \times 5 = 10{\cdot}8\,\text{mm}^2$$

and the bearing pressure when the tool is cutting close to this centre will be $\frac{4000\text{N}}{10{\cdot}8\,\text{mm}^2} = 370\ \text{N/mm}^2$, about half the ultimate failing stress of a good quality mild steel! The main bearing carries only the same load with an area of probably 3000 to 4000 mm^2.

Example 7. If the bearings for the shaft in Example 12, p. 171 are to be proportioned so that their length shall be $2\frac{1}{2}$ times the diameter, calculate their dimensions if the bearing pressure is not to exceed $0{\cdot}4\,\text{N/mm}^2$.

The biggest load to be carried = 460 N

If $L = 2\tfrac{1}{2}d,\ L \times d = 2\tfrac{1}{2}d \times d = 2\tfrac{1}{2}d^2 =$ Area of bearing.

$$\text{But area of bearing} = \frac{\text{Load}}{\text{Pressure}} = \frac{460}{0{\cdot}4} = 1150\,\text{mm}^2$$

Hence

$$2\tfrac{1}{2}d^2 = 1150$$

$$d^2 = \frac{1150}{2{\cdot}5} = 460\,\text{mm}^2$$

$$d = \sqrt{460} = 21{\cdot}5\,\text{mm}$$
$$L = 2\tfrac{1}{2} \times 21{\cdot}5 = \underline{53{\cdot}8\,\text{mm}}$$

Bearing friction

When a bearing is properly lubricated the two metals forming it are not in contact but are separated by a thin film of oil. The friction now is not that of one metal rubbing on another but is the internal friction of the lubricant itself. It has been found experimentally that the coefficient of friction in a bearing with film lubrication depends upon the rubbing speed and upon the pressure, and the relation between them is

$$\mu = \frac{K\sqrt{v}}{p},$$

where μ = coeff. of friction
v = surface speed of shaft in m/s
p = bearing pressure in N/mm² (i.e. MN/m²)
K = a Constant = 0·032 for the usual oils.

Work lost in bearing friction

The effect of friction in a bearing is to introduce a tangential resistance at the periphery of the shaft. If W = load on the bearing and μ = coefficient of friction, then the tangential resistance will be $W = \mu$. Calling this resistance F, we have $F = W\mu$ (Fig. 146).

The work lost per second will be Fv
and the power lost = Fv watts

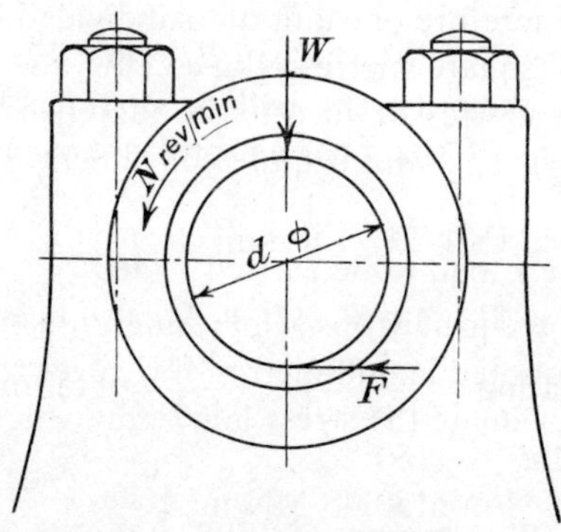

Fig. 146

Example 8. A 50 mm dia shaft running at 525 rev/min carries a load of 8000 N. The bearing is 100 mm long. Estimate (*a*) the coefficient of friction, (*b*) the tangential friction resistance, and (*c*) the power lost in friction.

We have that $\mu = \dfrac{0{\cdot}032\sqrt{v}}{p}$

$$v = \frac{\pi dN}{60\,000} = \frac{22 \times 50 \times 525}{7 \times 60\,000} = 1{\cdot}375\,\text{m/s}$$

$$\text{Bearing pressure } (p) = \frac{8000}{50 \times 100} = 1{\cdot}6\,\text{N/mm}^2$$

$$\mu = \frac{0{\cdot}032 \times \sqrt{1{\cdot}375}}{1{\cdot}6} = \frac{0{\cdot}032 \times 1{\cdot}172}{1{\cdot}6} = \underline{0{\cdot}0234}$$

Tangential frictional resistance $= 0{\cdot}0234 \times 8000$
$= 187$ N

Power lost in friction $= 187\text{ N} \times 1{\cdot}378$ m/s
$= \underline{257\text{ W}}$

Stress and strain

A material is placed in a state of stress when a load acts upon it, and the numerical value of the stress is given by

$$\frac{\text{Load acting}}{\text{Area subjected to load}} = \frac{F}{A}, \text{ when } F = \text{Load, and } A = \text{Area}$$

The SI unit of stress is therefore one unit of load divided by one unit of area, i.e. the newton per square metre (N/m^2). This unit is very small for practical purposes and so stresses will often be quoted in meganewtons per square metre (MN/m^2). This unit is quite convenient, since

$$1\,\text{MN/m}^2 = 1\,\text{N/mm}^2$$

and as loads are often quoted in newtons, while dimensions of engineering components are usually quoted in millimetres, if we ever require a stress in MN/m^2 it is useful to evaluate the stress in N/mm^2, e.g.

$$45\text{ N/mm}^2 = 45\text{ MN/m}^2.$$

It is possible that the unit adopted for fluid pressure will be the *bar*, a unit inherited from the previous metric system. In some ways this is a more convenient unit since it utilises the cm^2 as the unit of area.

$$1 \text{ bar (b)} = \text{da N/cm}^2 = 10 \text{ N/cm}^2$$
$$1 \text{ hectobar (hb)} = 10^3 \text{N/cm}^2$$

As a mental landmark, the bar is very near to atmospheric pressure:

$$1 \text{ bar} = 10 \text{ N/cm}^2 \qquad 1 \text{ atm} = 10{\cdot}13 \text{ N/cm}^2$$

The weight of a body is the effect of gravity on its mass. The effect of gravity on a mass of m kilogrammes can be taken as,

$$\text{weight} = \text{mass} \times \text{acceleration due to gravity}$$
$$= \text{mass} \times 9{\cdot}81 \text{ newtons.}$$

As we discussed in Chapter 1, the reader will find, in his normal life, that the mass of 1 kilogramme is referred to as "weight" or a kilogramme of mass and written 1 kg, with the inference of weight.

In our work it is sometimes expedient to express the weight of 1 kg of mass in its kg form and when doing this it should be written kgf. At the same time it should be remembered that 1 kgf = 9·81 newtons.

When materials are stressed they change their shape: for example, a bar will lengthen under tension or shorten under compression. This change of shape is called *strain*. We usually express the strain in terms of the natural length of the material, so that if a bar 100 mm long is subjected to tension and stretches 0·1 mm, the strain is expressed as $\frac{0{\cdot}1}{100} = 0{\cdot}001$.

Within certain limits the materials with which we have to deal behave in an elastic manner, i.e. the deformation caused by a load vanishes when the load is removed. If, however, the load on a bar is gradually increased, a point is reached beyond which the material will not return to its original shape when the load is removed. This point is called the *Elastic Limit* of the material. For most materials it has been found that within the elastic limit the change in length is proportional to the load producing it: e.g. if 1000 N causes an elongation of 0·05 mm, 2000 will cause 0·10 mm, and so on. Hence we may say that within the elastic limit:

Stretch is proportional to Load

or, since for the same bar, strain is proportional to stretch and stress to load:

Strain is proportional to Stress.

This is the same thing as saying: $\dfrac{\text{Stress}}{\text{Strain}} = \text{a constant quantity}$

This constant quantity is called *Young's Modulus*, and has a particular value for every material. It is usually denoted by the letter E. For steel E has a value of about 200 000 N/mm^2.

It is difficult at first to visualize and to appreciate what E = 200 000 N/mm^2 signifies. The following way of considering it might help the reader:

$\dfrac{\text{Stress}}{\text{Strain}}$ means *Stress per unit Strain* and a material would have unit strain if its length were doubled.

(Original length = 1; Stretch = 1; Strain = $\frac{1}{1}$)

If, then, a material could remain elastic whilst its length were doubled under a load, the stress in the material would have the value *E*.

Example 9. A 20 mm bolt 160 mm long carries a load of 20 kN. Calculate the extension in the bolt if $E = 200\,000\,\text{N/mm}^2$.

$$\text{Stress in the bolt} = \frac{\text{Load}}{\text{Area}} = \frac{20\,000}{\frac{\pi}{4}(20)^2} = \frac{20000}{314{\cdot}2} = 63{\cdot}7\ \text{N/mm}^2$$

$$\text{Strain} = \frac{\text{Extension}}{\text{Orig. length}} = \frac{\text{Ext}}{160}$$

$$E = \frac{\text{Stress}}{\text{Strain}}$$

$$E = 200\,000 \qquad \text{Stress } 63{\cdot}7$$

$$\therefore 200000 = \frac{63{\cdot}7}{\frac{\text{Ext}}{160}} = \frac{63{\cdot}7 \times 160}{\text{Ext}}$$

$$\text{Extension} = \frac{63{\cdot}7 \times 160}{200\,000} = \underline{0{\cdot}051\ \text{mm}}$$

Example 10. A 20 mm steel bolt is threaded through a brass sleeve 100 mm long, 24 mm bore and 32 mm outside diameter. A nut and washer are put on and the nut tightened up until the brass sleeve has shortened by 0·05 mm. Calculate the extension in the bolt.

E for steel = 200 000 N/mm² $\qquad$ E for brass = 80 000 N/mm²

$$\text{Strain in sleeve} = \frac{0{\cdot}05}{100} = 0{\cdot}0005$$

and since $E = \dfrac{\text{Stress}}{\text{Strain}}$: Stress = E(Strain) = 80 000 × 0·0005 = 40N/mm²

$$\text{Stress in sleeve} = 40\ \text{N/mm}^2$$

$$\text{Cross-sectional area of sleeve} = \frac{\pi}{4}(32^2 - 24^2) = \frac{22}{28}(1024 - 576)$$

$$= \frac{22 \times 448}{28} = 352\,\text{mm}^2$$

Hence compressive load carried by sleeve = (Stress)(Area)
= 40 × 352 = 14 080 N

This will be equal to the tension in the bolt.

$$\text{Hence stress in bolt} = \frac{14\,080}{\frac{\pi}{4}(20)^2} = \frac{14\,080}{314{\cdot}2} = 44{\cdot}8\,\text{N/mm}^2$$

$$E = \frac{\text{Stress}}{\text{Strain}} \text{ and Strain} = \frac{\text{Stress}}{E} = \frac{44{\cdot}8}{200\,000}$$

But
$$\text{strain} = \frac{\text{Extension}}{\text{Orig Length}} = \frac{\text{Ext}}{100}$$

$$\therefore \frac{\text{Ext}}{100} = \frac{44{\cdot}8}{200\,000}$$

$$\text{Ext} = \frac{100 \times 44{\cdot}8}{200\,000} = 0{\cdot}0224\,\text{mm}$$

$$\text{Extension of bolt} = \underline{0{\cdot}0224\,\text{mm}}$$

Exercises 7c

1. A bearing has to carry a load of 3000N, with a bearing pressure of 0·75N/mm². If the length of the bearing is to be made equal to twice its diameter determine its dimensions.

2. A 50mm diameter shaft runs in two bearings spaced at 2·5 m centres, the bearings each being 80 mm long. Loads of 700N, 800N and 750N act on the shaft at 0·5 m, 1·25 m and 1·8 m respectively, from the LH bearing. Determine the load and bearing pressure at each bearing.

3. A bearing 50mm diameter, 80mm long, carries a total load of 6000N. If the shaft is rotating at 210 rev/min estimate the coefficient of friction from the expression $\mu = \dfrac{0{\cdot}032\sqrt{v}}{p}$. Hence determine the number of joules of work lost in friction per second, i.e. the power lost in watts.

4. The end thrust on a spindle is taken by a collar on a 60 mm diameter portion of the shaft. If the maximum thrust is 2100 N, and the bearing pressure is not to exceed 0·7 N/mm^2 determine the necessary top diameter of the collar.

5. A line of 60 mm shafting runs in six bearings each 100 mm long. The average load on each bearing is 6000 N and the speed of the shaft is 315 rev/min. Estimate the coefficient of friction and the power being lost in friction.

6. If the Elastic Limit of a certain material were at 160 N/mm^2, what load would a 20 mm diameter bar of the material carry without sustaining a permanent stretch?

7. Taking the ultimate stress of a mild steel to be 500 N/mm^2, calculate the load in Newtons necessary to fracture an M6 metric bolt at the root of the thread. [Take the diameter at the root of the thread as 4·5 mm.] Hence taking the efficiency of the thread at 10%, find what force at the end of a 200 mm spanner will cause the bolt to fracture. [M6 thread has a pitch of 1 mm]

8. A drawbolt 20 mm dia, 800 mm long, is pulled up to a tension of 16 000 N. Calculate the stress in the bolt, and if E = 200 000 N/mm^2, determine the total extension.

9. An air cylinder is 140 mm diameter and the cylinder head is held on by six M 12 studs and nuts. If the nuts are tightened up to an initial tension of 1000 N, calculate the stress at the root of the thread when the air pressure in the cylinder is 0·6 N/mm^2. [Take the root diameter of the M 12 thread at 9·5 mm.]

10. A steel ring 20 mm wide, 10 mm thick and 149·85 mm inside diameter, is heated up and shrunk on to a shaft 150 mm diameter. If E = 200 000 N/mm^2, estimate the stress and the tension in the ring.

8 Mechanical principles – III

The equations of motion

The distance travelled during a given time by a body moving at a certain constant speed will be given by multiplying the speed by the time, or if

s = space travelled, v = velocity (or speed), and t = time,

$$s = vt \qquad (1)$$

It is important that the time units of v and t are coherent (e.g. if v is in metres/second, then t must be in seconds and s will then be in metres).

Acceleration

Acceleration is the rate of increase of velocity. For example: if a body starts from rest with an acceleration of 1 m/s every second (i.e. 1 m/s²), its velocity at the end of 1 second will be 1 m/s, at the end of 2 seconds it will be 2 m/s, and at the end of t seconds it will be t metres per second.

Hence we may say for a body starting from rest with an acceleration a: Final velocity (v) after time t; $v = at$

If, instead of starting from rest, the body already had an initial velocity of u, then: Final velocity after time $t = u + at$

This gives us
$$v = u + at \qquad (2)$$

Instead of accelerating, a body may be slowing down or decelerating. Its acceleration will then be a minus quantity, and we shall have for its final velocity:

$$v = u - at$$

This slowing down is generally termed retardation.

A graph of velocity-time for equation (1) above is shown in Fig. 147 (*a*) and the area under the graph is equivalent to the distance moved.

If we now plot a similar graph for equation (2) it will be as Fig. 147 (*b*). In this case, due to the acceleration, the velocity is increasing at a constant rate and the graph is a sloping line instead of a horizontal one. The distance moved will be, as before, the area under the graph (Area OABC).

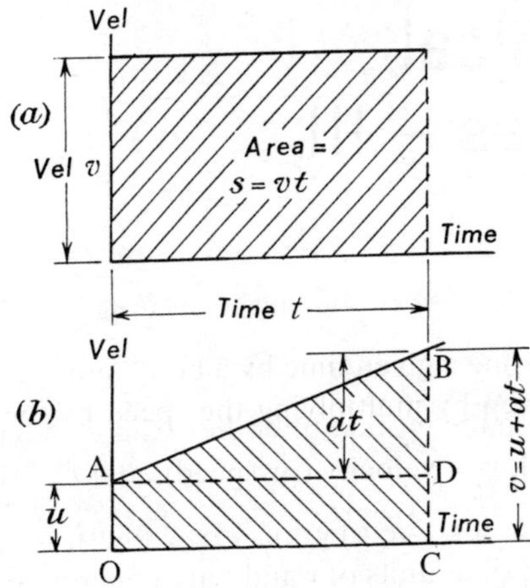

Fig. 147

But $$\text{OABC} = \text{OADC} + \text{ADB}$$
$$s = ut + \tfrac{1}{2}tat$$
This gives us $$s = ut + \tfrac{1}{2}at^2 \qquad (3)$$

If $u = \text{O}$ then the line starts at O and
$$s = \tfrac{1}{2}at^2$$

The reader is strongly advised to interpret problems of accelerated motion as far as possible with the help of a graph.

Equation (3) could have been obtained as follows: For any motion the space travelled = (average velocity) (time). In Fig. 147 (*b*) the average velocity is at a height midway between A and B, i.e. $u + \frac{1}{2}at$. Multiplying this by the time t we get $s = ut + \frac{1}{2}at^2$ as before.

Finally, we require an equation connecting v, s and a, so we must eliminate t.

In equation (2) we have $v = u + at$

and $$t = \frac{v - u}{a}$$

Substituting this value for t in equation (3) we have
$$s = ut + \tfrac{1}{2}at^2$$
$$s = u\left(\frac{v - u}{a}\right) + \tfrac{1}{2}a\left(\frac{v - u}{a}\right)^2$$
$$= \frac{uv - u^2}{a} + \tfrac{1}{2}a\left(\frac{v^2 - 2uv + u^2}{a^2}\right)$$

Putting on the common denominator $2a$

$$s = \frac{2uv - 2u^2 + v^2 - 2uv + u^2}{2a}$$

$$s = \frac{v^2 - u^2}{2a}$$

which gives us that $$v^2 - u^2 = 2as \qquad (4)$$

If the initial velocity $u = 0$ (body starting from rest)

then $$v^2 = 2as.$$

In problems dealing with the motion of bodies falling under the action of gravity then,

$$a = \text{acceleration due to gravity} = 9{\cdot}81\,\text{m/s}^2$$

This is generally signified by g instead of a, and the reader should note particularly that in using 9·81 for g the units are in *metres* and *seconds*. The units of all the other quantities in the equations *must* be kept in coherent units.

Example 1. A drop stamp falls freely for 6 m under the action of gravity. Find its velocity at the moment it strikes the tup.

Here $$u = 0 \quad s = 6\,\text{m} \quad a = 9{\cdot}81\,\text{m/s}^2$$

and
$$v^2 = 2as$$
$$= 2 \times 9{\cdot}81 \times 6 = 117{\cdot}72$$
$$v = \sqrt{117{\cdot}72} = \underline{10{\cdot}85\,\text{m/s}}$$

Example 2. A shaping machine ram is running on a stroke of 450 mm. It starts from rest, accelerates at a uniform rate until the centre of the stroke and then retards at a unifrom rate to a standstill at the end of the stroke. If the stroke occupies $1\frac{1}{2}$ second, find the acceleration and the maximum speed attained.

This problem is best illustrated graphically, and the motion is represented in Fig. 148.

The ram is accelerated from O to A, its velocity increasing uniformly and the reverse process takes place from A to B.

The area OAB represents the space travelled, which in this case is 450 mm = 0·45 m

Hence $\qquad 0{\cdot}45 = \frac{1}{2}\text{OB.AC}$ and since $\text{OB} = 1\frac{1}{2}$ seconds

$$0{\cdot}45 = \tfrac{1}{2}.1\tfrac{1}{2}.\text{AC} = \tfrac{3}{4}\text{AC}$$

$$\therefore \text{AC} = v = 0{\cdot}6\,\text{m/s}$$

For half the stroke $v = at$

$$0{\cdot}6 = a.\tfrac{3}{4} \quad \text{and } a = 0{\cdot}8\,\text{m/s}^2$$

Hence $\qquad$ acceleration $= \underline{0{\cdot}8\,\text{m/s}^2}$

max speed of ram $= \underline{0{\cdot}6\,\text{m/s}}$

Note that the *average* speed of the ram $= 0{\cdot}3\,\text{m/s}$

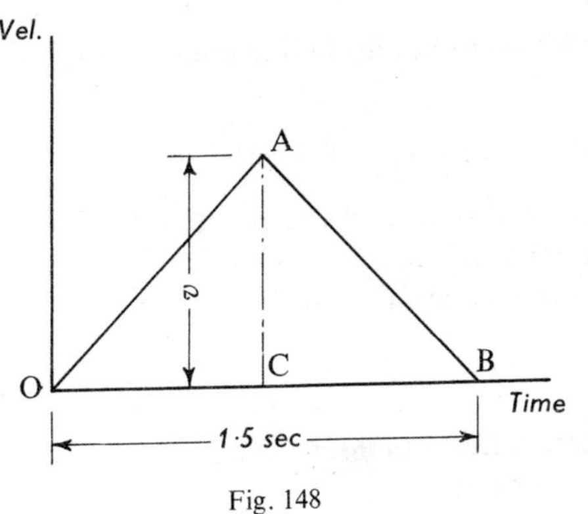

Fig. 148

Fig. 149

Example 3. A planing machine table is set for a travel of 900 mm. It starts from rest, accelerates uniformly during the first 150 mm, runs at a constant speed for 600 mm and then retards uniformly to rest during the last 150 mm of the travel. The total time taken travel the 900 mm is 4 seconds.

Find (*a*) the average speed, (*b*) the maximum speed, (*c*) the acceleration.

A graph showing the motion is shown at Fig. 149. Let the maximum velocity be v and the times of acceleration, uniform speed and retardation t_1, t_2 and t_3 as shown.

(*a*) The average speed will be

$$\frac{\text{distance}}{\text{time}} = \frac{0{\cdot}9\,\text{m}}{4\,\text{s}} = \underline{0{\cdot}225\,\text{m/s}}$$

Since the first and last portions of the travel are identical: retardation = acceleration (a).

For the first part of the stroke:

$$v^2 = 2as = 0{\cdot}3a \text{ (since } s = 0{\cdot}15\,\text{m)} \qquad (1)$$

Also, for the first and last portions of the travel

$$v = at_1 = at_3 \text{ and } t_1 = t_3 = \frac{v}{a}$$

and for the second $s_2 = vt_2$

$$t_2 = \frac{0{\cdot}6}{v} \text{ (since } s_2 = 600\,\text{mm} = 0{\cdot}6\,\text{m)}$$

$$\therefore t_1 + t_2 + t_3 = \frac{v}{a} + \frac{0{\cdot}6}{v} + \frac{v}{a} = 4 = \frac{2v}{a} + \frac{0{\cdot}6}{v} \qquad (2)$$

(since total time = 4 seconds)

From equation (1): $a = \dfrac{v^2}{0{\cdot}3}$

Substituting this in equation (2):

$$\frac{2v \times 0{\cdot}3}{v^2} + \frac{0{\cdot}6}{v} = 4$$

$$\frac{0{\cdot}6}{v} + \frac{0{\cdot}6}{v} = 4 \quad \text{i.e.} \quad \frac{1{\cdot}2}{v} = 4$$

and

$$4v = 1{\cdot}2, \; v = \underline{0{\cdot}3\,\text{m/s}}$$

Since from (1)

$$a = \frac{v^2}{0{\cdot}3} = \frac{0{\cdot}3 \times 0{\cdot}3}{0{\cdot}3} = \underline{0{\cdot}3\,\text{m/s}^2}$$

Exercises 8a

1. A shaft starts from rest and with uniform acceleration attains a speed of 300 rev/min in half a minute. Sketch the graph of velocity-time, and calculate (*a*) the acceleration in rev/min^2; (*b*) the number of revolutions made by the shaft during the period.

2. A drop stamp falls freely under the action of gravity from a height of 8 m. Calculate (*a*) the time of fall, and (*b*) the velocity at the instant it strikes the bottom block.

3. Starting from rest, a shaping machine ram, with uniform acceleration, reaches a speed of 24 m/mm during 240 mm of travel. Find the acceleration and the time taken.

4. A cam rotates at 180 rev/min. During 90° of its revolution it causes a plunger to rise a distance of 25 mm. Half the rise is made with uniform acceleration and the remainder with an equal retardation. Calculate the acceleration of the plunger and sketch the graph of velocity-time for it.

5. The total travel of a planer table is 2·1 m. Starting from rest, the table accelerates uniformly for $1\frac{1}{2}$ seconds, runs at a constant speed for 2 seconds, and retards to rest during $1\frac{1}{2}$ seconds. Calculate the acceleration, and the speed during the middle interval. Sketch the graph of velocity-time.

6. After the power has been shut off, a flywheel rotating at 180 rev/min slows down to rest during 90 turns. If the retardation is uniform finds its value in rev/min^2 and the time taken by the wheel in coming to rest.

7. A machine slide has an acceleration of 0·08 m/s^2. How far will this slide travel from rest before reaching a speed of 24 m/min, and how long will it take for this to be effected?

8. A slide starts from rest and travels a distance of 1·25 m with an acceleration of 0·1 m/s², and then comes to rest again with a retardation of 0·05 m/s². Calculate (*a*) the maximum speed attained, (*b*) the total time taken.

Sketch the graph of velocity-time.

Motion and force

Newton's First Law of Motion states that every object remains at rest or moves with uniform velocity in a straight line until compelled by some force to act otherwise. His Second Law states that change of motion is proportional to the impressed force, and takes place in the direction in which that force acts.

Before we can arrive at a quantitative relation between force and change of velocity we must consider the velocity of an object as something more than a rate of movement, since force required will depend upon the size or amount of material in the body.

Mass and weight

Every object is made up of a mass of material (iron, wood, stone or whatever it might be), and this mass is constant and invariable, so long as we do not cut away from or add material to it. Due to the gravitational pull of the earth acting on this material every body exerts a downward force. This force is the *weight* of the body. The weight of a body is not a constant quantity because the pull of gravity varies according to the distance from the centre of the earth. For example, the weight of the same amount of mass would be about $\frac{1}{2}$ percent greater at the poles than at the equator. We thus have the *mass* of a body, being the amount of substance in it, and a constant quantity, and the *weight*, being the downward force caused by the gravitational pull acting on the mass.

We may now define the quantity of motion of a body as being (mass) (velocity), and for the given velocity this will not vary since mass is a constant quantity. This product mv (m = mass) is called *Momentum*.

By Newton's Second Law: Force is proportional to change of motion, i.e. Force is proportional to change of mv.

But m cannot change as it is constant.

$$\therefore \text{ Force varies as } m \text{ (change of } v\text{)}$$

Now change of velocity is acceleration.

Hence $$\text{Force varies as } ma.$$

If the units of F, m and a are chosen so that unit force causes unit acceleration on unit mass we may say $F = ma$, and this is the fundamental relationship between the quantities.

The SI system of units is coherent. This means that the SI unit of force is the force that gives to one unit of mass one unit of acceleration. To honour the contribution of Sir Isaac Newton to Science this is called the newton. Hence

F (newtons) $= m$ (kilogrammes) $\times$ a (metres per second every second)

Let us now consider the action of gravity on a mass of m kilogrammes, i.e. the weight of the body.

$$\text{Using } F = ma$$
$$a = g$$
$$\text{and } F = mg$$

The weight of a body of mass m kilogrammes is, therefore, mg newtons; g may be taken as $9{\cdot}81\ \text{m/s}^2$.

Example 4. If the planing machine table in Example 3 has a mass of 400 kg, and the coefficient of friction at the slides is 0·1, calculate (*a*) the total force necessary to accelerate it, and (*b*) the power being taken to accelerate and overcome friction at the instant when the table has moved 75 mm from the beginning of its travel.

(*a*) Force to overcome friction $= (W)\mu$
$= (mg)\mu = 400 \times 9{\cdot}81 \times 0{\cdot}1 = 392{\cdot}4\text{N}$

Force to accelerate $= ma$
$= 400 \times 0{\cdot}3 = 120\text{N}$

Total force = force to overcome friction + force to accelerate
$= 392{\cdot}4 + 120\text{N} = 512{\cdot}4\text{N}$

(*b*) After 75 mm of movement, speed of table $= \dfrac{0{\cdot}6}{2} = 0{\cdot}3\ \text{m/s}$

Rate of doing work = (force)(speed)
$= 512{\cdot}4 \times 0{\cdot}3 = 153{\cdot}75\ \text{W}$

Power $= 154\ \text{W} = 0{\cdot}154\ \text{kW}$

We might add that during the middle portion of the stroke no acceleration is taking place and the table has merely to be kept moving against friction (neglecting any cutting force).

Here we have: frictional resistance $= 392{\cdot}4\text{N}$

$$\text{Speed} = 0{\cdot}6\,\text{m/s}$$
$$\text{Power} = 392{\cdot}4 \times 0{\cdot}6 = 235{\cdot}44\,\text{W} = 0{\cdot}235\,\text{kW}$$

Force of hammer blows

The force of a hammer blow may be estimated by considering the retardation of the hammer as shown by the following example:

Example 5. A hammer of mass 1 kg and moving at 2 m/s strikes a pin and is brought to rest by driving in the pin 5 mm. Calculate the average force of the hammer blow on the pin.

To find the retardation of the hammer we may use the equation

$$v^2 - u^2 = 2as$$

Here

$$v\ (\text{final velocity}) = 0$$
$$u\ (\text{initial velocity}) = 2\,\text{m/s}$$
$$s = 5\,\text{mm} = 0{\cdot}005\,\text{m}$$
$$-u^2 = 2as$$
$$a = -\frac{2^2}{2 \times 0{\cdot}005} = -400\,\text{m/s}^2$$
$$\text{Force} = ma = 1 \times 400 = \underline{400\,\text{N}}$$

Example 6. A machine slide, of mass 500 kg and moving at 24 m/min, takes 1 second to come to rest after the power is shut off. Calculate the average frictional resistance assumed as a force acting against the slide.

To find the retardation of the slide we may use the formula

$$v = u + at$$

Here $v = 0$: $u = \frac{24}{60} = 0{\cdot}4\,\text{m/s}$: $t = 1$ second

$0 = 0{\cdot}4 + a(1)$ $a = -0{\cdot}4\,\text{m/s}^2$ ($-ve$ because retardation)

If the average resistance is denoted by F

$$F = ma = 500 \times 0{\cdot}4 = \underline{200\,\text{N}}$$

Exercises 8b

1. A slide of mass 100 kg starts from rest and accelerates uniformly to a speed of 12 m/min in 2 seconds. Neglecting friction, calculate the force necessary to produce the acceleration.

2. A machine table has a mass of 60 kg and the frictional resistance at the slides is equivalent to a force of 50N. If a constant force of 80N is applied to this slide, what speed will it have attained after 2 seconds?

3. If the planer table in Ex. 7*a*, No. 5, had a mass of 300kg, and the coefficient of friction at the slides were 0·08, what force would have been required to accelerate it during the first portion of its travel?

4. A 1kg hammer head moving at 1·2m/s is brought to rest by driving a pin through a distance of 10mm. Assuming the retardation of the hammer to be constant, calculate the average force of the blow delivered to the pin.

5. Taking the mass of the cam plunger in Ex. 8*a*, No. 4, to be 1·2kg, calculate the vertical force exerted by the plunger on the cam face during the portion of the lift that the plunger is accelerating. [The plunger moves upward on a vertical centre line.]

6. A shaping machine ram has a mass of 150kg and on its return stroke it starts from rest and moves through a distance of 360mm in 0·75s with uniform acceleration. Neglecting friction, calculate the acceleration, the accelerating force, the velocity after the ram has moved 360mm and the power necessary to move it at that instant.

7. A drop stamp of mass 100kg falls freely from a height of 6m. Calculate its final speed. It is brought to rest by compressing the metal on the bottom block through a distance of 10mm. Determine the retardation of the stamp and the average force of the blow delivered.

8. A machine slide of mass 50kg is moving at 0·8m/s when the power is shut off. If the frictional resistance to its motion is equivalent to a force of 50N, how far will it travel before coming to rest?

Energy

There are various forms of energy (e.g. heat energy, chemical energy, electrical energy, etc) and the origin of all of them may be traced back to energy derived from the heat of the sun. The Law of the Conservation of Energy states that energy cannot be destroyed: one form may be changed into another, but we can neither create new energy nor destroy that which is in the universe. At the moment we are interested in the energy of mechanical movements, and in this connexion we may define the energy of a body as *the power of overcoming resistance or of doing work*.

A body may possess energy by virtue of its position, e.g. a weight on a cord wound round a shaft may rotate the shaft and do work as it descends to the floor. A wound-up clock-spring possesses energy. Energy of this kind is called *Strain Energy*.

When a body is moving, it possesses energy of a different kind called *Kinetic Energy*. A rotating flywheel or an oscillating machine slide are examples of moving bodies possessing kinetic energy.

Since we may convert energy from one form to another without loss, we may obtain an expression for kinetic energy:

Let a body of mass m (i.e. weight mg) be raised to a height h above some datum line (Fig. 150). When in this position the body will possess *mgh* units of potential energy, since this amount of work must be expended to lift it there. If now the body be allowed to fall, it will lose its potential energy, and gain an equal amount of kinetic energy and

$$\text{KE} = \text{PE} = mgh$$

We may express the K.E. in terms of v because

$$v^2 - u^2 = 2as.$$

$$u = 0;\ a = g, \text{ and } s = h.$$

$$\therefore v^2 = 2gh$$

and

$$h = \frac{v^2}{2g}.$$

$$\text{Hence KE} = mgh = mg \times \frac{v^2}{2g} = \frac{mv^2}{2}. \qquad (6)$$

An expression for kinetic energy in terms of m and v.
The SI unit of all forms of energy is the newton metre, i.e. the joule (J).

The reader is reminded that energy and work are interchangeable: to put a body in possession of a certain amount of energy requires the expenditure of an identical amount of work.

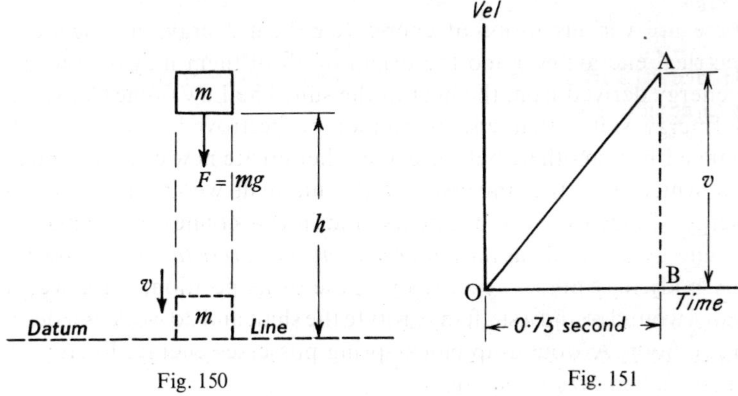

Fig. 150

Fig. 151

Example 7. A shaping machine ram has a mass of 200 kg and accelerates uniformly from rest, covering the first 360 mm of its travel in 0·75 s. Find the velocity at the end of this travel, and show that the kinetic energy of the ram at that point is equal to the work done in accelerating it.

In Fig. 151 the motion of the ram may be represented by the line OA, and AB represents the velocity v attained after 0·75 second.

Since space travelled = Area OAB = 360 mm = 0·36 m

$$\tfrac{1}{2}(v \times \tfrac{3}{4}) = 0{\cdot}36$$

and $$\frac{3v}{8} = 0{\cdot}36,\ v = 0{\cdot}96\,\text{m/s}$$

To find the acceleration we have $v = at$ or $a = \dfrac{v}{t}$

$$\frac{0{\cdot}96}{0{\cdot}75} = 1{\cdot}28\,\text{m/s}^2$$

$$\text{Force} = ma = 200 \times 1{\cdot}28 = 256\,\text{N}$$

$$\text{Work done} = (\text{force})(\text{distance}) = 256 \times 0{\cdot}36 = 92{\cdot}16\,\text{J}$$

Energy of 200 kg ram at 0·96 m/s $= \dfrac{mv^2}{2} = \dfrac{200 \times 0{\cdot}96^2}{2} = 92{\cdot}16\,\text{J}$, as before,

Example 8. Solve Example 6 by treating it from the aspect of energy.

Kinetic energy of 500 kg slide at 0·4 m/s

$$\frac{mv^2}{2} = \frac{500 \times 0{\cdot}4 \times 0{\cdot}4}{2} = 40\,\text{J}$$

The slide is stopped in 1 second from a speed of 0·4 m/s

$$\text{Average speed} = 0{\cdot}4 \div 2 = 0{\cdot}2\,\text{m/s}$$

$$\text{space} = (\text{velocity})(\text{time}) = 0{\cdot}2 \times 1 = 0{\cdot}2\,\text{m}$$

Hence 40 J of energy is dissipated over a distance of 0·2 m and if F is the force acting to do it

$$\text{Work} = (\text{force})(\text{distance})$$

$$40 = F \times 0{\cdot}2 \qquad F = 40 \div 0{\cdot}2$$

$$= \underline{200\ \text{N}}\ \text{as before.}$$

Example 9. A 250 kg drop stamp falls through a height of 4 m before striking the work. If it compresses the metal and is brought to rest in a distance of 25 mm, estimate the average force of the blow.

Work stored up in stamp when striking work

$$= \text{potential energy} = mgh = 250 \times 9{\cdot}81 \times 4 = 9810\,\text{J}$$

This is dissipated over a distance of 25 mm = 0·025 m

$$\text{Work} = (\text{force})(\text{distance})$$

$$9810 = F \times 0{\cdot}025$$

$$F = \frac{9810}{0{\cdot}025} = \underline{392\,400\,\text{N}}$$

Circular motion

Many of the problems of the shop deal with rotating masses (flywheels, pulleys, etc), so that we must adapt our knowledge of motion and force to circular as weil as linear movement.

It is quite permissible to use the equations of motion as they stand and apply them to some point on the rotating body. In general, this will be a point on the rim should the body in question be a flywheel or pulley.

It is better, however, when dealing with circular motion, to use the angular notation of quantities, since if we consider any rotating body the speed of points at different radii will vary according to their radius. The *angular* speed of the body, however, is constant, irrespective of the radius.

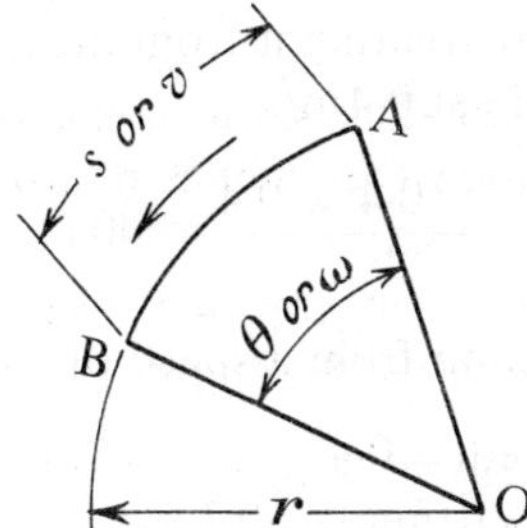

Fig. 152

We have seen that if we consider an angle AOB, where AB is the arc struck from the centre O, and r is the radius, then $\frac{\text{AB}}{r} = \theta$ in radians.

If this refers to a body having circular motion about O as centre:

if arc AB = space moved (s), then $\frac{s}{r}$ = angle θ (radians), or

$$s = \theta r$$

Again, if AB represents the velocity (v) of the body at radius r, then

$$\frac{v}{r} = \text{angular velocity } (\omega)$$

or

$$v = \omega r \qquad (7)$$

If v is in m/s, and r in m, then ω will be in radian per second.

In the same way the relation between the linear acceleration a and the angular acceleration α of a body moving in a circle is that

$$\frac{a}{r} = \alpha \text{ or } a = \alpha r$$

When the reader has become accustomed to these simple conversions from the linear to the angular notation, he will find the angular working is preferable to and more rational than linear working for problems of rotation.

The equations of motion given on pages 198 later may be used for angular notation when it is remembered that:

$$s = \text{space in radians; } v = \text{velocity in rad/s}$$
$$a = \text{acceleration in rad/s}^2$$

Since 1 revolution = 2π radian we may convert rev/min to rad/s by dividing by 60 and multiplying by 2π,

i.e. $$\omega(\text{rad/s}) = \frac{N}{60}.2\pi. \; [N = \text{rev/min}]$$

Example 10. A pulley revolving at 220 rev/min comes to rest with uniform retardation in 50 turns. Calculate the angular retardation and the time taken.

We may obtain the time very simply without using radians, for if the retardation is uniform, the velocity-time graph is a straight line and the average velocity $= \frac{220}{2} = 110$ rev/min

The pulley therefore comes to rest in 50 turns at a mean speed of 110 rev/min, i.e. in $\frac{50}{110}$ min $= \frac{50}{110} \times 60 = 27$ sec.

Using the equation $$\omega_2 = \omega_1 + \alpha t$$

$$0 = \frac{220}{60}.2\pi + \alpha.27.$$

$$\alpha = -\frac{220 \times 2\pi}{60 \times 27} = 0{\cdot}853 \text{ rad/s}^2$$

Example 11. A gas engine which normally runs at 500 rev/min takes 20 s to accelerate its flywheels to their full speed. Calculate the angular acceleration and the number of revolutions made by the engine. (Assume constant acceleration.)

We may obtain the number of revolutions from the average speed as before, since average speed $= \frac{500}{2} = 250$ rev/min

Using $s = vt$ we have $s = \frac{250}{60} \times 20 = 83{\cdot}3$ revolutions.

To find the acceleration we may use

$$\omega_2 = \omega_1 + \alpha t$$

$$\frac{500}{60}.2\pi = 0 + \alpha.20$$

$$a = \frac{500 \times 2\pi}{60 \times 20} = \frac{5\pi}{6} = 2{\cdot}63\,\text{rad/s}^2$$

Exercises 8c

1. Convert a speed of 175 rev/min to rad/s, and 110 rad/s to rev/min.

2. A pulley has an acceleration of 4 rad/s². How long will it take to reach a speed of 250 rev/min?

3. A shaft retards from a speed of 500 rev/min to rest in $3\frac{1}{2}$ second. Calculate its retardation in rad/s².

4. Calculate the kinetic energy of a car of mass 1400 kg and travelling at 54 km/h. If this is brought to rest by the brakes in 30 m, find the average force of resistance exerted.

5. Solve Ex. 8*b*, No. 7, from a consideration of energy.

6. A machine table of mass 150 kg is moving at 30 m/min. Calculate its kinetic energy. What force applied to it will bring it to rest in 600 mm? (Neglect friction.)

7. Find the energy stored in a 4 kg hammer-head moving at 2 m/s. If this hammer is brought to rest by compressing the metal under it through a distance of 25 mm, determine the average force of the blow.

Accelerating torque

When a torque acts on a rotating body or on a body capable of rotation it causes angular acceleration.

In Fig. 153 let the small mass m be rotating about the centre O at radius r and let the force F act on it.

Then $F = ma$, where a = linear acceleration of m.

But torque $T = Fr$, and angular accel $\alpha = \frac{a}{r}$, i.e. $a = \alpha r$.

Hence $F = ma = m\alpha r$ and $T = Fr = m\alpha r^2$.

But a rotating body is made up of many small masses m, each situated at its own particular radius.

The sum of all these small masses we will call M, the total mass of the body. If this mass could be concentrated at a single radius which we will call k, we could write for the whole rotating body: $T = Mk^2\alpha$. Actually it is possible to determine the value of a radius at which the whole of the mass of a body may be assumed as concentrated, and this radius is called the *Radius of Gyration*, being denoted by k.

We may thus write:

$$\text{Accel torque (T)} = Mk^2\alpha \qquad (8)$$

For a flywheel having a rim heavy in proportion to the rest of the wheel, k may be assumed as the mean radius of the rim.

For a plain disc of radius r, $k = 0{\cdot}707r$.

We might caution the reader again regarding the units of the above expression. If T is in newton metres (N m), M will be in kilogrammes, k will be in metres and α will be in rad/s^2.

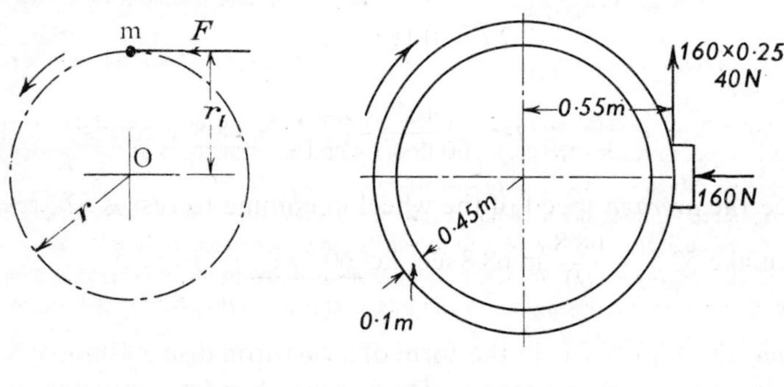

Fig. 153 Fig. 154

Example 12. A flywheel of mass 550 kg has a heavy rim, the inside and outside radii of which are 450 mm and 550 mm respectively. When this wheel is rotating at 105 rev/min a brake is pressed against the rim with a radial force of 160 N. If the coefficient of friction between the brake and the wheel is 0·25, calculate how long the wheel will take to come to rest and how many revolutions it will make in doing so.

The tangential force at the rim of the wheel tending to stop it is $160 \times \mu$.

$$= 160 \times 0{\cdot}25 = 40\,\text{N}$$

Since this acts at a radius of 550 mm = 0·55 m, the retarding torque will be $40 \times 0{\cdot}55 = 22$ N m.

As the rim is heavy in comparison with the rest of the wheel, we will take the Radius of Gyration at the mean rim radius, i.e. at 500 mm radius (0·5 m).

Using the torque equation $T = Mk^2\alpha$ we have

$$22 = 550 \times 0{\cdot}5 \times 0{\cdot}5 \times \alpha \text{ from which } \alpha = \frac{22}{550 \times 0{\cdot}5 \times 0{\cdot}5} = 0{\cdot}16\,\text{rad/s}^2$$

We may now use the equation $\omega_2 = \omega_1 + \alpha t$ to find the time to stop the wheel since

$$\omega_2 = 0; \quad \omega_1 = \frac{105}{60}(2\pi)$$

$$\text{and } \alpha = -0{\cdot}16 \text{ (retardation)}$$

Hence
$$0 = \frac{105}{60}.2\pi - 0{\cdot}16t$$

i.e.
$$\frac{105}{60}2\pi = 0{\cdot}16t$$

$$t = \frac{105 \times 44}{60 \times 7 \times 0{\cdot}16} = \underline{68{\cdot}8 \text{ seconds}}$$

Since the *average* speed of the wheel in coming to rest is 52·5 rev/min it will make $52{\cdot}5 \times \frac{68{\cdot}8}{60}$ in 68·8 sec, i.e. 60·2 rev.

Example 13. A pulley is in the form of a cast-iron disc 500 mm × 80 mm thick. It is driven from a source of power which exerts a constant torque of 10 N m. How long will this pulley take to attain to a speed of 210 rev/min when started from rest? Take the density of the cast iron to be 7280 kg/m³.

$$\text{Mass of pulley} = \frac{\pi}{4}D^2t \times \text{density}$$

$$= \frac{22}{28} \times 0{\cdot}5^2 \times 0{\cdot}08 \times 7280\,\text{kg} = 114{\cdot}4\,\text{kg}$$

Taking the radius of gyration as 0·707 × outside radius, we have $k = 0{\cdot}707 \times 0{\cdot}25 = 0{\cdot}172\,\text{m}$

The applied torque is 10 N m and applying the torque equation

$$T = Mk^2\alpha, \qquad 10 = 114{\cdot}4 \times 0{\cdot}172^2 \times \alpha$$

$$\alpha = \frac{10}{114{\cdot}4 \times 0{\cdot}172^2} = 2{\cdot}8\,\text{rad/s}^2$$

$$\omega = 210\,\text{rev/min} = 44\,\text{rad/s}$$

$$t = \frac{44}{2{\cdot}8}$$

$$= \underline{15{\cdot}7 \text{ seconds}}$$

Example 14. A steel level 300 mm long is of rectangular cross-section 40 mm × 20 mm, and is pivoted at its centre. One end bears on a cam which causes it to swing through a length of 25 mm, during the time that the cam makes $\frac{1}{4}$ revolution at 180 rev/min. If half the swing of the lever is made with constant acceleration, and the other half with constant retardation, estimate the torque required to accelerate the lever. [k for a lever pivoted at the centre $= \frac{L}{12}$ approx (L = length of lever).] Take the density of steel as 7840 kg/m³

The problem is shown in Fig. 155.

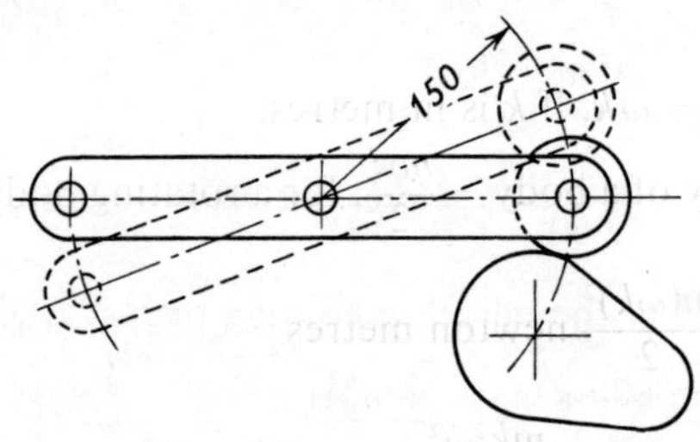

Fig. 155

Approximate mass of lever = 0·3 × 0·04 × 0·02 × 7840 = 1·88 kg.

The lever is accelerated through an arc 25 mm long on a 150 mm radius, i.e. through an angle of $\frac{1}{6}$ radian.

This takes place during $\frac{1}{8}$ turn of a cam revolving at 180 rev/min, i.e. $\frac{1}{8}$ rev at 3 rev/s

$$= \tfrac{1}{8} \times \tfrac{1}{3} = \tfrac{1}{24} \text{ second}$$

Since $\theta = \omega t + \frac{1}{2}\alpha t^2 = \frac{1}{2}\alpha t^2$ when $\omega = 0$

$$\therefore \theta = \tfrac{1}{2}\alpha t^2, \text{ and } \alpha = \frac{2\theta}{t^2} = \frac{2 \times \frac{1}{6}}{(\frac{1}{24})^2} = 192 \text{ rad/s}^2$$

For the lever we have radius of gyration $k = \frac{L}{12} = \frac{300 \text{ mm}}{12} =$ 25 mm = 0·025 m, and mass m = 1·88 kg.

Hence applying the torque equation

$$T = mk^2\alpha = 1{\cdot}88 \times (0{\cdot}025)^2 \times 192 = 0{\cdot}225 \text{ Nm}$$

This means that with the cam end of the lever being accelerated upward a torque of the above amount would have to be applied by the cam to the end of the lever. With the cam end falling, this torque would have to be applied to the lever by a spring or other means to prevent the roller from leaving the cam.

The above consideration is, of course, relative to the lever only, and neglects the effect of attachments to its free end.

The energy of rotating bodies

If we continue our consideration of a rotating body as having all its mass concentrated at the radius of gyration (k), if the body is rotating at a speed of ω radians/second the linear speed in metres/second of a point at radius k will be

$$v = \omega k, \text{ if } k \text{ is in metres.}$$

Since the kinetic energy of a body $= \frac{mv^2}{2}$; for a rotating body it will be

$$\frac{m(\omega k)^2}{2} \text{ newton metres}$$

Hence $$\text{KE} = \frac{mk^2\omega^2}{2} \text{ joules}$$

Rotating flywheels are used on presses and other machines for the purpose of storing a reserve of energy, so that when a sudden large output of work is required the machine will not stall, or undergo an undue slowing up in speed.

Example 15. Calculate the energy stored up in a solid disc of cast iron, 500 mm dia by 80 mm thick, when rotating at 180 rev/min. If this wheel is on a press, what will be its speed after a hole has been blanked if the blanking pressure is 100 kN and its duration extends over 5 mm.

From Example 13 the mass of this wheel is 114·4 kg and its radius of gyration, 0·172 m.

The angular speed $\omega = \frac{180}{60} \times 2\pi = 6\pi \text{rad/s}$

Putting these in the expression for Kinetic Energy

$$\text{KE} = \frac{mk^2\omega^2}{2} = \frac{114{\cdot}4 \times 0{\cdot}172^2 \times (6\pi)^2}{2}$$

Energy stored at 180 rev/min $= \underline{601{\cdot}5 \text{ J}}$

For a pressure of 100 kN extending over 5 mm, the work done

$$= 100\ 000 \times 0{\cdot}005 = 500\text{J}$$

This energy must be given up by the flywheel and its energy afterwards will be $601{\cdot}5 - 500 = 101{\cdot}5$ J

If ω_1 is the speed of the wheel after giving up the energy: re-applying the expression for kinetic energy

$$101{\cdot}5 = \frac{mk^2\omega^2}{2};\quad \omega^2 = \frac{2 \times 101{\cdot}5}{mk^2} = \frac{203}{114{\cdot}4 \times 0{\cdot}172^2}$$

$$= 60 \qquad \omega = \sqrt{60} = 7{\cdot}75 \text{ rad/s}$$

$$\text{rev/s} = \frac{\omega}{2\pi} = \frac{7{\cdot}75}{2\pi}$$

$$\text{rev/m} = \frac{7{\cdot}75 \times 60}{2\pi} = \frac{232{\cdot}5}{\pi} = 74 \text{ rev/min}$$

Hence speed of wheel after blanking hole = 74 rev/min

Example 16. Solve Example 12 from a consideration of energy and work done.

At 105 rev/min the work stored up in the flywheel = Energy $= \dfrac{mk^2\omega^2}{2}$

$$= \frac{550 \times 0{\cdot}5 \times 0{\cdot}5 \times 11 \times 11}{2}$$

$$= 8320 \text{ J}$$

The tangential force at the brake block = 40 N, and to dissipate 8320 J of energy this must travel $\dfrac{8320}{40} = 208$ m

Revs of wheel for 208 m on its circumference

$$= \frac{208}{\text{Circum}} = \frac{208}{\pi \times 1{\cdot}1} = 60{\cdot}2 \text{ rev, as before}$$

Average speed = 52·5 rev/min

Hence time to stop $= \dfrac{60{\cdot}2}{52{\cdot}5} \times 60$ min = 68·8 s

Example 17. A fly-press has two 150 mm diameter spherical cast-iron balls spaced at the ends of the arm, each ball being at 500 mm radius. At

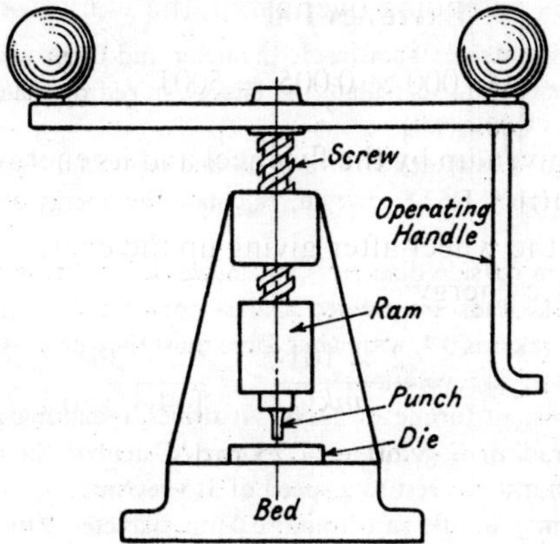

Fig. 156

what speed must the arm rotate if the punch is to be just capable of penetrating a thickness of 2·5 mm under a constant pressure of 20 000 N? Take the density of cast iron to be 7280 kg/m³.

The reader is no doubt acquainted with the fly-press, a sketch of which is shown in Fig. 156.

$$\text{mass of a ball} = \text{volume} \times \text{density}$$
$$= \frac{\pi \times 0{\cdot}15^3}{6} \times 7280 = 12{\cdot}9\,\text{kg}$$

Energy stored in 2 balls at a speed of ω rad/s.

$$= 2\left(\frac{mk^2\omega^2}{2}\right) = mk^2\omega^2$$
$$= 12{\cdot}9 \times 0{\cdot}5 \times 0{\cdot}5 \times \omega^2 = 3{\cdot}225\omega^2$$

This must be equal to the work output required at the punch, i.e. 20 000 N acting for a distance of 2·5 mm = 0·0025 m

$$= 20\,000 \times 0{\cdot}0025$$
$$= 50\,\text{J}$$

Hence $3{\cdot}225\omega^2 = 50$,

$$\omega^2 = \frac{50}{3{\cdot}225} = 15{\cdot}5,$$

$$\omega = \sqrt{15{\cdot}5} = 3{\cdot}94\,\text{rad/s} = \frac{3{\cdot}94}{2\pi} = \underline{0{\cdot}627\,\text{rev/s}}$$

Exercises 10d

1. A CI flywheel rim is 1 m outside, 0·8m inside diameter and 0·1 m wide. Taking the radius of gyration as the mean radius, calculate the energy stored up when the speed is 315 rev/min [Density of CI = 7280 kg/m³].

2. If the flywheel in Ex. No. **1** is attached to a press and a punching operation causes the speed of the wheel to drop to 262·5 rev/min, calculate the energy absorbed by the operation.

3. A CI flywheel, rim 1·4 m outside diameter, 1 m inside, and 0·1 m wide is revolving at 105 rev/min when two brake pads are pressed against opposite sides of its rim. If the coefficient of friction at the brakes is 0·4, with what force must they be pressed against the rim to bring the wheel to rest in 30 revolutions?

4. A motor develops a constant torque of 32 Nm. It drives a shafting and pulleys of mass 400 kg, and having a radius of gyration = 200 mm. Calculate the time taken for the motor to accelerate the shaft from rest to a speed of 315 rev/mm.

5. A flywheel is in the form of a solid cast-iron disc 0·6 m diameter, 80 mm thick, and is carried on a 50 mm diameter shaft. When the wheel is revolving at 315 rev/min it is disengaged from its drive and comes to rest in 75 seconds. If the retarding torque is due entirely to friction at the bearings, calculate the tangential frictional force at the surface of the 50 mm shaft upon which the wheel is mounted.

6. A press has a flywheel of mass 400 kg and radius of gyration = 0·707 m. The press is shearing metal bars 40 mm × 20 m, for which the ultimate shear strength is 400 N/mm². When a bar is being sheared the full load comes on and remains constant whilst the shear blade moves 5 mm, after which the load drops to zero. If the above flywheel is rotating at 52·5 rev/min when a bar is sheared, calculate the reduction in speed caused by the work absorbed.

7. A fly-press has two masses each of 5 kg attached to opposite ends of the arm at 400 mm radius. When the arm is rotating at 1 rev/s a punch in the ram makes contact with a pin and drives it a distance of 5 mm into a hole. Calculate the average pressure exerted on the pin by the punch.

8. A cylindrical mixing tank mass 160 kg, inside diameter 1 m, radius of gyration 250 mm, is rotating at 105 rev/min when 20 kg of material is tipped into it. If the material immediately moves to the sides of the tank and arranges itself at a mean radius of 400 mm, estimate the momentary reduction in speed caused by the extra mass.

Heat and Heat Energy

Temperature

The temperature of a substance is no indication of the amount of heat it contains, but merely a measure of its "hotness level."

There are two scales of temperature used in this country; the Celsius and the Kelvin. (The Celsius scale is a more modern name for the Centigrade scale, but the latter name is likely to persist for some time after the adoption of the SI conventions.) The freezing–boiling point limits of water are shown in Fig. 157.

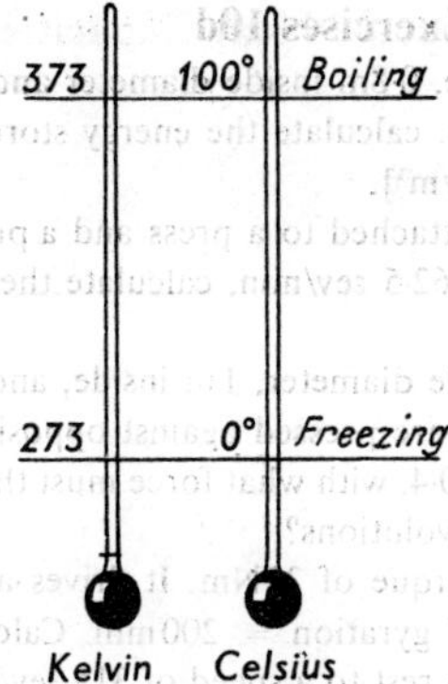

Fig. 157

The degrees of temperature on these systems are generally denoted °C and K respectively. The chief calculation concerning these is the conversion from one to the other. It will be noted that a very simple relationship exists,

i.e. temperature in Kelvin = temperature in Celsius + 273. For example

$$20°C = 273 + 20 = 293K$$
$$\text{and } 353\,K = 353 - 273 = 80°C$$

(The reader will note that the word "degree" is not used when referring to the Kelvin scale.)
Furthermore, 1°C of temperature rise = 1 K of temperature rise. The symbol relates to the kelvin scale of absolute temperature and goes down to absolute zero (0) of temperature. It is employed mostly in scientific and thermodynamic work.

Amount of heat
Heat is a form of energy, and hence the unit for a quantity of heat is the same unit as for a quantity of energy, i.e. the joule. For large quantities we occasionally refer to kilojoules and megajoules. The amount of energy needed to raise unit mass of a substance a unit increase of temperature is called the *specific heat capacity* of that substance. As an example, the specific heat capacity of water is about 4200 J/kg°C. Water has the greatest specific heat capacity of any substance, so that all other substances have a specific heat capacity of less than 4200 J/kg °C.

Table of Specific Heat Capacities

Substance	Specific Heat Capacity in J/kg °C
Water	4200
Alcohol (absolute)	2930
Olive oil	1300
Petroleum	2140
Turpentine	2000
Copper	400
Cast iron	540
Aluminium	900
Lead	1300
Steel	480
Brass	395
Oak	2400
Stone generally	880
Air (at constant pressure)	1000

When a substance is heated up the heat transferred to it will be given by

$$\text{(Mass of substance)(Rise in temperature)(Specific heat capacity)}$$
$$= mc\,(T_2 - T_1)$$
[m = mass; c = sp. ht. capacity; T_1 and T_1 = Temp limits.]

Heat calculations

Due to the fact that heat escapes so easily and so rapidly by conduction, convection and radiation, the results of heat and temperature calculations are not to be relied upon. It is possible, however, to obtain an approximate idea of the state of conditions, and the work involves important principles in which we cannot have too much practice.

Example 19. A piece of steel of mass 5 kg is heated up to 700°C and immersed in a tank 400 mm square containing 250 mm of water at 15°C. The steel is left until temperature conditions become steady. Assuming that 10% of the heat is lost, estimate the final temperature.

When the hot steel is placed in the water it will lose heat to the water, and if no heat were lost externally the heat lost by the steel would be equal to the heat gained by the water. As it is, 90% of the heat lost by the steel is gained by the water.

Let T be the final steady temperature.

$$\text{Heat lost by steel} = (\text{mass})(\text{sp. ht. cap.})(\text{fall in temp}) = 5 \times 480(700 - T)$$

The mass of 1 cubic metre of water = 1000 kg, so the mass contained in a tank 0·4 m square when the depth is 0·25 m

$$= 0{\cdot}4 \times 0{\cdot}4 \times 0{\cdot}25 \times 1000 = 40\,\text{kg}$$

$$\text{Heat gained by water} = 40 \times 4200(T - 15) \quad (2)$$

Since heat gained by water = $\frac{9}{10}$(heat lost by steel) we have

$$168000(T - 15) = \tfrac{9}{10}[5 \times 480(700 - T)] \quad (3)$$

Multiplying out the brackets we have:

$$168\,000T - 2\,520\,000 = 1\,512\,000 - 2\,160T$$

From which $170\,160T = 4\,032\,000$

and $$T = \frac{4\,032\,000}{170\,160} = \underline{23{\cdot}7°\text{C}}$$

Example 20. A piece of steel 1 kg in mass is taken from a furnace and placed in 2 litres of water. Conditions are made such that the minimum of heat escapes. If the initial temperature of the water was 20°C and the final steady temperature of steel and water 52°C, estimate the temperature of the steel when taken from the furnace.

If we assume no loss of heat we have

Heat gained by water = Heat lost by steel.

Let T = furnace temperature

Mass of 2 litres of water = 2 kg

$$\text{Heat gained by water} = 2 \times 4200(52 - 20) = 8400 \times 32 = 268\,800\text{ J}$$

$$\text{Heat lost by steel} = (\text{mass})(\text{sp. ht. cap.})(T - 52) = 1 \times 480(T - 52) = 480T - 24\,960$$

Equating: $480T - 24\,960 = 268\,800$

$$480T = 293760$$

$$T = \frac{293760}{480} = \underline{612°\text{C}}$$

Actually this would be a low estimate as some heat would be lost.

Exercises 8e

1. The dimensions of a workshop are 40 m × 16 m × 12·5 m and the ventilation system is such that the air in the shop is changed twice per hour. If the temperature in the shop is 20°C and the outside temperature 12°C, calculate the heat lost per hour by the shop due to the two air changes. [Sp. ht. capacity of air = 1000 J/kg °C, density of air = 1·3 kg/m³.] Give the answer in megajoules.

2. A piece of steel mass 5 kg is taken from a furnace at 700°C and plunged into 8 litres (8 kg) of water at 15°C. If 10% of the heat is lost, estimate the temperature of the water when steady conditions have been reached. [Sp. ht. capacity of steel = 480 J/kg °C.]

3. Water flows through a gas-heated boiler at the rate of 12 litres per minute, and its temperature is raised from 20°C to 70°C by the boiler. If the efficiency of the boiler is 70% and the gas used yields 18 MJ/m³ when burned, calculate the gas consumption of the boiler in cubic metres per hour.

4. A piece of steel of mass 1·25 kg is taken from a furnace and quickly transferred into a tank containing 3 litres of water. The initial temperature of the water was 15°C, and the final steady temperature was 50°C. Assume that no heat escaped during the process, and estimate the temperature of the steel when taken from the furnace.

5. An oil-cooling arrangement consists of a nest of tubes through which the oil flows, the tubes being subjected to a circulation of cooling water on their exterior. The oil flows through the tubes at the rate of 18 litres/min, its entering temperature is 80°C, and it is desired to cool this down to 30°C. Estimate what flow of water will be necessary if it enters at 18°C and leaves at 28°C. [1 litre oil = 0·9 kg, sp. ht. cap. of oil = 2000 J/kg °C.]

6. In a certain locality the cost of gas for industrial heating was 4p per cubic metre, and the cost of coal £12·00 per tonne (= 1000 kg). The heating value of the gas was 18 MJ/m³ and of the coal 25 MJ/kg. Assuming an efficiency of application of 90% for the gas and 60% for the coal, compare the relative costs of heating by gas and coal.

Heat energy

Heat is a form of energy, and when mechanical work is dissipated by friction it is converted into heat. Most of our mechanical energy is derived from heat by converting it through some form of heat engine. The relation between heat and mechanical energy was at one time called *Joule's Equivalent*, after the famous scientist Joule. The use of Joule's Equivalent is not required when using SI units, as heat and other forms of energy use the same unit.

Example 21. If 1 kg of coal when burned yields 25 MJ, estimate the mass of coal required per hour to generate 100 kW if the overall efficiency is 10%.

$$\text{We have that } \frac{\text{Output}}{\text{Input}} = \text{Efficiency} = \frac{10}{100}.$$

$$\text{Output} = 100\,\text{kW, Input} = 100\,\text{kW} \times \frac{100}{10} = 1000\,\text{kW}$$

$$1000\,\text{kW} = 1000\,000\,\text{W} = 1000\,000\,\text{J/s} = 10^6\,\text{J/s}$$

$$\text{Heat energy required per hour} = 10^6 \times 3600\,\text{J}$$

$$\text{Heat energy in 1 kg of coal} = 25\,\text{MJ} = 25 \times 10^6\,\text{J}$$

$$\text{Mass required} = \frac{3600 \times 10^6}{25 \times 10^6} = \underline{144\,\text{kg}}$$

Example 22. A machining operation is cooled by soluble oil having a specific heat capacity of 3000 J/kg°C, flowing at the rate of 60 litres/min. If 10 kW is being absorbed at the cutting point and 80% of the heat generated is taken away by the cooling oil, calculate its rise in temperature. [1 litre of coolant = 0·9 kg].

Assuming all the power to be dissipated as heat at the cutting point, we have:

Heat generated per minute at the cutting point
= 10 kW for one minute = 10 000 J/s × 60 s = 600 000 J

$$\text{Heat taken away by coolant} = \tfrac{8}{10} \times 600\,000\,\text{J} = 480\,000\,\text{J}$$

$$\text{Heat taken up by coolant} = (\text{mass})(\text{sp. ht. cap.})(\text{temp rise})$$
$$= (60 \times 0{\cdot}9)(3000)(\text{temp rise})\text{ joules}$$

Equating these we have:

$$(60 \times 0{\cdot}9 \times 3000)\text{ temp rise} = 480\,000\,\text{J}$$

$$\text{Temp. rise} = \frac{480\,000}{60 \times 0{\cdot}9 \times 3000} = \underline{2{\cdot}96\,°\text{C}}$$

Example 23. The surface speed of a grinding wheel is 1200 m/min. The end of a steel bar of 40 mm square cross-section is pressed against the wheel for ¼ min, with a force of 100 N. If the coefficient of friction between the steel and the wheel is 0·4, and if half of the heat generated is absorbed by the steel, being momentarily confined to a depth of 2·5 mm, estimate the temperature rise at the surface in contact with the wheel face.

If the coefficient of friction is 0·4 and the radial pressure 100 N, the tangential resistance will be 100 × 0·4 = 40 N and the work dissipated per second $= 40\,\text{N} \times \dfrac{1200\,\text{m}}{60} = 800\,\text{Nm} = 800\,\text{J}$.

$$\therefore \text{Work dissipated in 15 s} = 12\,000\,\text{J}$$

$$\text{Heat input from work} = \tfrac{1}{2} \times 12\,000\,\text{J} = 6000\,\text{J}$$

Taking the density of steel as 7840 kg/m³, the layer of metal to which this heat is assumed to be confined = volume × density.

$$= 0{\cdot}04 \times 0{\cdot}04 \times 0{\cdot}0025 \times 7840$$
$$= 0{\cdot}031\,36\,\text{kg}$$
$$\text{Heat given} = (\text{mass})(\text{sp. ht. capacity})(\text{temp rise})$$
$$6000 = (0{\cdot}031\,36)(480)(\text{temp rise})$$
$$\text{Temp rise} = \frac{6000}{480 \times 0{\cdot}031\,36} = \underline{399\,°\text{C}}$$

Exercises 8f

1. A cutting operation is absorbing 2 kW at the tool point. Calculate the heat being generated in kilojoules per minute. If this operation is being cooled by oil flowing at the rate of 10 litres per min, and if 90% of the heat is taken away by the oil, calculate its rise in temperature. [1 litre oil = 0·9 kg; sp. ht. cap. of oil = 2500 J/kg°C.]

2. Estimate the gas consumption of an engine when it is developing 12 kW with a thermal efficiency of 20%. Take the heat value of the gas used at 18 MJ/m³, and express the answer in cubic metres of gas per hour.

3. A bearing is 140 mm diameter and runs at 500 rev/min. It carries a load of 20 kN and the coefficient of friction is 0·06. Calculate the work spent per minute in friction. If the bearing is to be cooled by a circulation of oil [sp. ht. cap. = 1600 J/kg°C], and if the temperature rise of the oil is not to exceed 8°C, what mass of oil must flow through the bearing per minute?

4. A flywheel of mass 250 kg and having a radius of gyration of 400 mm is rotating at 210 rev/min, when it is brought to rest by a brake. Calculate the heat generated at the brake. If the brake shoe is cast iron of mass 4 kg, and it absorbs half the heat generated, estimate its rise in temperature. [Spec. ht. cap. of C.I. = 540 J/kg°C.]

5. A grinding operation is absorbing 5 kW at the wheel. Calculate the rate of flow required for the cooling water if all the heat generated is taken away by the water and its rise in temperature is not to exceed 4°C. Give the answer in litres/min.

Appendix I

ISO Shafts (Hole Basis)

Tolerance Limits for Selected Grades (From BS 4500: 1969)

(Unit = 0·001 mm)

Nominal Sizes		c11		d10		e9		f7		g6		h6		k6		n6		p6		s6	
Over	Up to and Incl.	UL −	LL −	UL −	LL −	UL −	LL −	UL −	LL −	UL −	LL −	UL −	LL −	UL +	LL +	UL +	LL +	UL +	LL +	UL +	LL +
mm	mm																				
6	10	80	170	40	98	25	61	13	28	5	14	0	9	10	1	19	10	24	15	32	23
10	18	95	205	50	120	32	75	16	34	6	17	0	11	12	1	23	12	29	18	39	28
18	30	110	240	65	149	40	92	20	41	7	20	0	13	15	2	28	15	35	22	48	35
30	40	120	280	80	180	50	112	25	50	9	25	0	16	18	2	33	17	42	26	59	43
40	50	130	290																		
56	65	140	330	100	220	60	134	30	60	10	29	0	19	21	2	39	20	51	32	72	53
65	80	150	340																	78	59
80	100	170	390	120	260	72	159	36	71	12	34	0	22	25	3	45	23	59	37	93	71
100	120	180	400																	101	79
120	140	200	450	145	305	85	185	43	83	14	39	0	25	28	3	52	27	68	43	117	92
140	160	210	460																	125	100
160	180	230	480																	133	108
180	200	240	530	170	355	100	215	50	96	15	44	0	29	33	4	60	31	79	50	151	122
200	225	260	550																	159	130
225	250	280	570																	169	140

UL = Upper Limit LL = Lower Limit

Appendix II

ISO Standard H Holes (Hole Basis)

Tolerance Limits for Selected Holes. (Selected from BS 4500: 1969)

(Unit = 0·001 mm)

Nominal Sizes		H7		H8		H9		H11	
Over	Up to and includ-ing	UL	LL	UL	LL	UL	LL	UL	LL
mm	mm								
6	10	15	0	22	0	36	0	90	0
10	18	18	0	27	0	43	0	110	0
18	30	21	0	33	0	52	0	130	0
30	50	25	0	39	0	62	0	160	0
50	80	30	0	46	0	74	0	190	0
80	120	35	0	54	0	87	0	220	0
120	180	40	0	63	0	100	0	250	0
180	250	46	0	72	0	115	0	290	0

UL = Upper Limit LL = Lower Limit

Appendix III

British Standard H Hole

[Limits for H6 to H11 over the Range 6 mm to 180 mm
Abstracted from BS 1916 (1953)]

Nominal Size		High Limit (unit + 0·001 mm)						Low Limit
over	to	H6	H7	H8	H9	H10	H11	H6 to H11
6	10	9	15	22	36	58	90	0
10	18	11	18	27	43	70	110	0
18	30	13	21	33	52	84	130	0
30	50	16	25	39	62	100	160	0
50	80	19	30	46	74	120	190	0
80	120	22	35	54	87	140	220	0
120	180	25	40	63	100	160	250	0

Appendix IV

British Standard Shafts

Tolerance Limits for Selected Grades [From BS 1916 (1953)]

Shaft	Limit	Over 6 To 10	10 14	14 18	18 24	24 30	30 40	40 50	50 65	65 80	80 100	100 120	120 140	140 160	160 180
		Nominal Diameter Range (mm) and Corresponding Limits (0·001 mm)													
b9	High	−150	−150		−160		−170	−180	−190	−200	−220	−240	−260	−280	−310
	Low	−186	−193		−212		−232	−242	−264	−274	−307	−327	−360	−380	−410
c9	High	−80	−95		−110		−120	−130	−140	−150	−170	−180	−200	−210	−230
	Low	−116	−138		−162		−182	−192	−214	−224	−257	−267	−300	−310	−330
d9	High	−40	−50		−65		−80		−100		−120		−145		
	Low	−76	−93		−117		−142		−174		−207		−245		
e8	High	−25	−32		−40		−50		−60		−72		−85		
	Low	−47	−59		−73		−89		−106		−126		−148		
f7	High	−13	−16		−20		−25		−30		−36		−43		
	Low	−28	−34		−41		−50		−60		−71		−83		
g6	High	−5	−6		−7		−9		−10		−12		−14		
	Low	−14	−17		−20		−25		−29		−34		−39		
h6 & 7	High	0	0		0		0		0		0		0		
h6	Low	−9	−11		−13		−16		−19		−22		−25		
h7	Low	−15	−18		−21		−25		−30		−35		−40		
j6	High	+7	+8		+9		+11		+12		+13		+14		
	Low	−2	−3		−4		−5		−7		−9		−11		
j7	High	+10	+12		+13		+15		+18		+20		+22		
	Low	−5	−6		−8		−10		−12		−15		−18		
k6	High	+10	+12		+15		+18		+21		+25		+28		
k7	High	+16	+19		+23		+27		+32		+38		+43		
k6 & 7	Low	+1	+1		+2		+2		+2		+3		+3		
m7	High	+21	+25		+29		+34		+41		+48		+55		
	Low	+6	+7		+8		+9		+11		+13		+15		
s6	High	+32	+39		+48		+59		+72	+78	+93	+101	+117	+125	+133
s7	High	+38	+46		+56		+68		+83	+89	+106	+114	+132	+140	+148
s6 & 7	Low	+23	+28		+35		+43		+53	+59	+71	+79	+92	+100	+108

Appendix V

CONVERSION TABLE

Fractional sub-divisions of an inch to decimals and to millimetres

in	in	milli-metres	in	in	milli-metres
1/64	0·015625	0·3969	39/64	0·609375	15·4781
1/32	0·03125	0·7938	5/8	0·625	15·875
3/64	0·046875	1·1906	41/64	0·640625	16·2719
1/16	0·0625	1·5875	21/32	0·65625	16·6688
5/64	0·078125	1·9844	43/64	0·671875	17·0656
3/32	0·09375	2·3812	11/16	0·6875	17·4625
7/64	0·109375	2·7781	45/64	0·703125	17·8594
1/8	0·125	3·175	23/32	0·71875	18·2562
9/64	0·140625	3·5719	47/64	0·734375	18·6531
5/32	0·15625	3·9688	3/4	0·75	19·05
11/64	0·171875	4·3656	49/64	0·765625	19·4469
3/16	0·1875	4·7625	25/32	0·78125	19·8438
13/64	0·203125	5·1594	51/64	0·796875	20·2406
7/32	0·21875	5·5562	13/16	0·8125	20·6375
15/64	0·234375	5·9531	53/64	0·828125	21·0344
1/4	0·25	6·35	27/32	0·84375	21·4312

Millimetres to inches
Based on 1 inch = 25·4 millimetres

mm	0	1	2	3	4	5	6	7	8	9
	in	in	in	in	in	in	in	in	in	in
—	—	0·03937	0·07874	0·11811	0·15748	0·19685	0·23622	0·27559	0·31496	0·35433
10	0·39370	0·43307	0·47244	0·51181	0·55118	0·59055	0·62992	0·66929	0·70866	0·74803
20	0·78740	0·82677	0·86614	0·90551	0·94488	0·98425	1·02362	1·06299	1·10236	1·14173
30	1·18110	1·22047	1·25984	1·29921	1·33858	1·37795	1·41732	1·45669	1·49606	1·53543
40	1·57480	1·61417	1·65354	1·69291	1·73228	1·77165	1·81102	1·85039	1·88976	1·92913
50	1·96850	2·00787	2·04724	2·08661	2·12598	2·16535	2·20472	2·24409	2·28346	2·32283
60	2·36220	2·40157	2·44094	2·48031	2·51969	2·55906	2·59843	2·63780	2·67717	2·71654
70	2·75591	2·79528	2·83465	2·87402	2·91339	2·95276	2·99213	3·03150	3·07087	3·11024
80	3·14961	3·18898	3·22835	3·26772	3·30709	3·34646	3·38583	3·42520	3·46457	3·50394
90	3·54331	3·58268	3·62205	3·66142	3·70079	3·74016	3·77953	3·81890	3·85827	3·89764
100	3·93701	3·97638	4·01575	4·05512	4·09449	4·13386	4·17323	4·21260	4·25197	4·29134
10	4·33071	4·37008	4·40945	4·44882	4·48819	4·52756	4·56693	4·60630	4·64567	4·68504
20	4·72441	4·76378	4·80315	4·84252	4·88189	4·92126	4·96063	5·0000	5·0394	5·0787
30	5·1181	5·1575	5·1969	5·2362	5·2756	5·3150	5·3543	5·3937	5·4331	5·4724
40	5·5118	5·5512	5·5906	5·6299	5·6693	5·7087	5·7480	5·7874	5·8268	5·8661
50	5·9055	5·9449	5·9843	6·0236	6·0630	6·1024	6·1417	6·1811	6·2205	6·2598
60	6·2992	6·3386	6·3780	6·4173	4·4567	6·4961	6·5354	6·5748	6·6142	6·6535
70	6·6929	6·7323	6·7717	6·8110	6·8504	6·8898	6·9291	6·9685	7·0079	7·0472
80	7·0866	7·1260	7·1654	7·2047	7·2441	7·2835	7·3228	7·3622	7·4016	7·4409
90	7·4803	7·5197	7·5591	7·5984	7·6378	7·6772	7·7165	7·7559	7·7953	7·8346
200	7·8740	7·9134	7·9528	7·9921	8·0315	8·0709	8·1102	8·1496	8·1890	8·2283

17/64	0·265625	6·7469
9/32	0·28125	7·1438
19/64	0·296875	7·5406
5/16	0·3125	7·9375
21/64	0·328125	8·3344
11/32	0·34375	8·7312
23/64	0·359375	9·1281
3/8	0·375	9·525
25/64	0·390625	9·9219
13/32	0·40625	10·3188
27/64	0·421875	10·7156
7/16	0·4375	11·1125
29/64	0·453125	11·5094
15/32	0·46875	11·9062
31/64	0·484375	12·3031
1/2	0·5	12·7
33/64	0·515625	13·0969
17/32	0·53125	13·4938
35/64	0·546875	13·8906
9/16	0·5625	14·2875
37/64	0·578125	14·6844
19/32	0·59375	15·0812

55/64	0·859375	21·8281
7/8	0·875	22·225
57/64	0·890625	22·6219
29/32	0·90625	23·0188
59/64	0·921875	23·4156
15/16	0·9375	23·8125
61/64	0·953125	24·2094
31/32	0·96875	24·6062
63/64	0·984375	25·0031
1	1	25·4
2	2	50·800
3	3	76·200
4	4	101·600
5	5	127·000
6	6	152·400
7	7	177·800
8	8	203·200
9	9	228·600
10	10	254·000
11	11	279·400
12	12	304·800

10	8·2677	8·3071	8·3465	8·3858	8·4252	8·4646	8·5039	8·5433	8·5827	8·6220
20	8·6614	8·7008	8·7402	8·7795	8·8189	8·8583	8·8976	8·9370	8·9764	9·0157
30	9·0551	9·0945	9·1339	9·1732	9·2126	9·2520	9·2913	9·3307	9·3701	9·4094
40	9·4488	9·4882	9·5276	9·5669	9·6063	9·6457	9·6850	9·7244	9·7638	9·8031
50	9·8425	9·8819	9·9213	9·9606	10·0000	10·0394	10·0787	10·1181	10·1575	10·1969
60	10·2362	10·2756	10·3150	10·3543	10·3937	10·4331	10·4724	10·5118	10·5512	10·5906
70	10·6299	10·6693	10·7087	10·7480	10·7874	10·8268	10·8661	10·9055	10·9449	10·9843
80	11·0236	11·0630	11·1024	11·1417	11·1811	11·2205	11·2598	11·2992	11·3386	11·3780
90	11·4173	11·4567	11·4961	11·5354	11·5748	11·6142	11·6535	11·6929	11·7323	11·7717
300	11·8110	11·8504	11·8898	11·9291	11·9685	12·0079	12·0472	12·0866	12·1260	12·1654
10	12·2047	12·2441	12·2835	12·3228	12·3622	12·4016	12·4409	12·4803	12·5197	12·5591
20	12·5984	12·6378	12·6772	12·7165	12·7559	12·7953	12·8346	12·8740	12·9134	12·9528
30	12·9921	13·0315	13·0709	13·1102	13·1496	13·1890	13·2283	13·2677	13·3071	13·3465
40	13·3858	13·4252	13·4646	13·5039	13·5433	13·5827	13·6220	13·6614	13·7008	13·7402
50	13·7795	13·8189	13·8583	13·8976	13·9370	13·9764	14·0157	14·0551	14·0945	14·1339
60	14·1732	14·2126	14·2520	14·2913	14·3307	14·3701	14·4094	14·4488	14·4882	14·5276
70	14·5669	14·6063	14·6457	14·6850	14·7244	14·7638	14·8031	14·8425	14·8819	14·9213
80	14·9606	15·0000	15·0394	15·0787	15·1181	15·1575	15·1969	15·2362	15·2756	15·3150
90	15·3543	15·3937	15·4331	15·4724	15·5118	15·5512	15·5906	15·6299	15·6693	15·7087
400	15·7480	15·7874	15·8268	15·8661	15·9055	15·9449	15·9843	16·0236	16·0630	16·1024
10	16·1417	16·1811	16·2205	16·2598	16·2992	16·3386	16·3780	16·4173	16·4567	16·4961
20	16·5354	16·5748	16·6142	16·6535	16·6929	16·7323	16·7717	16·8110	16·8504	16·8898
30	16·9291	16·9685	17·0079	17·0472	17·0866	17·1260	17·1654	17·2047	17·2441	17·2835
40	17·3228	17·3622	17·4016	17·4409	17·4803	17·5197	17·5591	17·5984	17·6378	17·6772
50	17·7165	17·7559	17·7953	17·8346	17·8740	17·9134	17·9528	17·9921	18·0315	18·0709
60	18·1102	18·1496	18·1890	18·2283	18·2677	18·3071	18·3465	18·3858	18·4252	18·4646
70	18·5039	18·5433	18·5827	18·6220	18·6614	18·7008	18·7402	18·7795	18·8189	18·8583
80	18·8976	18·9370	18·9764	19·0157	19·0551	19·0945	19·1339	19·1732	19·2126	19·2520
90	19·2913	19·3307	19·3701	19·4094	19·4488	19·4882	19·5276	19·5669	19·6063	19·6457
500	19·6850	19·7244	19·7638	19·8031	19·8425	19·8819	19·9213	19·9606	20·0000	20·0394

For full list of conversions refer to BS S 350 parts 1 and 2

GKN Bolts and Nuts Limited

Appendix VI
The Trigonometrical Addition Formulae

It is sometimes necessary to express the trigonometrical ratios of the sum or difference of two angles in terms of their individual ratios. The conditions are shown in Fig. 158 and the formulae are quoted without proof. If the reader wishes to pursue the proof he can do so by consulting any trigonometrical textbook.

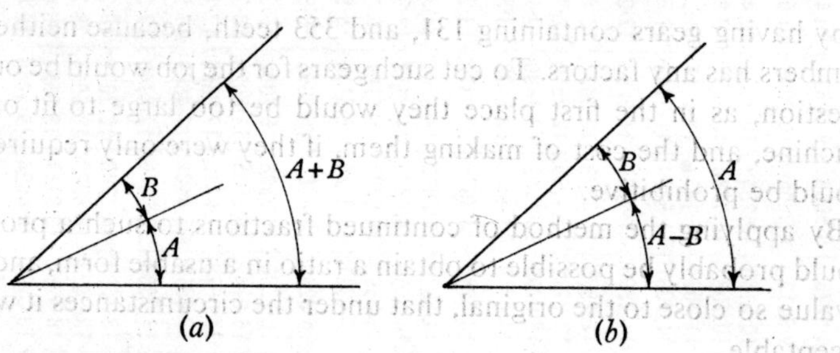

Fig. 158

In Fig. 158 (a),

$$\sin(A+B) = \sin A\cos B + \cos A\sin B$$
$$\cos(A+B) = \cos A\cos B - \sin A\sin B$$
$$\tan(A+B) = \frac{\tan A + \tan B}{1 - \tan A\tan B}$$

In Fig. 158 (*b*),

$$\sin(A-B) = \sin A\cos B - \cos A\sin B$$
$$\cos(A-B) = \cos A\cos B + \sin A\sin B$$
$$\tan(A-B) = \frac{\tan A - \tan B}{1 + \tan A\tan B}$$

By writing B = A in (A + B) we get:

$$\sin 2A = 2\sin A\cos A$$
$$\cos 2A = \cos^2 A - \sin^2 A = 2\cos^2 A - 1 = 1 - 2\sin^2 A \text{ (since } \cos^2 A + \sin^2 A = 1)$$
$$\tan 2A = \frac{2\tan A}{1 - \tan^2 A}$$

Appendix VII
Continued Fractions

A continued fraction is a series of fractions derived from a single complicated fraction, each fraction in the series approaching more nearly to the value of the fraction from which the series was derived.

If during the course of our work we required to obtain a gear ratio (e.g. for cutting an obscure screw pitch) of, say, $\frac{131}{353}$, we could only do it by having gears containing 131, and 353 teeth, because neither of the numbers has any factors. To cut such gears for the job would be out of the question, as in the first place they would be too large to fit on to the machine, and the cost of making them, if they were only required once, would be prohibitive.

By applying the method of continued fractions to such a problem, it would probably be possible to obtain a ratio in a usable form, and having a value so close to the original, that under the circumstances it would be acceptable.

For the purpose of explaining the method we will convert the above ratio to a continued fraction:

Example 18. Put the numbers down as a division sum only *divide the numerator into the denominator*

```
                                131)353(2
                                    262
Now divide this into the             91)131(1
    original divisor                     91
Divide into the last divisor             40)91(2
                                            80
Divide into the last divisor                11)40(3
    (and so on every time)                     33
                                                7)11(1
                                                   7
                                                   4)7(1
                                                     4
                                                     3)4(1
                                                       3
                                                       1)3(3
                                                         3
```

The quotients obtained from the continued division are

2, 1, 2, 3, 1, 1, 1 and 3.

These may now be written as the denominators of a continued fraction as follows:

```
A
1     C
-------
2 + 1      E
    ---------
    1 + 1      G
B       ---------
        2 + 1      J
D           ---------
            3 + 1      L
    F           ---------
                1 + 1      N
        H           ---------
                    1 + 1
            K           ---------
                        1 + 1
                M           ---
                            3
                        P
```

We now have to find what are called the "convergents" of this fraction. In simpler terms, the convergents are approximations to the actual value of the fraction. They are, in value, alternately too large and too small, but each time they approach nearer to the actual value (hence the term convergent).

1st convergent [Down to line AB] $= \frac{1}{2}$

2nd convergent [To line CD] $= \cfrac{1}{2 + \cfrac{1}{1}} = \frac{1}{3}$

3rd convergent [To line EF] $= \cfrac{1}{2 + \cfrac{1}{1 + \cfrac{1}{2}}} = \cfrac{1}{2 + \cfrac{1}{1\frac{1}{2}}} = \cfrac{1}{2 + \frac{2}{3}}$

$= \cfrac{1}{\frac{8}{3}} = \frac{3}{8}$

4th convergent [to line GH] $= \cfrac{1}{2 + \cfrac{1}{1 + \cfrac{1}{2 + \cfrac{1}{3}}}} = \cfrac{1}{2 + \cfrac{1}{1 + \cfrac{1}{2\frac{1}{3}}}}$

$$= \cfrac{1}{2 + \cfrac{1}{1 + \frac{3}{7}}} = \cfrac{1}{2 + \cfrac{1}{\frac{10}{7}}} = \cfrac{1}{2 + \frac{7}{10}} = \cfrac{1}{\frac{27}{10}} = \frac{10}{27}$$

5th convergent [to line JK] $= \cfrac{1}{2 + \cfrac{1}{1 + \cfrac{1}{2 + \cfrac{1}{3 + \cfrac{1}{1}}}}} = \cfrac{1}{2 + \cfrac{1}{1 + \cfrac{1}{2 + \frac{1}{4}}}}$

$$= \cfrac{1}{2 + \cfrac{1}{1 + \frac{4}{9}}} = \cfrac{1}{2 + \cfrac{1}{\frac{13}{9}}} = \cfrac{1}{2 + \frac{9}{13}} = \cfrac{1}{\frac{35}{13}} = \frac{13}{35}$$

6th convergent [to line LM] $= \cfrac{1}{2 + \cfrac{1}{1 + \cfrac{1}{2 + \cfrac{1}{3 + \cfrac{1}{1 + \cfrac{1}{1}}}}}}$

$$= \cfrac{1}{2 + \cfrac{1}{1 + \cfrac{1}{2 + \cfrac{1}{3 + \frac{1}{2}}}}} = \cfrac{1}{2 + \cfrac{1}{1 + \cfrac{1}{2 + \frac{2}{7}}}} = \cfrac{1}{2 + \cfrac{1}{1 + \cfrac{1}{\frac{16}{7}}}}$$

$$= \cfrac{1}{2 + \cfrac{1}{1 + \frac{7}{16}}} = \cfrac{1}{2 + \cfrac{1}{\frac{23}{16}}} = \cfrac{1}{2\frac{16}{23}} = \cfrac{1}{\frac{62}{23}} = \frac{23}{62}.$$

7th convergent [to line NP]. (The reader should now be able to check this for himself) $= \frac{36}{97}$
8th convergent [whole fraction] $= \frac{131}{353}$

The values of the convergents, their decimal equivalents and the error (+ or −) from the true value of the original fraction, are set down in the following table.

Original Fraction = $\frac{131}{353}$ = 0·3711

Convergent No.	Value.	Decimal Equiv.	Error + or −.
1	$\frac{1}{2}$	0·5000	+0·1289
2	$\frac{1}{3}$	0·3333	−0·0378
3	$\frac{3}{8}$	0·3750	+0·0039
4	$\frac{10}{27}$	0·3704	−0·0007
5	$\frac{13}{35}$	0·3714	+0·0003
6	$\frac{23}{62}$	0·3710	−0·0001
7	$\frac{36}{97}$	0·37113	+0·00003
8	$\frac{131}{353}$	0·3711	0·0000

If a graph of the error against the convergent No. is plotted it will be somewhat like Fig. 159. It will be noticed that the error is only 0·0007 even at the 4th convergent, even although this is a very simple fraction ($\frac{10}{27}$).

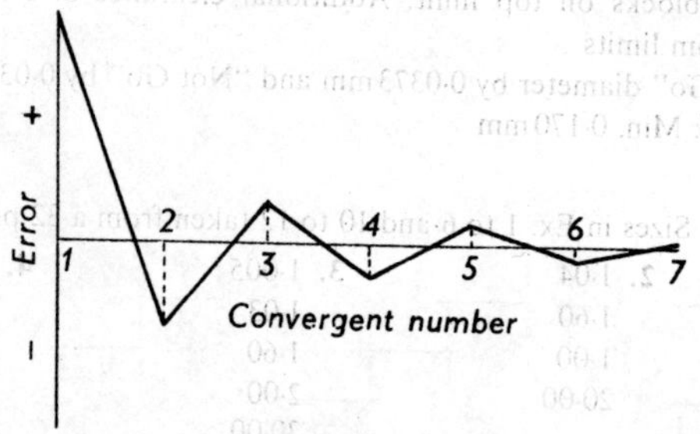

Fig. 159

Answers to exercises

Exercises 2a

	Hole (mm)	Shaft (mm)	Clearance (mm)	
1.	75·120	74·940	max	0·226
	75·000	74·894	min	0·060
2.	35·062	35·018	max	0·060
	35·000	35·002	min	−0·018 (interference).
3.	20·021	19·980	max	0·062
	20·000	19·959	min	0·020
4.	57·046	57·083	max	−0·007
	57·000	57·053	min	−0·083 (interference).

5. Centre distance 108·98 mm; "Not Go" diameter 12·06 mm
6. 40·0062 mm diameter
7. Open out "Go" and "Not Go" ends by 0·052 mm
8. Same fit with blocks on top limit. Additional clearance of 0·017 mm with pair of blocks on bottom limits
9. Yes. Reduce "Go" diameter by 0·0373 mm and "Not Go" by 0·036 mm
10. Max. 0·271 mm: Min. 0·170 mm

Exercises 2b. Sizes in Ex. 1 to 6 and 10 to 12 taken from a 32 piece set of ships

1. 1·01, 1·10, 9·00

2. 1·04, 1·60, 1·00, 20·00

3. 1·005, 1·03, 1·60, 2·00, 30·00

4. 1·08, 1·70, 6·00, 60·00

5. 1·70, 4·00, 10·00, 60·00

6. 1·06, 1·30, 3·00, 20·00, 30·00, 60·00

7. 0·105, 0·170, 0·100

8. 0·150, 0·600, 1·000

9. 0·1005, 0·108, 0·180, 0·800, 2·000

10. (*a*) 1·005, 1·12, 1·80, 1·00, 30·00
(*b*) 1·05, 1·90, 2·00, 10·00, 20·00

11.

"Go" end.	"Not go" end.
1·005	1·05
1·17	1·90
1·80	9·00
6·00	8·00
20·00	10·00

12. 1·08, 4·00, 10·00

Exercises 2c

1. 0·30 mm **3.** 10·31 mm **4.** One end 41·40 mm higher
5. 0° 6′ too steep **6.** BC = 41·725 mm; CD = 47·84 mm;
AD = 86·84 mm; y = 13·10 mm; x = 29·17 mm
7. True angle = 37° 43′; error 0° 1′ **8.** 500·09 mm; 0·108 mm
9. 75·79 mm. **10.** 10·16 mm **11.** 10·5 mm

Exercises 2d

1. 35° 18′ **2.** 22° 20′ **3.** 47° 4′ **4.** (a) 39° 46′; (b) $a = 8$, $b = 16$; (c) 25·01
5. 25° 50′ **6.** a = 46·23 mm, α = 30° 18′ **7.** A = 152·19 mm; B = 57·81 mm
8. AB = 103·5 mm; 29° 32′; 34° 12′

Exercises 2e

1. 4·366 mm; 25° 2′ **2.** 11·67 mm **3.** A = 58·506 mm; B = 56·006 mm
4. $(25 - H)^2 = 225 - \dfrac{(102 - D)^2}{4}$; 16·708 mm **5.** $d = \dfrac{D}{3}$; 26·67 mm **6.** 9° 12′

Exercises 2f

1. (a) 20·53 mm; (b) 36·43 mm; (c) 0·767 in
2. Normal to axis, 58·9 mm diagonally across plugs, 59·26 mm
3. 10·99 mm **4.** 12·94 mm **5.** 15·4 mm **6.** 52·804 mm
7. 14·16 mm **8.** 64·05 mm

Exercises 3a

1.

28	39	54	75	104	145	202	280	rev/min
250	180	130	94	68	49	35	25	mm Dia

2.

877	1260	1820	2630	rev/min
6	4	3	2	mm Dia

4. 413 rev/min; 237 mm, 119 mm, 60 mm **5.** 5500 rev/min

Exercises 3b

1. C = 32·28; 35·15 h **3.** 25·2 m/min **4.** $\dfrac{\text{Tung. Carb.}}{\text{H.S.S.}} = \dfrac{2{\cdot}8}{1}$ approx
5. $T = \dfrac{1500 - 27v}{v - 20}$; 165 **6.** Rake 12° 10′, Clearance 14° 50′
7. 2·61 mm; 21° **8.** 15° 1′ **9.** α = 7° 18′; β = 22° 13′
10. Rake 19° 36′; Clearance 15° 36′

Exercises 3c

1. 58° 30′ **2.** 1 in 6·08; **3.** 29°
4. (a) 1·55 mm; (b) 0·65 mm; (c) 7° 32′

5. 8·05 mm; 3° 55′ to 4° 2′
6. 7·07 mm; 2·47 mm; 70° 38′
7. Angle 41° 18′: Depth 6·95 mm Land 3·8 mm
8. 4·78 mm; 1·66 mm
9. 2·44 mm; 6·08 mm; 21° 57′ with Horiz.
10. (*a*) 2·04 mm; (*b*) 29·6 mm; (*c*) 11° 23′

Exercises 3d

1. $\frac{13}{55} = \frac{20 \times 65}{50 \times 110}$; 1·5009 mm
2. $\frac{22}{35}$; Actual lead 3·1428 mm; Error + 0·0012 mm
3. 4·433 mm; nearest 4·432 with $\frac{39}{44}$ ratio; 66·47 mm/min
4. (*a*) 1·93 kW; (*b*) 1·11 mm³/J
5. 3·12 mm; **6.** 10 mm
7. 38·4*p*
8. 13·98 Nm (*a*) 0·44 kW; (*b*) 1·12 J/mm³
9. 1400 rev/min; 73·21 Nm; 13·9 kW
10. 53·3 mm; 1·1*p*
11. Nearest Ratio $= \frac{20}{49} = \frac{40 \times 25}{35 \times 70}$; Pitch = 2·041 mm

Exercises 4a

1. 6·69 mm; (*a*) 69·52 mm (*b*) 0·56 mm
2. (*a*) w = 9·435 mm; h = 6·1 mm; (*b*) w = 10·00 mm; h = 6·37 mm
3. Cutting 0·06 mm too shallow.
4. Cutting 0·17 mm too deep; Tooth 0·12 mm thin; Space 0·13 mm wide.
5. (*a*) w = 11·10 mm, h = 5·98 mm; (*b*) w = 11·04 mm, h = 5·95 mm
6. 7·38 mm; (*a*) 257·38 mm (*b*) 183·56 mm **7.** 197·47 mm
8. (*a*) 23·63 mm; (*b*) 18·79 mm
9. (*a*) 184·5 mm; (*b*) 140·6 mm; (*c*) 98 mm; (*d*) 78 mm

Exercises 4b

1. P.D. = 210 mm; T.D. = 218 mm; Depth = 9 mm
2. w = 8·66 mm; h = 4·02 mm
3. T = 40T; P.D. = 200 mm; T.D. = 208 mm; t = 24t;
p.d. = 120 mm; *t.d.* = 128 mm; Depth = 9 mm
4. 179·7 mm **5.** 0·233°
6. (*a*) 221·35 mm; (*b*) 229·35 mm; (*c*) 9 mm; (*d*) 1910 mm; (*e*) 63.
7. (*a*) 27; (*b*) P.D. 124·71 mm, T.D. 132·71 mm; (*c*) 678 mm; (*d*) 35.
8. 2 P.D. = 70·71 mm; T.D. = 74·71 mm; lead = 222 mm; 4·5 mm
9. Gear: 45T, 120 mm P.D.; 125 mm T.D.; Helix angle, 20° 22′; lead, 1016 mm
Pinion: 30T, 80 mm P.D., 85 mm T.D.; Helix angle, 20° 22′, lead, 677 mm

Exercises 4c

1. T.D. = 46·36 mm; R.D. = 32·23 mm; λ = 9° 2′.
2. 35T; P.D. 111·40 mm; T.D. 117·76 mm; Centre Dist 75·70 mm; Throat rad. 16·82 mm; Whole dia. 124·71 mm; 32·71 mm [Face angle 75°.]
3. 6; λ = 30°26′; 8·62 mm
4. Wheel: 75T; P.D. 238·73 mm; throat dia. 245·09 mm; rad. 27·45 mm. Worm: 5 start; P.D. 61·27 mm; T.D. 67·63 mm; λ = 14°34′

5. $T = 24$; P. angle, 45°; Cone dist., 42·42 mm; Add. angle, 3° 22′; Ded. angle, 4° 14′; Face, 48° 22′; Root, 40° 46′; Whole dia., 69·54 mm; Tip dist., 28·23 mm.

6. Wheel: 39T; $D = 195$ mm; Angles: $P = 56° 18′$; Add., 2° 27′; Ded., 3° 3′; Face, 58° 45′; Root, 53° 15′; Whole dia., 200·55 mm.

Pinion: 26t; $d = 130$ mm; Angles: $P = 33° 42′$; Add., 2° 27′; Ded., 3° 3′; Face, 36° 9′; Root, 30° 39′; Whole dia. 138·32 mm; Cone dist., 117·16 mm.

7. 5·9 mm; 5° 58′.

8. Wheel: 24T; P.D. = 120 mm; Angles: $P = 73° 54′$; Add., 4° 34′; Ded., 5° 43′; Whole dia, 122·77 mm; Cone dist., 62·45 mm.

Pinion: 18T; P.D. = 90 mm; Angles: $P = 46° 6′$; Add., 4° 34′; Ded., 5° 43′; Whole dia., 96·93 mm.

Exercises 5a

1. (*a*) 14; (*b*) 6·51 mm; (*c*) 4·57 mm **2.** 25 to 30; 31·19 mm.

3. 7° 31′; negative. **4.** 9° 26′. **5.** $82\frac{1}{2}°$ **6.** 4·82 mm.

Exercises 5b

1. 70 rev/min, 189 mm/min **2.** 60 480 mm³, 983 W **3.** 6 mm.

4. 2·04 min **5.** Spiral mill. **6.** 0·43 kW, 2·5 min, 0·035p.

Exercises 5c

[In the answers to Exercises 5c and 5d, whole numbers refer to complete turns of the crank, numerators of fractions to holes, and denominators to hole circles. When the fraction is a simple one (e.g. $\frac{1}{3}$) it has been left in that form. Numerators of gear ratios are drivers, and denominators are driven gears.]

1. (*a*) $3\frac{1}{3}$; (*b*) $2\frac{2}{3}$; (*c*) $1\frac{27}{33}$; (*d*) $1\frac{3}{17}$; (*e*) $\frac{40}{41}$; (*f*) $\frac{4}{5}$; (*g*) $\frac{20}{31}$; (*h*) $\frac{10}{19}$

2. (*a*) $3\frac{3}{39}$; (*b*) $2\frac{18}{51}$; (*c*) $1\frac{15}{25}$; (*d*) $1\frac{6}{54}$; (*e*) $\frac{48}{54}$; (*f*) $\frac{40}{54}$; (*g*) $\frac{24}{39}$; (*h*) $\frac{20}{41}$

3. (*a*) $1\frac{2}{3}$; (*b*) $2\frac{16}{18}$; (*c*) $3\frac{2}{3}$; (*d*) $5\frac{15}{18}$; (*e*) $7\frac{2}{27}$.

4. (*a*) $1\frac{45}{54}$; (*b*) $2\frac{2}{24}$; (*c*) $3\frac{26}{54}$; (*d*) $8\frac{1}{4}$; (*e*) $15\frac{9}{54}$

5. $1\frac{4}{9}$; 3 mm

6. (*a*) $\frac{2}{17} + \frac{12}{18}$; (*b*) $\frac{4}{21} + \frac{12}{27}$; (*c*) $\frac{23}{29} - \frac{9}{27}$; (*d*) $\frac{6}{21} - \frac{2}{17}$

7. $\dfrac{40\text{C}.c}{c\text{N} - \text{C}n}$

8. (*a*) 13 holes; 33 circle; Gears, $\frac{32}{44} \times \frac{64}{48}$; plate to turn in same direction as crank. (*b*) 20 holes; 27 circle; Gears, $\frac{40}{72} \times \frac{64}{48}$; plate turn same direction as crank. (*c*) 8 holes; 20 circle; Gears, $\frac{40}{100}$; plate to turn opposite to crank. (*d*) 10 holes, 33 circle; Gears, $\frac{40}{44} \times \frac{27}{42}$; plate to turn same direction as crank.

[*Note.*—Other solutions are possible to 8(*a*), (*b*), (*c*) and (*d*).]

9. 33° 20′ **10.** $5\frac{35}{49}$; $8\frac{28}{49}$; $11\frac{21}{49}$; $14\frac{14}{49}$

Exercises 5d

1. (*a*) $1\frac{5}{28}$; 10° 36′ 26″; (*b*) $4\frac{3}{5}$; 41° 24′; (*c*) $8\frac{5}{12}$; 75° 45′

2. $1\frac{2}{9}$. [$1\frac{3}{14}$ is nearer and could be obtained on Cincinnati.]

3. $7\frac{4}{15}$ **4.** (*a*) $\dfrac{100 \times 32}{48 \times 56}$; (*b*) $\dfrac{100 \times 24}{72 \times 48}$; (*c*) $\dfrac{32}{72}$; (*d*) $\dfrac{40 \times 24}{64 \times 48}$

5. $\frac{80 \times 24}{82 \times 48}$; $\alpha = 37° 28'$
6. $\frac{44}{56} \times \frac{48}{24}$; 24° 1′ between axes of work and cutter
7. 720 mm lead; $\frac{10}{36}$ ratio; 19° 14′ **8.** Nearest = $\frac{48}{44} \times \frac{24}{24}$ (based on 245 mm lead)
9. 72 mm; gear ratio $\frac{2}{1}$; $\alpha = 33° 10'$
10. Gear ratio $\frac{3}{1}$; $\alpha = 22° 1'$; lead = 25 mm
11. Lead = 60 mm; gear ratio = $\frac{5}{3}$; $\alpha = 30°$
[*Note*.—Other solutions are possible to Nos. 9, 10 and 11.]

Exercises 5e

1. 29°58′ **2.** 67°23′ **3.** 49°6′ **4.** (*a*) 41°6′; (*b*) 97°2′
5. 55·4 mm; 245·8 mm; 12° 52′ **6.** (*a*) 50° 46′; (*b*) 104° 28′

Exercises 6a

[In the solutions to Ex. 6*a* the angle given is that made with the vertical or horizontal drawn to the commencing end of the vector.]

2. (*a*) 7·21 upwards; 34° to R of vert
(*b*) 10·85 downwards to L; 41° below horiz
(*c*) 10·94 downwards; 4° to R of vert
(*d*) 3·1 R to L; 44° below horiz
(*e*) 3·4 downwards; 13° to L of vert
(*f*) 12 L to R; 5° below horiz
3. (*a*) 7·2 upwards; 34° to L of vert
(*b*) 10·85 upwards; 41° above horiz
(*c*) 2·2 upwards; 21° to R of vert
(*d*) 13·4 R to L; 32° above horiz
4. (*e*) 14·5 upwards; 40° to R of vert
(*f*) 9·3 downwards; 12° to L of vert
5. $ac = 6{\cdot}6$; $cb = 5{\cdot}5$; $\widehat{abc} = 50°$.
6. 5 units L to R; 37° above horiz
7. $ac = 21$; $cb = 7{\cdot}6$ vert downwards.
8. $ab = 8{\cdot}7$ L to R; 30° above horiz; $bc = 5$ downwards; 30° to R of vert

Exercises 6b

1. R to L (outwards); 3°38′ to lathe centre line. **2.** Horiz 38·3 N; vert 32·1 N
3. 212 N; 53 N/mm² **4.** 0·085 m/s; 45° to horiz. **5.** 250 N
6. Suspension chain 200 N; pulling chain 102 N **7.** 233 N; 552 N

Exercises 6c

1. 1 530 N in a plane at 34° to vertical; line of action inclined at 71° to 500 N force.
2. 11 mm **3.** 309 N; 904 N **4.** 216 lb.; 34° to horiz.
5. 130 N; 200 N **6.** 520 N; 26° to horiz. **7.** 176 N horiz. L. to R.
8. 2860 N **9.** 242 mm rad; 98° from 50 kg mass **10.** 5540 N
11. 64 800 mm³; 112° from A

Exercises 6d

1. (*a*) 5·36 m/s,; (*b*) 4·64 m/s **2.** 6·34 m/s **3.** (*a*) 1·14; (*b*) 16·8 rpm.
4. 0·8 m/s, 0·96 mm³ **5.** 0·00296 m/s; 24° to OA **6.** 0·8 m/s
7. 0·088 m/s **8.** 856 N **9.** 0·0051 m/s; 7840 N
10. (*a*) $\frac{3}{1}$; (*b*) 0·244 m/s. **11.** 0·000 52 m/s

Exercises 6e

1. 170 N **2.** 8 N **3.** Headstock 319 N; tailstock 531 N
4. Front bearing 1620 N upwards; rear bearing 417 N downwards.
5. Right 285 N; left, 374 N **6.** 1600 N, 600 N
7. 177 N **8.** 80 N

Exercises 7a

1. 25·6 N; 25·4 N at 6° 57′ to horiz. **2.** 750 N **3.** 12 300 N
4. 75·6 lb **5.** 0·112 kW **6.** 0·792 kW

Exercise 7b

1. 36·4; 93·9 N **2.** 1·97 kW **3.** 51·9 N **4.** 118 N
5. 69%; 15 600 N **6.** 121 N **7.** 5·30 N **8.** 35·1%
9. 2340 J, 385·7 N **10.** 1200 N **11.** 10 Nm

Exercises 7c

1. $d = 44{\cdot}7$ mm; $L = 95{\cdot}4$ mm
2. RH load = 1160 N; B. press = 0·29 N/mm²
LH load = 1740 N; B. press = 0·435 N/mm²
3. $\mu = 0{\cdot}0158$, 52·2 J **4.** 84·6 mm **5.** $\mu = 0{\cdot}032$, 1·14 kW
6. 50 300 N **7.** 7950 N 63·2 N **8.** 50·9 N/mm²; 0·204 mm
9. 21·7 N/mm² **10.** Stress = 200 N/mm²; tension = 40 000 N

Exercises 8a

1. 10 rev/min²; 75 revs **2.** 1·28 s, 12·5 m/s **3.** 0·75 m/s²; 0·8 s
4. 14·4 m/s² **5.** 0·4 m/s²; 0·6 m/s **6.** 3 rev/min²; 1 min
7. 2·25 m; 7·5 s **8.** 0·5 m/s; 15 s

Exercises 8b

1. 10 N **2.** 1 m/s **3.** 355 N **4.** 72 N
5. 17·3 N **6.** 1·28 m/s²; 144 N; 0·96 m/s; 0·138 kW
7. 10·8 m/s; 5890 m/s²; 589 kN **8.** 320 mm

Exercises 8c

1. 18·31; 1050. **2.** 6·55 s **3.** 14·9 rad/s²
4. 157 500 J; 5250 N **6.** 18·75 J; 31·25 N **7.** 8 J; 320 J

Exercises 8d

1. 22 700 J **2.** 6940 J **3.** 101 N **4.** 16·5 s
5. 131 N **6.** 3·6 rev/min **7.** 63 200 N **8.** 13·6 rev/min

Exercises 8e

1. 83·2 MJ **2.** 56·4°C **3.** 12 m^3
4. 785°C **5.** 38·6 litres/min **6.** $\dfrac{\text{Cost gas}}{\text{Cost coal}} = \dfrac{3{\cdot}09}{1}$

Exercises 8f

1. 120 kJ; 4·8°C **2.** 12 m^3/h **3.** 264 000 J; 20·6 kg
4. 9680 J; 2·24°C **5.** 17·9 litres/min

Index

An *Easy* ... ARITHMETIC

Ruth Beechick

Mott Media

112 East Ellen, Fenton, MI 48430

Other books in ***The Three R's*** series include:

A Strong Start in Language

A Home Start in Reading

More homeschooling books by this author include:

You CAN Teach Your Child Successfully: Grades 4-8

Dr. Beechick's Homeschool Answer Book

The Language Wars and other Writings for Homeschoolers

GENESIS: Finding Our Roots

Adam and His Kin: The Lost History of their Lives and Times

Printed in the United States of America.

ISBN 0-940319-01-2

Contents

Arithmetic Can Be Easy for Your Child

Does arithmetic have to be dull and difficult? Does it have to be frightening for you or your pupils? Must children grow up with the epidemic disease "Arithmetic Anxiety?"

The answer, as we shall show in this manual, is no.

You can make the difference. You can make arithmetic easy for your child whether you are teaching him in a home school or helping in his preschool years and his after school hours. In the following sections, we will examine four attitudes which are important for home educators—attitude 1) toward arithmetic, 2) toward the child, 3) toward teaching, and 4) toward testing.

1. Attitude Toward Arithmetic

Some parents, and professional teachers too, are afraid of arithmetic themselves, and thus lack confidence for teaching it. This can lead to an impersonal teaching approach and overdependence on a textbook. Just assign page 7 today and page 8 tomorrow and the child will learn arithmetic, the teacher hopes, and never discover that she doesn't understand it herself.

The cure for this brand of anxiety is to learn arithmetic yourself. You're an adult after all, and elementary school children are expected to learn arithmetic. So it can't be that hard. Get a good book and learn right along with your child. Or stay a few pages ahead.

A couple of unexpected bonuses await you after a few months of this. One is the exhilarating self-confidence that comes once you find that you don't have to go through life either hiding your arithmetic fear or apologizing for it. No longer need you excuse, "I never liked arithmetic when I was in school," or "They had that modern math and didn't teach the basics in my school." The second bonus is the joy of learning that you will experience. Your child will catch this joy from you. Your teaching in all subjects will vastly improve as you discover this heart of the teacher-pupil relationship. A teacher who loves learning earns the right and the ability to help others learn.

2. Attitude Toward Your Pupil

Some parents have a psychological or spiritual problem in relating properly to their child. One problem arises when a parent tries to live out his or her own ego through the child, perhaps pushing the child to do better in school than the parent himself did, or pushing him to do better than his neighbor's or his brother's child.

Another problem is thinking of teacher and pupil as on opposite sides of the game. A parent with this view may have had teachers who were rigid authority figures holding the answer book and the weapon of grades. If you find this tendency in your thinking, try to turn around and see teacher and pupil as on the same team. This attitude will pay off richly as you and your pupil score points together.

Some pupils learn arithmetic easily. If yours does, you can enjoy much variety, using ideas from this manual and elsewhere to give your child rich experiences in arithmetic. You may teach shortcuts, alternate methods, and almost anything you want. On the other hand, if your child has a difficult time with arithmetic, teach him one way to add and subtract. And give him lots of practice with it.

The Bible teaches us to discipline our children and to love them. These are not opposites. They blend together. Loving discipline will grow in the child into self-discipline. And that is a prerequisite for the life of learning we hope he will lead.

3. Attitude Toward Teaching

If you rate yourself reasonably high on arithmetic knowledge and on proper relationship with your child (points 1 and 2 above), then this third problem is not likely to be yours. The problem is an attitude that "they" know all kinds of things about teaching your child that you don't know.

If this problem does happen to be yours, try looking back at the decades of teaching methods and see how "science" often changes its mind. For instance, you surely have heard of stimulus-response learning even if you never signed up for Psychology 101. Just show the stimulus 2 + 3, and reward the child for responding 5. Then drill, drill, drill so the child "learns" a strong bond between 2 + 3 and 5. Don't let him think for himself because he may give a wrong answer and, horrors, he may learn an incorrect bond and you will have the job of erasing it.

That was the scientific method a few decades ago. It was developed first through the study of rats and pigeons and it dehumanized teaching methods. But it was called "science," so many teachers were hoodwinked into going along with it. The inevitable backlash followed, and in the name of science, turns and twists and fads followed one another. Science changed its mind from decade to decade. Whatever fad was on top while you were in elementary school probably influenced the way you were taught.

Can teaching and its methods really be a science in the same manner as physics and chemistry? No, it can't.

Fortunately, throughout the decades of "scientific teaching" good teachers continued to be fully human. They continued to use their intuitive common sense. They looked into children's minds as only a human can, in intense mind-to-mind contact. Such teachers led children along exciting paths of learning. Mental challenge and fun played their part—memory and drill, too. These teachers used science when they believed in it, but they used their own judgment above all.

Your child's years of growing up with arithmetic will span about one of the changing decades of teaching. Will the decade bring some "new math" not yet in view at this writing? Will it bring an earlier-is-better push because of foreign competition in business or war? Will it bring a new "scientific" method of teaching?

Whatever it brings, you can remain in control. You may read about education research, but you should digest these into your unique thinking. Your child may be an Edison who doesn't fit into an ordinary mold. Remember, no researcher knows your child as well as you do. So you can feel free to use whatever modern educators say, as long as you can digest it and live with it. But you are also free to use your own commonsense judgment. Make decisions that seem right to you.

4. Attitude Toward Testing

There is far less need for testing in home schools than there is in classrooms. Most kinds of tests could be dispensed with until about third grade. But one kind of test will be quite useful, especially for older primaries. To help you be comfortable with decisions about testing, we include here a few comments on major kinds of tests.

Readiness tests are often given to help decide which children are "ready" for certain kinds of arithmetic work. But parents find these unnecessary because they usually know their child's abilities quite well. If there is doubt, you can simply try something and see if your pupil can do it. If it's too hard, he's not ready. Readiness tests are an attempt to manage classroom groups of children. Home schools, at their best, should not have to imitate this testing feature of schools.

Achievement tests are those which have "norms" for comparing your child with others. Some parents, both in and out of the home school movement, fight achievement tests for various reasons. Some home schoolers welcome them as a way to show the strength of home schooling. Whatever your general attitude toward achievement tests, we recommend that you try to avoid them at first grade level, and second, too. if possible.

What if your child can do quite complex arithmetic when you pose real-life problems, but your local district wants to test him on problems written in abstract form? Professional teachers have long argued that it weakens education when we "teach to the test," and in this situation, they are right. Thus achievement tests generally don't help your child, and the pressure and misteaching which may preceed them can actually harm the child. Tests also don't help you. No arithmetic test will tell you more than you already know about your child's ability after you have been working with him for a few months. Who gains, then? The legislator, or school official, or society? Even these don't gain if your child is pressured or harmed by the testing.

So if it is within your control, try to see that your child does not meet achievement tests until at least third grade.

One test universally found in books and correspondence courses is the **unit test** appearing at the end of a unit of study. Most teaching parents feel they can skip these tests because they already know what the child can do and can't do. But correspondence schools usually require unit tests. If you are able to diminish the tyranny of this testing, especially in primary grades, it will be an improvement over the present situation. Unit tests, as other tests, help in managing large classroom groups.

But one kind of testing can be quite valuable for the child. That is **self-testing,** or testing used for motivation purposes. Use these tests after you begin formal arithmetic teaching, which will be second or third grade in most cases. Once a child can grasp the nature of the task of learning all the addition combinations, he can be motivated to study the hard ones in order to pass a test. Or he can take a test in order to see which ones he should make flashcards for. After he knows all the combinations, he can be motivated to increase his speed by taking timed tests. All such uses are part of the learning process. Teacher and pupil are on the same team. Teacher is not holding a club over the pupil.

Some unit tests can be used in this motivating way. Certain children enjoy the feel of finishing a unit and passing a test on it. Occasionally you can build a child's confidence with a unit test. "See, you *do* know it," you might say to him.

Testing decisions are many. In making decisions you are comfortable with, remember always the uniqueness of home schools. They should not be miniature copies of classrooms.

Modes of Thinking

Children grow through three modes of thinking about arithmetic. When you understand these three modes you can easily make numerous day to day decisions about teaching. Should your child learn to recite numbers to 100 now? Does she need drill on multiplication tables or more real-life examples? You can have confidence in making these decisions.

1. The Manipulative Mode

Using this mode of thinking, children can work problems with real objects: marbles, M&M's, spoons, people. When your three-year-old helps you set the table, a lot of arithmetic thinking can happen, especially if you help it along: How many more spoons do we need? Are there enough chairs? The idea is for the child to see and manipulate real objects.

With real objects, three-year-olds can do problems that are not introduced until second grade, or later, in textbooks. Children can think about spoons, candy, fruit, and friends very early in life. And they can figure out some surprisingly complex problems. Just give them a chance.

If you happen to be familiar with Piagetian stages often mentioned in psychology books, this kind of thinking is like the "preoperational" stage. It means that arithmetic operations are not done inside the head, as we do when we multiply 5×8, for example. The spoons or apples are physically present and can be counted or manipulated to figure out problems.

Piagetian theory says this thinking predominates up to about ages six and seven. But it happens at all ages. Have you lately learned about computers or auto engines or anything else new? Did you get impatient with someone trying to explain and explain, feeling that if you could only get your hands on the equipment and use it then you would understand? Such an experience will help you know what the manipulative mode is.

The difference between young children and us is that we can switch freely from the manipulative mode of thinking to other modes we have learned to use. But very young children can't switch. They are tied to the manipulative mode. They must become proficient in this mode as a preparation for other modes to follow. This thinking—this actual experience with objects—is the foundation upon which all later arithmetic understandings are built.

Thus, we must teach young children in the manipulative mode. Failure to do this is probably the greatest single cause of children's arithmetic difficulties. It is why people grow up with Arithmetic Anxiety.

2. Mental Image Mode

After your child gains enough experience with spoons and other real objects, she becomes able to make images of objects in her head. She no longer needs to see and handle actual objects in order to figure out some of the easier problems you give her. Instead, she can image the objects in her head and work out problems using those images.

In the Piagetian system, this is called the concrete operational stage. This means children can do mental operations with images of objects. They can think of four family members, add one guest, and get the answer that five people will be at dinner. Or they can think of the four plates they usually put on the table and mentally add one more plate to get five.

How can you know when your child no longer needs real objects to manipulate? She, herself, will let you know by simply dispensing with their use. When she can image the objects, she finds it quicker and easier to work out a problem in her head. She becomes impatient with the slow process of counting and moving groups of checkers or plates or M&M's.

According to Piagetian theory, children use this mental image mode—along with the manipulative—until about ages twelve and thirteen. We adults find it useful, too. For example, let's say we have a story problem where we can't immediately see which number should be divided into the other to get the percentage we need. A helpful procedure is to change the numbers to small ones that we can easily image in our heads. With small numbers, our mental image tells us what the correct answer is, and we can see which number divided into the other gives that answer. After that, we translate back to the large, original numbers and work out the problem.

If you have a good feel for the mental image mode of thinking, you can be an excellent teacher of arithmetic. Children of elementary grades must do a lot of their thinking in this mode. And you will be able to communicate with them in the proper mode.

When we say that a child doesn't understand something, we usually mean that he is not able to image it in his head. The cure for that is to provide more manipulative experience. Try showing something one way and a second way and a third way. Approach it from different angles. Wait awhile and teach it again next month. After sufficient manipulative experience, the child eventually will image the troublesome process in his head. He will understand it.

3. Abstract Mode

In this mode, finally, children can think about an abstraction such as "four." They don't have to picture four plates or four dots on a domino. They have become so familiar with "fourness" that they can add and subtract this number easily. They can think of 4×3, where the 3 may be imaged as something quite concrete, and the four not so concrete, being the number of groups of the threes.

When do children gain the ability to think in the abstract mode? Piagetian theory puts the age at the beginning of adolescence, about twelve. In elementary school arithmetic, the abstract mode of thinking does not play a large role. You may often think abstractly yourself, but you must guard against trying to push children into this mode before they are ready. Pushing does not work. It only leads to the kinds of problems you wish to avoid: anxiety, frustration, dislike of arithmetic, and so forth.

The only route to good abstract thinking in a child's later years is through lots of manipulative and mental image thinking in early years.

How To Use the Modes

We have looked at three modes of arithmetic thinking:

1. manipulative (outside the head)
2. mental image (inside the head)
3. abstract (inside the head)

Children develop these in the order given. They can always switch back to use a previously learned mode, but they cannot jump ahead to use a mode they have not grown into. Hidden in this principle is a secret that can start you on an exciting adventure with your young pupil. Here is the secret: look at the three modes with a broad, long-term view, not with a tight, daily view.

Have you ever seen an arithmetic workbook that uses pictures to illustrate combining a group of three and a group of two, then on the same page it has problems using the symbols $3 + 2 = 5$? That's two modes. And if the book tells the teacher to begin with real objects, it actually is trying to use all three modes of thinking. This is the tight, daily view. It leads through all modes of thinking in one short lesson. The next page probably takes a different set of numbers and again moves through the modes. But, of course, the young child doesn't use abstract thinking, even though he is required to use the abstract symbols.

With the broad view, you can take advantage of the young child's strengths—her manipulative and image thinking. You will spend less time with the child's weakness—abstract symbols. While thinking in her strong modes, a child can learn much more actual arithmetic. She can think more deeply, work more complex problems, and better prepare for learning and enjoying advanced arithmetic. With this broad view, you can delay teaching abstract symbols somewhat longer than is usual. Later, when you do begin to use symbols, your child will learn them faster and understand them better.

To put all this in another way, the secret is to begin the child's arithmetic at a young age by using real objects. Then spend a year or two having the child do a lot of arithmetic in her head. And after she can do that well, you finally begin working with abstract symbols. There will naturally be overlap of these three broad phases. For instance, a child may do some problems in her head while she still does most with real objects. Or she may occasionally write some problems with symbols before she is ready to use symbols all the time.

The key is that you know which mode of thinking the child does best, and you take advantage of that strong mode. This way you can teach more arithmetic. You will not waste time trying to lead up to the abstract mode each day. And you can confidently make decisions about how to use arithmetic textbooks.

A teacher once wrote, "I used to think that the fault was mine. I couldn't explain well enough, I was too impatient, I didn't motivate, and on and on. Or the fault was the child's. He didn't try hard enough. Or the family's. They didn't get him to bed on time; there was too much stress in family life. I never thought of the textbook being the problem. But then I saw that books sometimes don't fit the thinking modes of children.

You, too, can be free from slavery to a textbook. Of course, you may wish to use time-saving features a book offers. You can appreciate the ready-made problems, helpful pictures and diagrams, creative game ideas, and so on. But when you run into trouble, don't rule out the possibility that the book might not be exactly right for your particular child at that particular time.

Enjoy arithmetic. The mental challenge it offers stimulates both teacher and pupil. Sometimes it's hard work, of course. Sometimes it takes perseverance. Sometimes one must memorize. But along the way be sure to find moments of great mental exhilaration. They will come more often if you help your child use the appropriate thinking mode.

The Child's Early Years

Every day a portion of our children's conversations and problems should involve numbers and other arithmetic concepts: big, small, long, high. Comparisons. Measurements. Counting.

Three-year-old Angie counted seven people at the dinner table. "How many would be left if you and your sister go play?" Mother asked. After a moment of silent thinking, Angie answered, "Five."

Seven minus two is a problem arithmetic textbooks introduce during first or second grade. But Angie was looking at real people, not symbols on a sheet of paper. She was operating in the manipulative mode of thinking (see the preceding chapter). Her parents posed problems like this every day.

Angie gradually learned to read house numbers, page numbers, and clock numbers almost without trying. She occasionally wrote them, too. One day when she was five years old, her sister came home from school and showed her how to write a 1 in front of each number for the teens, and how to put a 2 in front of each number for the twenties. "It keeps going like that," Jill told her. Angie caught on to the pattern and spent several days filling sheets of paper with numbers. She was going on to a billion, to tentillion, she said. But one day she joined her brothers digging roads in a hillside. Roads overtook numbers as the new game in her life.

Meanwhile the first graders in Jill's class were laboriously chanting and writing numbers day after day, trying to learn them up to one hundred. A few, like Jill, had sufficient experience counting toes and counting people at dinner tables so that they understood the counting idea. They could "image" it. Thus they didn't need that much practice. Others lacked the insight Jill had, but with lots of practice they could learn by rote how to count. For both groups of children it was inefficient learning.

Not many first grade teachers operate that way today. Most realize that children must understand the meaning of numbers, and not just memorize number names. Parents could help them.

Later in this chapter are some ideas for real-life home teaching. But first, let's take a moment to see some of the many levels of teaching you might use. Consider the addition fact $3 + 2 = 5$.

MANIPULATIVE MODE	*Real objects, with touching and moving:* Three plates (spoons, marbles, jacks, etc.), put two more with them. Now there are five. *Real objects, with only sight:* Three jacks in this group, two jacks in the other group. There are five all together.
TRANSITION	*Pictures:* Picture of three jacks in a group and two in another group. Five total. *Symbolic pictures:* Three dots in this group and two in another group. Five total.
MENTAL IMAGE MODE	*Touchable objects:* Think of three jacks and two jacks. They make five all together. ("Story problems" often are of this type.) *Non-touchable ideas:* A team won three games and lost two games. They played five games all together. (Some story problems are this type.)
SYMBOLIC MODE	*Digits only:* 3 and 2 are 5. *Digits and signs:* $3 + 2 = 5$

Levels for Thinking about "3 + 2 = 5"

With this chart, it is easy to see how it happens that many people make arithmetic more difficult than it needs to be. When a parent decides to teach arithmetic, what pops into his mind? Often it is the last of these modes—the symbolic. Or it may be the transitions, as found in workbooks, that pop into mind.

Unfortunately, there is a tendency to think that the manipulative mode doesn't qualify as real arithmetic. Teachers use objects to explain the meaning of symbols, or to build understanding for difficult concepts. But the goal in these strategies is to get back to the symbolic as quickly as possible. Objects are seen as only a temporary crutch.

These strategies, in one sense, are a backwards approach. If you teach a child how to read and write the digit 3 and then, with objects, teach the meaning of 3, that is backwards. That order is: 1) symbol, then 2) real objects. If a workbook lesson shows three airplanes, has the child draw lines around three toy airplanes, and then at the bottom of the page has him practice writing the digit 3, that may still be committing the same error. The order here is: 1) pictured objects, then 2) symbol. So it seems right according to the chart. But the problem is that it's all on one page. The lesson expects the child to move from manipulative mode to symbolic mode in one lesson. This kind of page should be given to a child after he already has an understanding of three. Then he may use the page to learn the digit 3. But he won't need to learn how to count three airplanes or draw a ring around three of them.

Let's examine a point further down on the chart. Children using the mental image mode (most primary children) are able to figure out many story problems by imaging them in their heads. But if they also are required to translate their thinking into symbols and write digits and signs on paper, the task is more difficult. Thus, many children who really are good thinkers in their proper modes are made to feel like failures.

This chart and the accompanying discussion is given here to remind us adults of the complexity of thinking skills we acquired during our growing up years. Symbolic thinking doesn't happen overnight. We need to give our children time. We need to be patient with them. We should not start arithmetic teaching with $3 + 2 =$ ______ .

Real-Life Arithmetic

Parents teaching their children at home have an exciting opportunity. Future progress in education can happen more in the homes than in schools. One reason is that parents can use real-life situations for teaching. Another reason is that parents have the advantage of using the child's early years. As more parents become interested in teaching, society is likely to develop a new attitude toward these early years. No longer will we want to put children in classrooms earlier and earlier. Home is the best environment.

If you are home schooling, you are pioneering in a highly significant movement. Don't throw away your opportunity by imitating school too closely. Use real life for teaching. Your family is unique and will have other kinds of situations than are listed in this manual. But all families can follow two important principles, no matter what the specific activities are.

The first principle is to use real-life situations to teach bits of arithmetic and to build a "need" to know arithmetic. When you read stories to children, they learn that books contain stories and they develop a "need" to learn how to read stories for themselves. That same principle must apply in arithmetic. Daily events involve arithmetic. Share these with your child so he develops an awareness of arithmetic and a need to know it.

The second principle is to do this sharing in the mode appropriate for your child's age and development. At preschool ages, that will practically always be the manipulative mode. At primary ages the manipulative will gradually give way to the mental image mode. Occasionally, your child may wish to read and write numbers. That is all right. Just don't push him to work problems written in symbols. Most arithmetic should be mental. It happens in conversation, not in written assignments.

The following list gives some of the places these conversations can occur.

Game Area. Is this your family room, kitchen table, or living room rug? Wherever it's located, you must have this. We list the game area first, so you will read it even if you don't take time to read the rest of the list. We cannot overemphasize the importance of games for growing children. Much arithmetic is learned as children count moves, compute scores, take turns. But that is only a fraction of the benefits. Numerous thinking skills are developed as children learn to operate within various kinds of rules, plan strategy, and so forth. Sportsmanship and other social skills gradually develop. When children later learn that rules don't have to be rigid, they can develop new twists and live by their own agreed-on rules. One fifth grader developed an insurance system to accompany Monopoly. He calculated the chances of a player landing on Park Place with a hotel on it, and other expensive events, and balanced this against money he could collect as players pass Go. Then he sold insurance against expensive contingencies. Players could purchase various kinds of policies and make installment payments each time they passed Go. This is complex for young children, of course, but the point to notice here is that years of game experience lead to advanced thinking skills and creativity.

Supermarket. Young toddlers sitting in the basket can watch as you put in *one* loaf of bread, *two* cartons of milk, and so forth. Older children can help select *six* apples. Still older children can carry pocket calculators and figure out that the chocolate Santas, even at half price, cost more per ounce than other chocolate in the store.

Kitchen. Young toddlers can find you a "bigger" pan and a stirring spoon with a "longer" handle. Slightly older children can help you measure and count to follow a recipe. They can begin reading ingredient lists. Children don't have to be very old to follow some simple recipes entirely on their own. Making milk drinks, fruit drinks, sandwich fillings, and other snacks will teach them to read both the words and the numbers in a recipe. Learning about measuring cups and spoons, quarts, ounces, pounds, and such kitchen matters comes to children bit by bit through regular experience in using them. You don't need to get preachy. Just have fun making the cookies.

Dining Area. Setting the table, arranging chairs, and such preparations are ideal for counting and adding experiences. Sometimes subtraction and multiplication are needed too. Later, when the family is eating, arithmetic can be one of the topics. Does anyone have game scores to report? Simple money matters to discuss? Did you walk *two* miles instead of your usual *one*? If arithmetic doesn't accidentally come up, you can invent problems, such as Angie's mother had a habit of doing.

Yard, Garage, and Workshop. Chores carried on in these areas all have their natural arithmetic. Measuring, counting, planting rows. Here is where families show their uniqueness more than in the kitchen. One father had his seven-year-old son help with carpentry work almost daily. The boy learned many skills along with arithmetic. Another father let his son help fix the motorcycle. He learned about bolt and wrench sizes and other mechanical matters. What kind of arithmetic experiences does your home offer?

Car. Speed limits, miles to the next town, street numbers, license numbers—the list is endless. Don't feel that your child needs to completely understand these concepts as you talk about them or read them from signs. This is a time for him to meet them over and over and gradually develop meaning. Older children can read road maps and compute mileage. Younger children can count three cows or find the tallest building. There's something for everyone.

Television. If you have this in your home, let your child learn more than what's on the screen. He can learn to tell the times of his favorite programs. He can plan for the number of viewing hours per day or per week that you allow him. He can read channel numbers and program listings.

Real life is daily. It is close at hand. It offers the best learning opportunities your child will ever have. Think arithmetic!

First Grade

Arithmetic goals are not the same everywhere. Textbooks and school curriculum guides vary in what they suggest teaching in each grade. Thus there can be no one "right" curriculum plan for you to follow. This chapter gives guidelines which are "typical" of most first grade courses, and you should feel free to use them somewhat flexibly. If you don't get it all taught this year, don't panic. Just plan to teach it next year. A more likely situation is that you will find your child well ahead of these guidelines, particularly if you have done a thorough job of real-life, manipulative mode teaching.

The first section below gives you a scope and sequence chart. It shows the knowledge and skills typically taught at first grade level. The second section adds comments and teaching suggestions especially for home schools.

First Grade Knowledge and Skills

Numbers. Count cardinal numbers to 100. Ordinal numbers (first in order, second, third, etc.) up to "tenth." Child must understand and use numbers, not simply chant their names. He should be able to count out fifteen sheets of paper, point to the fourth person in line, count beads, and so forth. Some experience in reading numbers and a little experience in writing numbers may be offered if the child seems ready for writing in general.

Groups. Ability to see how many are in a group such as dots on dominoes. Ability to count by groups of five and ten, using materials such as an abacus or nickels and dimes. Ability to count by twos, using pairs—eggs in a carton, eyes and ears of the people present, socks in the wash, and so forth.

Measurement. Gain simple practical experience with clocks (both dial and digital), calendars, rulers, measuring cups and other measuring devices. Use money—at least pennies, nickels, and dimes.

Vocabulary. Grow in ability to use words having to do with size, quantity, shape, and other arithmetic and geometry concepts. Examples: taller, larger, less, circle, square, one-half, hour, minute.

Addition. Ability to add any two groups with sums of six or less, not including zero as a group. Some children may proceed to problems with sums up to ten. (Refer to the addition chart in the second grade section.)

Subtraction. Ability to "take away" a group from six (or ten) or any lesser number and tell what is left. (Other kinds of subtraction problems, such as finding how much more are in one group than another, are not used when children first learn to subtract.)

Notation. Ability to read and perhaps to write the digits from 1 to 10. If addition and subtraction problems are written out, begin with the "sentence" form, thus: 4 and 2 are 6.

First Grade Teaching Suggestions

Practically every item in the first grade curriculum can be taught using real-life methods. In fact, they are better taught in real life, including games, than in daily sit-down arithmetic lessons. Let the child spend real money at the store. Let him help make cookies. Read again the previous chapter, and use those ideas, extending them to fit your child's growing understanding.

As a home school teacher you do not need a workbook and daily written assignments such as a classroom teacher might use. Your one-on-one teaching can accomplish more. But if your child likes it, occasional use of a workbook is all right. If you are using a correspondence course which requires daily written work, see if you can reduce the writing and have the child do some of the problems mentally or with objects. Also, you may look into local law. It may be the case that your child doesn't have to be enrolled in anything until age seven or eight.

If you feel bold enough to strike out on your own without a workbook or mail-order course, be sure to plan regular check-ups for yourself. Reread the scope and sequence several times during the year. Mark it up. What does your child know quite well? What weak area will you give special attention to? Plan a game or activity and some arithmetic conversations for each day. (See the activity list below if you want help in getting started.) At this level it not important in which order you teach the topics. Just be sure the child keeps meeting arithmetic.

If you feel more secure following a textbook, a good compromise is to look at the book yourself but have the child do much of the work in his head or with objects.

Don't be deceived by the short list of first grade topics and by how simple they look to us adults. For a child of first grade age, it takes a considerable amount of learning to master the knowledge and skills listed for this grade.

Notation. This last item on the list is, surprisingly, less important than any of the others. The others involve genuine arithmetic thinking and learning. This item involves only a skill in writing things the way our society has decided they should be written. If a child labors too hard at this task, you can safely wait until his physical development allows for easier small muscle movements.

Measurement. This should only be learned through practical, real-life experiences. No attempt need be made to work problems. The emphasis is on learning the principles of measurement, which are: 1) Any measurement, such as an inch or hour, is always the same no matter what ruler or clock it is on. 2) To measure correctly requires practice in being exact. 3) Two people measuring the same object should get the same results. Repeated use of simple measurements builds an understanding of these principles.

A ruler with inches only, no fractions, is helpful. These can be bought at educational supply stores. Teach inches, not fractional parts thereof. Teach time only to hours, not halves and fourths. Teach anything that comes up in everyday life—*pound* of margarine, *cup* of sugar, *gallon* of milk.

Activity Ideas. This list is given to show how easy it is to achieve arithmetic learning in the daily activities around your home.

Domino-type games (matching, recognizing groups)
Lotto-type games (reading numbers)
Board games (counting moves, following rules, reading numbers)
Jacks (counting, recognizing groups)
Pick-up-sticks-type games (counting, scoring)
Building toys—Lego, blocks, and others (size, pattern, comparison, planning, counting)
Snacks (counting, sharing equally, cutting in half)
Follow simple recipe (reading numbers, measuring)
Help fix things (accuracy, conversation, measuring, comparing)
Help with shopping (money, counting, comparing)
Follow directions for an art or craft project (straight lines, folding in half, following steps 1, 2, 3, etc.)
Collect rocks, stamps, other (sorting, comparing, classifying)

Second Grade

Every second grade teacher meets a problem each fall that no other teacher faces to the same degree. The problem is the forgetting that occurs over the summer between first and second grades. It is wise to begin each topic by going over first grade work. Review adding and subtracting. Reteach measurements. Play number games. Ease back into arithmetic. This time will not be wasted. It will pay off in faster progress as you move ahead to new understandings.

Thus, in the second grade topics listed below, you will see the first grade curriculum included in each. If the child learned numbers to 100 in first grade, we do not say that second grade curriculum covers the numbers 101 to 200 or higher. But we say that second grade curriculum covers all the numbers to 200. This is standard procedure, and many years of experience have proven to second grade teachers that it is necessary and that it works well.

As suggested in the first grade section, you may teach most of the knowledge and skills without expensive workbooks. Your second grader may enjoy a little book work. But use books in addition to real life teaching, not instead of it.

Second Grade Knowledge and Skills

Numbers. Read, write, and count up to at least 200. Ordinal numbers up to "tenth." If a child understands calendars well enough, she may learn ordinal numbers up to "thirty-first."

Place Value. Understand the tens and ones places in numbers up to at least 39. This is simply an introduction to the place value idea; the concept will be taught again in third grade. (See teaching suggestions below.)

Groups. Ability to count by tens and fives at least to 30, and on to 100 if the child can. Ability to count by twos to 10 or higher. (Use real objects—stacks of books, checkers, popsickle sticks, squares on a game board. Use dimes, nickels, and pennies after a child understands the value of these coins.)

Measurement. Time in hours and half hours; length in inches and feet (no fractions); coins of pennies, nickels, dimes and perhaps, also, quarters and half dollars; and a few other simple measures such as pound, pint, quart, and dozen.

Vocabulary and Signs. Learn the words *subtract* and *minus* to use instead of *take away*. Learn *plus, add,* and *equals*. Extend vocabulary of comparison: long, longer, longest; high, higher, highest; left and right; top and bottom; and so forth.

Fractions. One-half, one-fourth, and sometimes one-third. By cutting apples or candy bars, the child learns these fractional parts. No work on writing fractions is done. No adding or subtracting of fractions. And no fractions with numerators other than 1.

Addition. Ability to add two numbers up to sums of 12. Ability to add three numbers. For children who understand place value and who write problems in their vertical form, you may begin addition of two-place numbers without carrying.

Subtraction. Ability to take away a group from twelve or any lesser number and tell what is left. With the same prerequisites mentioned for addition, you may teach subtraction of two-place numbers without borrowing. (See teaching suggestions for further comments on this.)

Multiplication and Division. Begin to understand the meaning of combining similar groups two "times" or three "times." Begin to understand the meaning of dividing a large group into smaller groups of twos or threes or fives or tens. (Work with real objects rather than with problems written in abstract form.)

Notation. Learn to write addition and subtraction problems in both their horizontal "sentence" forms and their vertical forms, using and knowing the signs. Examples:

$$4 + 2 = 6 \qquad \begin{array}{r} 4 \\ +2 \\ \hline 6 \end{array} \qquad 6 - 2 = 4 \qquad \begin{array}{r} 6 \\ -2 \\ \hline 4 \end{array}$$

Two-place numbers in addition and subtraction and columns of three numbers in addition may be added to these notation skills for children who are proficient in working the problems. (See teaching suggestions below for a discussion of early notation versus delayed notation teaching.)

Problem Solving. Much experience in solving problems is usually given in second grade. This will not be new or difficult for children brought up from an early age in real-life arithmetic. Continue to use the manipulative and mental image modes of thinking. Occasionally write problems in their abstract forms.

Second Grade Teaching Suggestions

Place Value. Perhaps the most difficult concept you will have to teach is that of place value. This is helping your child to understand why digits 1 and 4 occupy the places they do in the number 14. Fourteen is a good first lesson on place value because it sounds almost like four-ten. Eleven, twelve, and thirteen are words invented by someone other than a primary teacher.

To teach place value manipulatively, you need some kind of objects which can be easily bundled into groups of ten. Popsickle sticks are often used. You could have the child count fourteen sticks and notice that it's a rather slow way to find out how many sticks there are. Would she like a faster way to count them? Have her count ten sticks and bundle them together with a rubber band. Put the group of ten at the left and four single sticks beside it at the right. How many? Was that faster than counting each one singly? Put six single sticks at the right of the ten. How many? Continue playing with the sticks in this manner, sometimes letting the child make problems for you to count.

When this is easy to do with one bundle of ten, proceed to two tens and three tens. When you can't stump your pupil on any number up to 39, proceed to writing the numbers. Lay out fourteen sticks and directly below them show how we write 1 to tell that there is one "ten" and we write 4 to tell that there are four "ones." Practice other numbers, giving your pupil turns at being "teacher."

Repeat some of the same procedures using dimes and pennies. Repeat using an abacus or other teaching aids you happen to have. Sometimes use the mental image mode. For example, while driving in the car you may ask, "How would you show the number 26 with the sticks?" Answer: two bundles of ten and six single sticks.

This technique of teaching a concept several times in several ways is a secret of good teachers everywhere. You will find it useful for any subject your child finds difficult.

Abstract Notation. Understanding this item is the key to choosing your strategy for the early years of arithmetic teaching. The question is: Should you teach abstract notation as early as the child can learn it, or should you use the time, instead, to teach in greater depth in the mental image mode?

Abstract notation includes writing out a column of numbers to add, and writing one number under another before subtracting it. The digits and signs used are "symbols." The position of the numbers is an arbitrary decision of society. They are conventions that adult, abstract thinkers use as a kind of shorthand to speed up our thinking.

When we teach these to children, we must realize that we simply are introducing them to our abstract "tools." We are not suddenly turning children into abstract thinkers. And the danger of starting too early and pushing this kind of work is that we will spend an inordinate amount of time with it. We will be teaching the importance of making straight columns, writing numbers in certain places and other trivial matters. By calling them trivial, we don't mean that they are unnecessary. But they are small matters compared to real arithmetic thinking.

If you stay with meaningful mental arithmetic longer, you will find that your child, if she is average, can do problems much more advanced than the level listed for her grade. You will find that she likes arithmetic more. And when she does get to abstractions, she will understanding them better. She will not need two or three years of work in primary grades to learn how to write out something like a subtraction problem with two-digit numbers. She can learn that in a few moments time, if you just wait until she is pretty good at mental image subtraction.

Mental Image Mode. While delaying abstract work, do plenty of real-life arithmetic. Use games a lot. These don't have to be "educational" arithmetic games, since most popular children's games require arithmetic thinking. If your child can do it, begin some experiences with the hundred chart described in the third grade teaching suggestions.

Addition and Subtraction Chart. The following chart shows in a concise way what your teaching task is in addition and subtraction. You can be flexible, of course, in order to meet the needs of your particular pupil. But this chart will help you know the general grade levels for teaching the various facts.

For addition, the chart reads like an old-fashioned multiplication table. That is, you choose a number in the left column and a number in the top row, and the sum of these is found in the chart where the row and the column meet.

For subtraction, the procedure is reversed. Start with a number within the chart, subtract the number at the beginning of its row, and the answer is the number at the top of its column.

The dark lines mark off the grade levels. Most first graders learn everything down to the line below the sixes, and many continue to the line below the tens. Most second graders learn up to the twelves. And third graders learn the whole chart.

	1	2	3	4	5	6	7	8	9
1	2	3	4	5	6	7	8	9	10
2	3	4	5	6	7	8	9	10	11
3	4	5	6	7	8	9	10	11	12
4	5	6	7	8	9	10	11	12	13
5	6	7	8	9	10	11	12	13	14
6	7	8	9	10	11	12	13	14	15
7	8	9	10	11	12	13	14	15	16
8	9	10	11	12	13	14	15	16	17
9	10	11	12	13	14	15	16	17	18

ADDITION AND SUBTRACTION CHART
Grade 1: to sixes or to tens. Grade 2: to twelves.
Grade 3: to eighteen.

Activity and Game Ideas. The following list of activities shows how everyday items can be used for arithmetic. Regular use of such activities achieves the "life application" that school teachers are always striving for. As a home teacher, you have an advantage. Life application is all around you.

Learn to make phone calls to Grandma, to a friend. Prepare a list of emergency numbers and post them in a convenient place.

Try to read some household bills. Talk about how to save money.

Read advertisements and cents-off coupons. Talk about them. Would this really save us money? Do we need the item, or would we just be letting the advertiser talk us into spending money? Is this brand with its cents-off coupon a better buy than some other brand?

Make up problems about news stories. If the team had made one more touchdown, what would the score be? Were there fewer traffic deaths this year or last year?

Read the calendar, the thermometer, the speedometer, the scales.

Read all the numbers in headlines on the front page of the newspaper.

Use commercial games a lot. They help to develop many arithmetic, logic, and thinking skills. Here are a couple of homemade games to add to your game collection.

Secret Number

For two players. Each has twenty nickels (or other coin). Player A writes a secret number from 1 to 100. Player B guesses and pays one nickel for the guess. Player A points upward if the secret number is higher than the guess, and she points downward if it is lower. Player B continues guessing and paying until he guesses correctly. Then he writes a secret number and Player A pays him to guess.

If one player runs out of money, the other is the winner. If neither player runs out of money, they can stop after an even number of turns and count to see who has the most money.

Variations. For easier games adjust the range of numbers. For instance, guess numbers from 1 to 10, and use only five coins.

The Greatest Number

For two or three players. Each player needs a set of ten cards, with the digits from 0 to 9. Players each mix up their cards and put them in a pile face-down in front of themselves.

To begin, all players draw three cards and make the greatest number they can with them. The player with the greatest number wins a point. Mix the cards again and take another turn. The player with the most points by the end of a specified time period is the winner.

Variations. For practice in writing numbers, you may draw and show the cards, and your pupil is to write the largest number she can with them. If you can make a larger number, you win. If you cannot make a larger number, she wins.

Draw two cards or four cards to make the game easier or harder.

Third Grade

At about third grade age, pupils can profit from more sit-down, formal arithmetic lessons. They may write their computations more often than before, and they may work in more systematic fashion toward mastering arithmetic skills. Now is the time to consolidate the real-life learning of previous years.

During this time of consolidation, point out often to your child what he knows and what he is now learning. Say things like, "I remember when you couldn't add big numbers like 7 and 8. Now you can add practically anything." Without such help from you, your pupil is not likely to be aware of his progress. You can see progress, since adult minds can take a sweeping view above the ground. But young children are down among the blades of grass. They can't see well where they have been and where they are going. Your frequent reminders can help keep your pupil motivated.

At third grade, you may feel a need for using a textbook for the first time. If you do use one, remember to continue teaching the meaning of arithmetic operations. Don't depend too heavily on pages in a book to do all the teaching for you. And feel free to skip parts in a book that your child is already proficient with. A common situation is that a book may teach what pennies, nickels, and dimes are, while the child may have extensive experience handling these coins in real situations. In cases like this, don't feel guilty passing over the pages, or letting the child do them simply "for fun," if he wishes to. You are teaching the child, not the book.

Third Grade Knowledge and Skills

Numbers. Read, write, count, and use numbers up to at least 1000.

Place Value. Review ones and tens places. Extend to the hundreds place. Notice the use of zero in a number like 106.

Groups. Expand skills in counting by groups. Become proficient in counting by tens and fives up to 30 or higher. Count by twos up to 20. Try counting by threes and fours. Sometimes begin the counting at numbers besides zero.

Addition and Subtraction. Master all facts in the addition and subtraction chart. (See chart in the second grade section.) Games, flashcards, speed tests, and other drill devices should be used to achieve ease and speed in using these facts. Learn carrying, borrowing, checking, and bridging (adding across the decades, as from the twenties to the thirties).

Multiplication and Division. Understand the principles that multiplication is a way to add equal groups and division is a way to subtract equal groups. Learn multiplication tables of twos and threes first. Tens and fives may follow if pupils have sufficient background in counting by these groups. Ones may be added when pupils understand the rather odd concept of one "times" something. All together, about half of the 81 multiplication facts should be taught. (See teaching suggestions below.)

You may introduce the multiplying of two-digit numbers which do not require carrying. This may involve more attention to zeros than has been given heretofore.

Fractions. Extend understanding of fractional parts of a real object, using only 1 as a numerator: one-half, one-fourth, one-third, one-fifth. Learn to write a few fractions which have 1 as a numerator. For some children, fractional parts of groups may be introduced. For instance, one-half of twelve or one-half of four may be learned using real eggs, candy, or other objects.

Measurements. Ability to work with all coins and with dollar bills. Write amounts, using decimal points and dollar signs. Compute problems involving money (within the guidelines given above for addition, subtraction, multiplication, and division). Build understanding of hours, half hours, and quarter hours. Learn about days, weeks, months, and years. Use the measures of inches, feet, and yards, and convert from one to another. Use pints, quarts, gallons, ounces, and pounds in realistic situations. Read scales and thermometers.

Problem Solving. Continued and expanded experience in solving realistic problems is the most valuable part of third grade arithmetic. Use problems involving games, sports, and other topics of high interest to your child. Solve many of these mentally or on the hundred chart or number line. Solve some by writing the figures in their proper positions.

Teaching Suggestions for Third Grade

Subtraction with Borrowing. The word *borrowing* has been used for centuries. But teachers have long pointed out that nothing is returned, as we usually do when we borrow items. If your child has a good understanding of place value, if he has bundled sticks into groups of tens and hundreds, then you may wish to use the term "regrouping." For instance, in the problem below, a ten is mentally moved to the ones place. Thus the top number is regrouped as 3 tens and 13 ones. Then the subtraction can proceed.

$$\begin{array}{r} 43 \\ -\ 6 \\ \hline 37 \end{array}$$

Multiplication. A multiplication table which goes as high as 9×9 includes 81 multiplication "facts." Third grade curriculums generally teach about half of these facts. But they do not all teach the same half. The facts you teach will depend on the approach you wish to take. One approach is to teach by "tables." That is, you may teach the table of twos up to 2×6 or 2×9. Then follow that with the tables of threes, fives, tens, and perhaps ones.

Another approach is to teach by "families." A full family includes two multiplication facts and two division facts, thus:

$$\begin{array}{r} 6 \\ \times 2 \\ \hline 12 \end{array} \qquad \begin{array}{r} 2 \\ \times 6 \\ \hline 12 \end{array} \qquad 6\overline{)12}\ \text{quotient } 2 \qquad 2\overline{)12}\ \text{quotient } 6$$

Since you probably will use both approaches at different times, it may become a bit confusing to keep track of which facts your pupil knows. Besides, when you are consistent in teaching the meaning behind arithmetic facts and operations, the child can figure out facts which you have not specifically taught him.

For these reasons, we do not show on a chart the exact facts to teach. But if your child knows about 40 of the easier facts, he has done well. He may not know 7×8, but he should know 3 x 5.

Fractions. Third grade curriculums ordinarily do not include adding or other computations with fractions. Instead, children should continue to gain real-life experience and build meaning for the difficult concept of fractions. Cut fruit into halves or fourths. Cut candy bars into thirds. See how many ways the child can cut a sheet of paper into halves.

To teach how fractions are written, you may show the meaning this way:

$$\frac{\text{1 of the}}{\text{4 equal parts}} \quad \text{is shortened to} \quad \frac{1}{4}$$

Textbooks. If you are using a workbook or textbook of some kind, learn to see it as a guide through the many topics of arithmetic. Realize that the child need not work every problem on every page. As mentioned earlier, it sometimes is appropriate to skip pages. Often it is best to talk through a problem with the pupil. Let him try to image it in his head, or if he cannot do this, let him work it manipulatively with objects. Teaching in this manner, you will not cover as many problems each day, but your pupil will learn more from the problems he does work.

Teaching Aids. Two extremely valuable teaching aids are a hundred chart and a number line. These have so many uses that it is worthwhile to make one or both of these. An example of a hundred chart is shown on the back cover of this manual. You or your pupil may wish to make a larger or sturdier version of it. To make a number line, number from 1 to 100 in one long row. Use a strip of adding machine paper, tape a strip of masking tape along a wall, or whatever creative way you can manage this in your house. A string of 100 wooden beads could also be used—ten yellow, ten blue, ten yellow, ten blue, and so on.

These teaching aids can help children to visualize numerous aspects of arithmetic operations. See the list of suggested primary grade uses on the last page of this manual.

Game Ideas. At third grade level, you should continue to use commercial games and other standard games and puzzles. These develop skills in thinking, planning, strategy, logic, and arithmetic processes. As your child grows in ability he may become the family scorekeeper, to add more arithmetic even to word games. Here we provide you with a few game and activity ideas specifically for use during arithmetic class periods.

A Problem a Day

Each day either you or your child can make up a problem from some piece of paper that comes into your family life. Possibilities are: menu, cash register tape, airline or bus schedule, newspaper bill, grocery ad.

Zap

For two or more players. One player begins counting with 1, the next says 2, and so on. But for 5 and all multiples of 5 players must say

"Zap." When this is easy, try Zap for multiples of 3 and of other numbers.

Concentration

Make eight pairs of cards with addition or multiplication facts your child needs to learn. Put a problem on one card and its answer on another. Example: 8 + 9 on a card and 17 on another. Mix the cards and lay them face down in random positions or in rows.

The first player turns over two cards. If they match he keeps them. If they do not, he turns them down again. The second player then takes his turn. When all pairs are matched, the one with the most cards is the winner. Later, add a rule that each player must name the match he is looking for before turning over a second card.

Invent a Game

Use old game boards, spinners, markers, and other game parts. The pupil is to think up a new use for the board. He may make cards or any new parts he needs for his game. For a language assignment, he can write the rules. Rules should tell: 1) how to prepare, 2) how each player takes a turn, and 3) how to determine the winner.

Advanced Skill Drill

Write numbers from 0 to 99 on cards. Mix them and place them face down. The pupil selects two cards and subtracts the smaller number from the larger. If the subtraction is too difficult for him to do on paper, let him work it on the hundred chart or with objects such as popsickle sticks. For addition practice, write numbers to 50. (This activity is especially helpful for people teaching without textbooks. A day's allotment of problems can be determined in this way.)

Exactly Twenty

For two players. Prepare forty-five cards by printing 1 on five cards, 2 on five cards, and so on up to the number 9. Mix the cards and place them face down in a pile. To begin, each player draws two cards.

The object of the game is to collect cards which total exactly 20. The first player starts his collection by laying one of his cards face-up in front of him. He then draws another card. The second player does the same. Turns continue. When either card in a player's hand would make his collection total more than 20, he cannot add to his collection, but must use his turn to discard and draw a new card. The discard pile is face-up beside the main pile. The first player to collect exactly 20 is the winner.

Ways to Use the Hundred Chart

The hundred chart on the back cover is one of the most flexible and useful devices you will ever find for helping your child to understand numbers and the basic arithmetic processes. Use it almost every day in your teaching. The list of ideas below will help you get started. (Most of these activities may be done on a number line, as well.)

Easy

Count to 10. Count to 20. Count as high as you want.

What is 5 and 1 more? Three and 2 more? (Count forward for any simple addition problem.)

What is 1 less than 6? One less than 8? Two less than 5? (Count backward for any simple "take-away" subtraction problem.)

Advanced

Count by tens on the chart. Count by fives. By twos.

Count by tens, but start on the 3, or 6. Start on other numbers.

Count by any size group you can. Start anywhere you wish.

Add 5 to 7. Add 5 to 17. To 27. To 37. (This bridges from one row, or one decade, to the next.)

Add 3 to 9. Add 3 to 19. To 29. To 39.

Add 9 to any number. (Nine is especially fascinating because of its position as one less than 10. Later on, 11 can be fascinating in a similar way.)

Write a rule for adding 9 to any number. For adding 11. Write rules for other discoveries you make on the chart.

Make up addition problems with bridging. Can you bridge all rows?

Begin with 100 and count by tens backwards. Count by fives or twos backwards.

Begin with 20 and count by twos backwards.

Subtract 4 from 51. Subtract 4 from 41. From 31. From 21. From 11.

Subtract 5 from 53. From 43. From 33. From 23. From 13.

Make up subtraction problems with bridging. Can you do them on all the rows?

When you have a difficult problem to figure out, see if you can work it on the hundred chart.